JUNIOR CYCLE HOME ECONOMICS

ÚNA SHELLY

CONSULTANT EDITOR:
MARGARET P. KINSELLA

I wish to thank everyone who helped in the preparation of *Zest for Life*, especially my consultant editor, Margaret P. Kinsella, and my friends and family, especially Dec, Stephen, Sarah and Andrew. –U.S.

Gill Education
Hume Avenue
Park West
Dublin 12
www.gilleducation.ie

Gill Education is an imprint of M.H. Gill & Co.

ISBN: 9780717179671

Design and layout: Outburst Design
Illustrations: Derry Dillon and Andriy Yankovskyy
Index: Cliff Murphy

The paper used in this book is made from the wood pulp of managed forests. For every tree felled, at least one tree is planted, thereby renewing natural resources.

Contents

* Note these chapters do not have corresponding material in the Skills Book and the Teacher's Resource Book.

Introduction

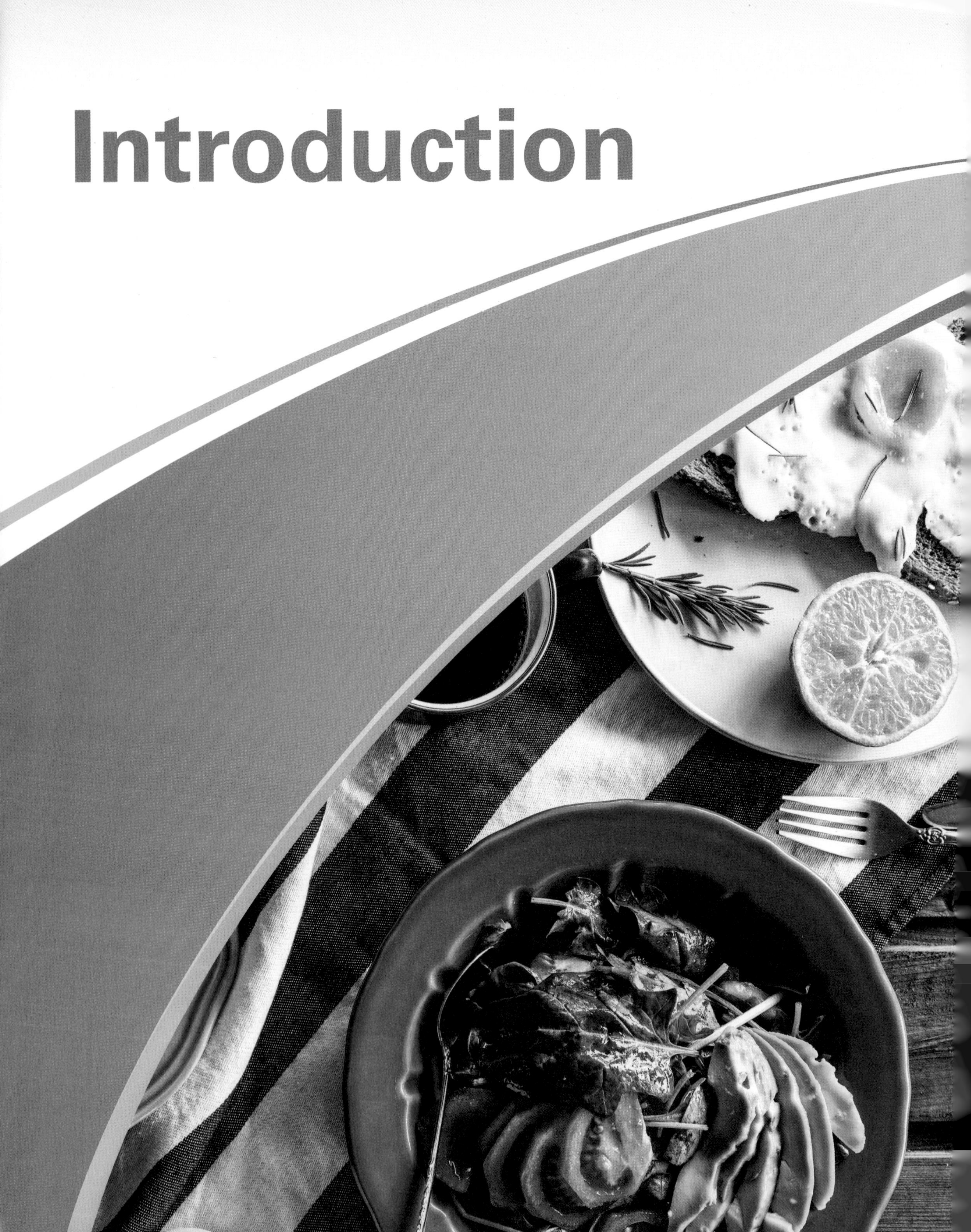

Welcome to Junior Cycle Home Economics and your new textbook, *Zest for Life*. Throughout the course you will learn how to be **healthy**, **sustainable** and **make good choices**. Home Economics is an excellent subject to prepare you for life and living and *Zest for Life* takes you on a journey of learning through many important life skills.

This textbook and the free accompanying Skills Book provide everything you need to meet the objectives of the new Junior Cycle Home Economics Specification and is written fully in line with the Junior Cycle Framework. This means that you will be fully prepared for your Classroom-Based Assessments and Final Examination when the time comes.

Structure of the book

The book contains all three strands:
Strand 1: Food, Health and Culinary Skills
Strand 2: Responsible Family Living
Strand 3: Textiles and Craft

The content prepares you for the two aspects of the Final Examination:
Practical Food Skills examination (50%)
Written examination (50%)

It also contains detailed guides on how to approach the practical and written examinations, as well as the two Classroom-Based Assessments:
CBA1: Creative Textiles
CBA2: Food Literacy Skills Brief

Key features

Learning Outcomes 1.8, 1.9, 2.4, 3.5

Learning Outcomes

Each chapter begins with a reference to the relevant Learning Outcomes that form the basis of the content.

Learning Intentions

The Learning Outcomes are then broken down into student-friendly learning intentions to help focus lessons and help students to understand the aims of the topic.

What I Will Learn

- to discuss the steps to good health
- to explain why it is important to develop a healthy lifestyle in childhood
- to state the benefits of exercise
- to define stress and explain how to avoid it
- to identify health hazards

Key Terms

Key terms are highlighted and explained throughout the book to enhance the student's literacy development.

A **staple food** is a food that is plentiful and is a main part of the diet in a particular country. It is usually cheap and readily available.

Cross-References

(see p. 100)

Cross-references link up related topics and issues, facilitating an integrated approach to learning.

Don't Forget!

'Don't Forget' information in clouds encourages the student to remember the Key Skills.

Don't Forget!

If consumers complain every time a service is unsatisfactory, they will eventually force suppliers to improve the service.

Key Words

Being litera te is one of the Key Skills students are asked to demonstrate, so Key Words are identified at the start of each chapter to enrich the student's vocabulary.

Key Words

- ✓ Balanced diet
- ✓ Food pyramid
- ✓ Serving
- ✓ Portion
- ✓ Composition
- ✓ Healthy
- ✓ Supplements

Cross-Curriculum Links

Cross-curriculum links provide the students with a wider context for their studies, and prompt further independent research.

Did You Know?

Extra information and interesting facts are included throughout the book.

Did You Know?

Even though advertising adds to the cost of products, it reduces the cost to the public of TV, radio, concerts, festivals, sporting events, newspapers and magazines.

Discovery Learning

Active learning is encouraged as students find evidence of the topic in their own lives and communities.

Discovery Learning

Pick out a TV, radio and magazine advertisement, and look at what persuasive techniques are being used in each. Which do you think is most effective and why?

Additional resources for teachers

The *Zest for Life Teacher's Resource Book* supports teachers with their planning, teaching and assessment. It includes:

- Diverse activities, quizzes and discussions for different group sizes
- Direct links to relevant parts of the textbook
- Guidance for practical classes and assessments
- Exam preparation materials
- Links to additional external resources

GillExplore.ie for teachers, which includes:

- Chapter Learning Checklists
- PowerPoint presentations
- Graphic organiser templates
- Full-colour worksheets and resources
- Glossary of key definitions in the textbook

Further Investigation

These refer students to relevant websites, videos, articles and revision aids.

Further Investigation

The Consumers' Association of Ireland is an independent voluntary organisation working on behalf of Irish consumers. It also produces the monthly *Consumer Choice* magazine. To find out more, visit **www.thecai.ie**.

Revision Toolkit

Revision Toolkit boxes provide helpful hints, tips and mnemonics to help students be exam ready.

Revision Toolkit

It is a good idea to keep a key term notebook. These terms should be listed alphabetically and include definitions. This is very important for revision and extending your vocabulary.

Be Numerate

In the kitchen, we use grams and kilograms to measure our ingredients. Minerals are measured in much smaller units:

- Milligrams: A unit of mass equal to one thousandth of a gram
- Micrograms: A unit of mass equal to one millionth of a gram

Be Numerate

Relevant figures and calculations are displayed in an accessible format.

Revision Questions

1. What is a nutrient?
2. List the five nutrients contained in food.
3. What is the other essential constituent in food?

Revision Questions

Using examination language, revision questions feature at the end of each topic to check for understanding.

Zest for Life Skills Book

The *Zest for Life Skills Book* provides a huge bank of differentiated questions, marked as follows:

- (E) Easy – these require a basic statement of fact.
- (M) Medium – these require some further discussion or explanation.
- (C) Challenging – these require more in-depth analysis or evaluation.

Used throughout the course, it is an invaluable independent learning aid for students, and once complete it serves as a comprehensive revision book. Key Skills are developed through each exercise, and end-of-chapter 'Learning Checklists' promote self-evaluation and help focus revision.

Strand 1
Food, Health and Culinary Skills

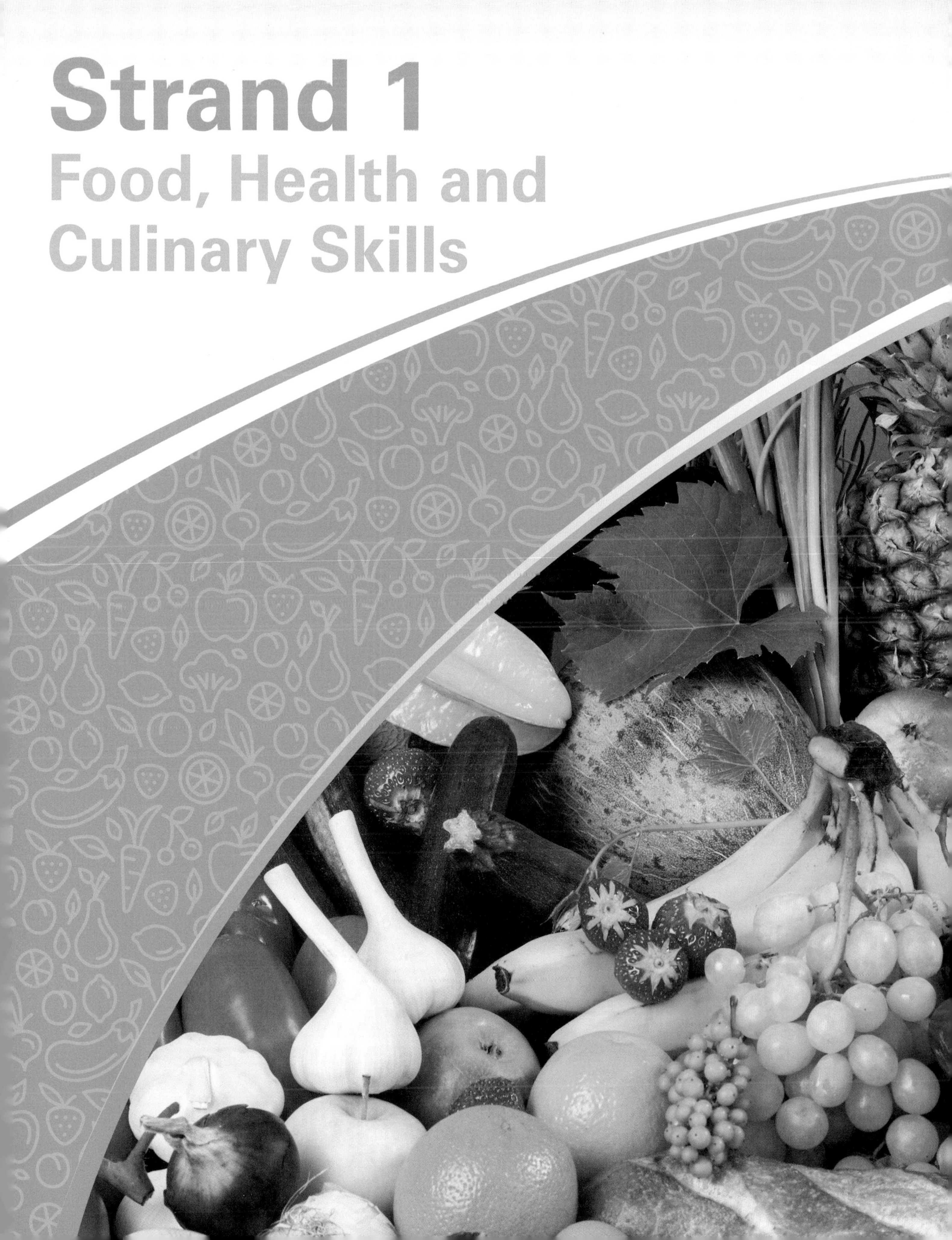

Section 1: Good Health

01 HEALTHY LIVING

 **Learning Outcomes** 1.8, 1.9, 2.4, 2.5, 3.5

What I Will Learn

- to discuss the steps to good health
- to explain why it is important to develop a healthy lifestyle in childhood
- to state the benefits of exercise
- to define stress and explain how to avoid it
- to identify health hazards

Key Words

- ✓ Health
- ✓ Rest
- ✓ Sleep
- ✓ Exercise
- ✓ Attitude
- ✓ Posture
- ✓ Leisure
- ✓ Emotions
- ✓ Stress
- ✓ Smoking
- ✓ Drugs
- ✓ Alcohol

Revision Toolkit

It is a good idea to keep a key term notebook. These terms should be listed alphabetically and include definitions. This is very important for revision and extending your vocabulary.

Steps to good health

According to the World Health Organisation (WHO), **health** is a complete state of physical, mental and social well-being, and not simply the absence of disease or infirmity.

A person's **health** is determined partly by inheritance and partly by other factors. Even the healthiest body can be damaged by neglect or abuse of substances such as cigarettes, alcohol and drugs.

Physical health is about keeping the body fit and healthy.

Emotional health is about feelings like happiness, fear and anger.

Mental health is about how we feel about ourselves and behave towards others.

Spiritual health is about our beliefs and moral values.

Social health is about how we get on with others and form relationships.

So, to lead a healthy lifestyle, a person should:

- Eat a **balanced diet**
- Get sufficient **rest** and **sleep**
- Take regular **exercise**
- Maintain good **personal hygiene**
- Take **precautions** against illnesses
- Develop a **positive attitude** to life
- **Avoid** unhealthy habits

A healthy lifestyle begins in childhood by:

- Immunising or vaccinating against certain diseases, e.g. measles and mumps.
- Getting booster shots in later years to reinforce these vaccinations.
- Receiving development checks during early childhood.
- Establishing healthy habits, i.e. having good eating patterns, getting plenty of exercise, maintaining personal hygiene and getting enough rest and sleep.

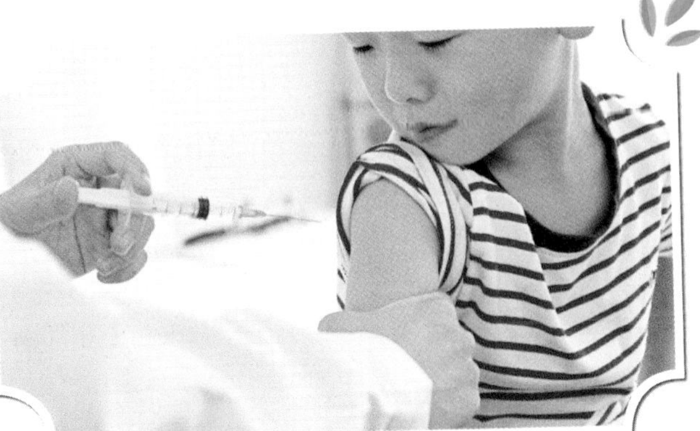

Immunisation

Further Investigation

In Ireland, the Health Service Executive runs a national immunisation programme covering from early childhood up until post-primary school. To find out more go to **www.hse.ie**, click on 'Health A–Z' on the top of the home page and then click on 'Immunisation'.

A balanced diet

Eat a healthy and balanced diet; follow the healthy eating and meal planning guidelines (**see p. 56**).

Rest and sleep

- Rest and sleep restore energy and relax the mind, so they are an important part of staying healthy at any age. They are particularly important for young children and teenagers, as they support their growth and development.
- Sleep helps the brain work better and improves concentration, which, in turn, improves learning and problem-solving.
- Getting a good night's sleep helps us look and feel better.
- Everyone needs different amounts of sleep. For example, teenagers generally need between seven and nine hours' sleep per night. Some people suffer from **insomnia**, which is an inability to fall asleep or to remain asleep long enough to feel rested. Ongoing sleep deficiency can lead to an increased risk of heart disease, kidney disease, high blood pressure, diabetes and strokes in adults.

Relaxation and leisure

- Leisure time gives us a chance to relax and take a break from the stresses of daily life. It should be enjoyable and, if possible, should be spent on interesting and rewarding activities.
- Many people choose activities that contrast with their work, e.g. a person who works in an office might cycle as a hobby.
- Using leisure time wisely can reduce stress, relieve boredom, keep your brain active, maintain your fitness, enable you to learn something new, help someone else and help you make friends.

Did You Know?

Youth clubs are a great way for teenagers to socialise and learn new skills. To find out more visit ***www.foroige.ie***.

Exercise and fitness

Exercise is vital for good health. If you do not exercise, you will be unfit. Lack of fitness can lead to obesity, stress, heart disease and breathing difficulties.

The benefits of exercise

- Improves fitness levels.
- Keeps joints flexible and muscles toned.
- Improves health and well-being.
- Leads to more efficient heart and lungs, which reduce the risk of coronary heart disease.
- Can lead to weight loss if combined with a healthy diet.
- May reduce blood pressure.
- Keeps the brain active and alert.
- Can slow the ageing process down.
- Team sports help people to increase in confidence and communicate better.
- Social activities can reduce loneliness and isolation for older people.
- Improves posture and balance.

Discovery Learning

Find out what **aerobic exercise** is and explain why it is beneficial to people of all ages. **Be creative** in how you present your findings to the class.

Stand tall and be confident!

Correct **posture** involves walking, standing or sitting tall and upright. It is an essential part of looking and feeling well. Slouching inhibits breathing and can affect your digestion. Even if you are healthy and fit, you will not look good unless you have good posture.

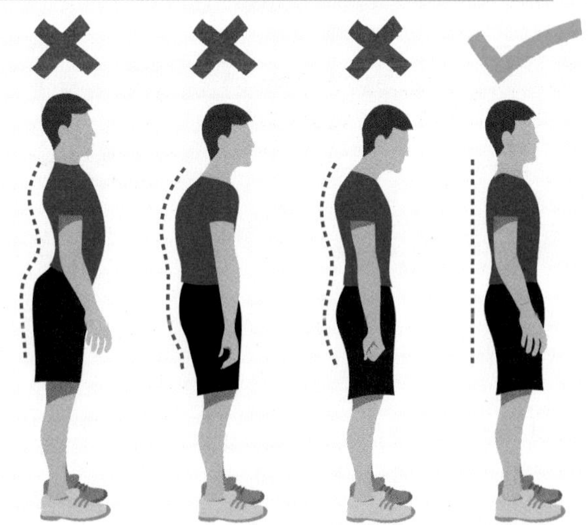

Good and bad posture

Good personal hygiene

Good personal hygiene is very important for personal comfort and the comfort of others.

Wash your hands frequently during the day, particularly after using the toilet and before eating.

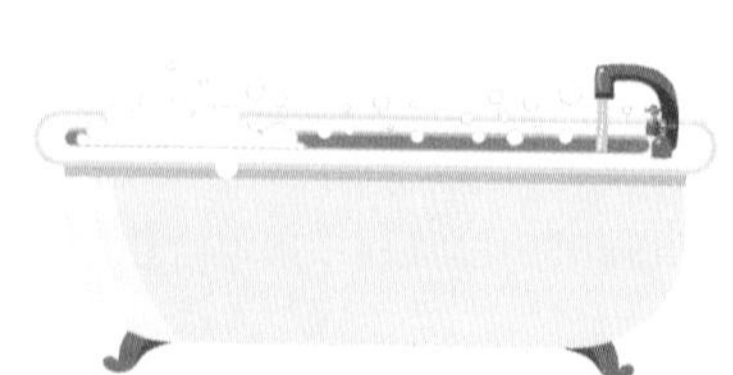

Take a shower or have a bath every day.

Wash your hair at least once a week.

Use warm water, soap/gel and friction to clean skin thoroughly.

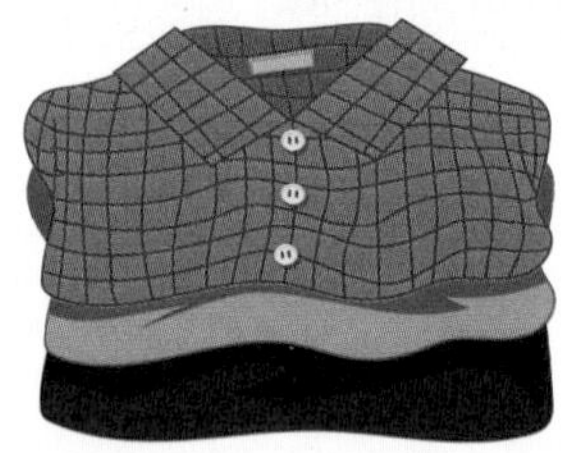

Change underwear and socks every day and change and wash outer garments on a regular basis.

Brush your teeth every morning and night and, if possible, after meals.

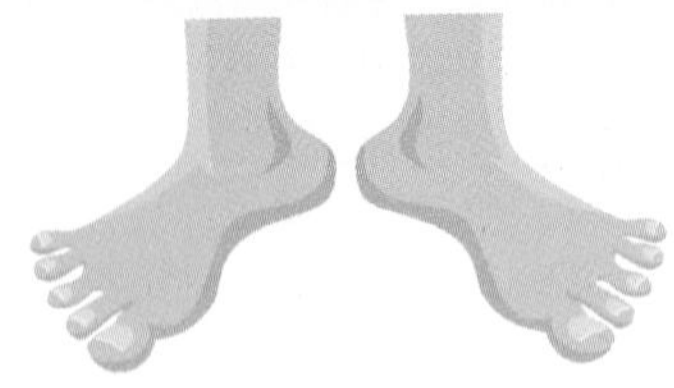

Parts of the body that need particular attention are the feet, the groin and the underarms, as these areas perspire most frequently.

Use a deodorant or antiperspirant after washing.

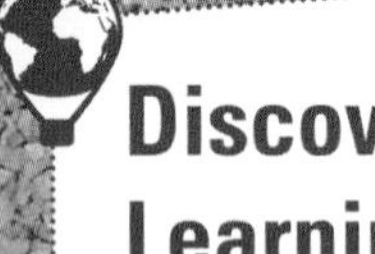

Discovery Learning

Do you know what the difference between an antiperspirant and a deodorant is? Go ahead and find out.

Good mental health

Mental health is concerned with the health and well-being of the mind. It affects our reactions to our relationships and those around us. A mentally healthy person is:

- Free from mental illness.
- Able to cope with the ups and downs of day-to-day life.
- Reasonably content and has a positive attitude to life, i.e. has high self-esteem.
- Confident enough to deal comfortably with other people.

Mental health guidelines

- Look after your physical health – eat well, exercise regularly, relax and get plenty of sleep.
- Avoid unhealthy habits – do not smoke or use drugs. If drinking alcohol, consume within healthy limits (**see p. 10**).
- Think positively about yourself.
- Form a few close friendships with people you can trust. Discuss any problems and feelings with them. Try not to neglect these people if you start a new relationship.
- Have a good routine, eat regularly and get enough sleep.
- Make good use of your leisure time.
- Avoid stress as much as possible. Mindfulness and meditation can help with this.

Don't Forget!
Physical and mental health go hand in hand – neglect one and the other suffers. Sometimes advice from your doctor, a counsellor or dietitian may be needed, so don't ever be afraid to ask for help.

Attitudes

- Our attitudes are the way we feel about life in general.
- Attitudes may be positive or negative.
- People with positive attitudes look on the bright side of life.
- People with negative attitudes tend to see only problems.

Further Investigation
Our attitudes are greatly influenced by how we were treated as children. Read the poem 'Children Learn What They Live' by Dorothy Law Nolte online. What do you think about this poem?

Emotions

Emotions are the feelings that we have. The basic emotions are:

- **Happiness:** This is a feeling that is nurtured by love and security. It is very important to love yourself – this means that you concentrate on your good qualities and try to change or accept your flaws. If a person does not love or accept themselves, it is difficult to love others. We do not feel happy all the time, but it is important to maintain a level of contentedness with oneself and one's life.
- **Anger:** Sometimes anger is seen as a negative emotion, but sometimes we are entitled to be angry. It is how we cope with anger that is important. Children often get angry when they do not get their own way – they can stamp, scream or throw a tantrum. However, it is unacceptable for a teenager or adult to react in this way. If you react calmly by explaining how you feel and why, this is a positive and constructive response.

- **Sadness:** This can range from mild sadness to depression. It can be caused by many things, such as loss, disappointment or loneliness. It is important to talk to others when you feel sad as this feeling is helped by the insight and support of others.
- **Fear:** This can be real or imaginary. We can be afraid of big things like exams, illness and the future, or little things like spiders. Anxiety is a condition that is associated with fear. It is a feeling of worry or unease about something and can range from mild to severe. It is very common to feel anxious – talking to others helps, but see a doctor if anxiety or low mood is affecting your day-to-day life.

Stress

- Stress is a normal reaction to difficulties in our lives. Some stress is healthy but sometimes we can experience too much of it. When someone is experiencing a lot of pressure and tension, they are said to be under stress.
- Different factors cause stress in different people – unemployment, marital breakdown and poverty are just a few examples.
- Stress can affect a person's mental and physical health; it can affect behaviour and lead to health problems.
- Continuous stress may result in symptoms such as anxiety, aggression, depression, fatigue, moodiness, low self-esteem, guilt and apathy.

Stress in teenagers

Caused by	Relieved by
• School work and exams • Peer pressure • Bullying • Conflict at home • Relationships	• Talking problems over with a friend or someone you can trust • Being organised and prepared • Trying to take complete breaks from the stressful situation • Taking physical exercise • Taking part in craftwork, such as knitting, crochet or patchwork, is known to have therapeutic (healing) effects, making you feel calmer and more relaxed.

Health hazards

Every year in Ireland, thousands of people get ill or die prematurely because they expose themselves to health hazards like smoking, excessive alcohol or illegal drugs use.

Quick facts on smoking

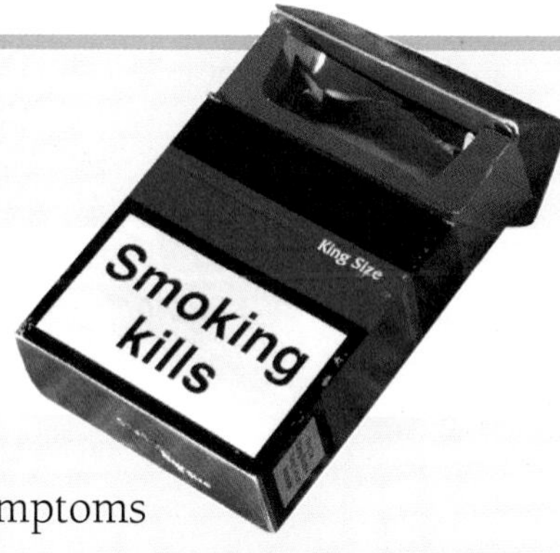

Reasons why people start to smoke	Curiosity, image, peer pressure and bad example
Harmful substances in cigarettes	Nicotine, tar, carbon monoxide, irritants and carcinogens
Harmful effects of smoking	• Affects your sense of taste and smell • Smoking is addictive and people can have withdrawal symptoms when they try to stop • Makes it difficult to stay fit and active • Causes bad breath, stained fingers and teeth, and lingering bad odour on clothes • Causes premature ageing and wrinkles • Can cause cancer in the lungs, stomach, mouth and throat • Increases risk of heart disease and can lead to strokes • Respiratory conditions: emphysema, bronchitis and smoker's cough
On a pregnant woman	• Miscarriages • Stillbirths
On children of smokers	• Lung infections • Asthma
Passive smoking	Passive smoking means breathing in tobacco smoke from the air in a smoky atmosphere. This is known as environmental tobacco smoke (ETS). Passive smokers can also suffer from smokers' diseases such as lung cancer, heart disease and bronchitis.
Government actions on smoking	• Smoking is banned in public places • There are high taxes on cigarettes so they cost a lot • Cigarettes and tobacco are not on display in shops and they cannot be advertised • Advertisements highlight the ill effects of smoking • It is illegal to sell cigarettes or tobacco to anyone under 18 • Packaging must carry health warnings and have graphic images of the effects of smoking • There is a plan in place (at the time of writing) to use plain packaging on cigarettes and tobacco to reduce appeal • There is a ban on selling packs of 10 cigarettes

Discovery Learning

Find out how much a packet of cigarettes costs and calculate how much money a person who smokes 20 cigarettes a day would spend over a year. Are you surprised at how much it costs?

Did You Know?

Alcohol is measured in units. Different drinks contain different amounts of alcohol. Consumption guidelines for alcohol are:

- **Men**: Not more than 17 units per week.
- **Women**: Not more than than 11 units per week.

1 unit =
100 ml glass of wine

Half a pint of beer

A small spirit or alcopop

Quick facts on alcohol

Reasons why young people abuse alcohol	• Curiosity • Peer pressure and image • Bad example • Easily available and reasonably cheap • Acts as a relaxant and gives people confidence
The dangers of drinking early in life	• Interferes with the ongoing physical, intellectual and emotional development of teenagers • Teenagers who drink can develop drinking problems more easily • Alcohol hits young drinkers more quickly – they may lose self-control or become involved in antisocial behaviour • Negatively affects school or college work • Can lead to taking sexual risks, which can cause pregnancy or the spread of disease
A person's reaction to alcohol is affected by …	• How **much** they drink • How **quickly** they drink • Their **body size** • Their **gender** • Whether or not the person has recently **eaten**
Immediate effects of drinking alcohol	• Face turns red • Loss of co-ordination, slurred speech and staggering • Mood alters – a person can become sad or aggressive • Brain slows down so powers of reasoning and judgement are decreased • Poor driving skills • Excessive drinking can cause vomiting or loss of consciousness • Alcohol is poisonous – binge-drinking can result in death
Long-term effects of alcohol abuse	**On the individual** • Addiction • Brain damage resulting in loss of judgement and co-ordination • Mental illness, e.g. depression • Cirrhosis of the liver (scarring) • Damage to unborn baby during pregnancy (foetal alcohol syndrome) • Cancer of mouth, throat or stomach • Heart disease, stomach ulcers and obesity • Death

	On the family • Domestic unhappiness and uncertainty • Separation and divorce • Financial problems **On the community** • Violence • Increase in road deaths • Increase in crime, e.g. public order offences, rape, homicide • High costs of treating people for alcohol-related health problems • Absenteeism from work, which can lead to job losses
Where to get help	• Alcoholics Anonymous for individual • Al-Anon for partners or adult relatives • Alateen for children of problem drinkers
Government action on alcohol	• It is illegal to sell alcohol to anyone under 18 years and an offence to buy it for them • It is an offence for anyone under 18 to drink alcohol in a public place • Children are not allowed in pubs after 9 p.m. • The hours for selling alcohol in supermarkets and off-licences are restricted
Guidelines for drinking sensibly	• Drink slowly and in moderation (see recommended units below) • Eat before or while drinking • Avoid drinking in 'rounds', which means having to drink as fast as others • Never drink if you are taking medication • Do not mix alcoholic drinks • Do not drive after drinking or travel with anyone who has been drinking • Do not pressure anyone else to drink

Further Investigation

To find out more about the support available for those with problem drinkers or drug addicts in the family, visit the following websites:

www.alcoholicsanonymous.ie
www.al-anon-ireland.org
www.aiseiri.ie

Quick facts on drugs

What are drugs?	• A drug is any substance other than food that has an effect on the body • Some drugs contain chemicals that can be helpful to the body if used correctly • Drugs can be ingested, inhaled, smoked or injected • Drugs fall into three categories: 1. **Commonly used drugs (legal drugs)**, e.g. alcohol, nicotine, caffeine in tea and coffee, and painkillers 2. **Controlled drugs (by prescription only)**, e.g. antibiotics, sleeping pills and sedatives 3. **Illegal drugs**, e.g. cannabis, cocaine, ecstasy, LSD and heroin
Why do people take drugs?	• Curiosity • Peer pressure and image • Bad example • Easily available and reasonably cheap • Drugs act as either relaxants or stimulants and give people confidence
Effects of drug abuse	**On the individual** • Addiction and severe withdrawal symptoms • Health is damaged by the effects of drugs and self-neglect • A tolerance to the drug is built up, so more is needed to get the same effect • Mental illness, e.g. depression, psychosis • HIV and other infections can be spread through the use of dirty needles • Death – many addicts die from overdosing, suicide, inhaling solvents or as a result of AIDS **On the family** • Domestic unhappiness and uncertainty • Financial problems • Violence • Separation and divorce **On the community** • Increase in road deaths • Increase in crime – possessing, buying and selling drugs are illegal • Many addicts resort to crime to feed their habit • High costs of medical care and law enforcement • Absenteeism from work can lead to job losses

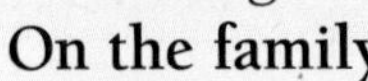

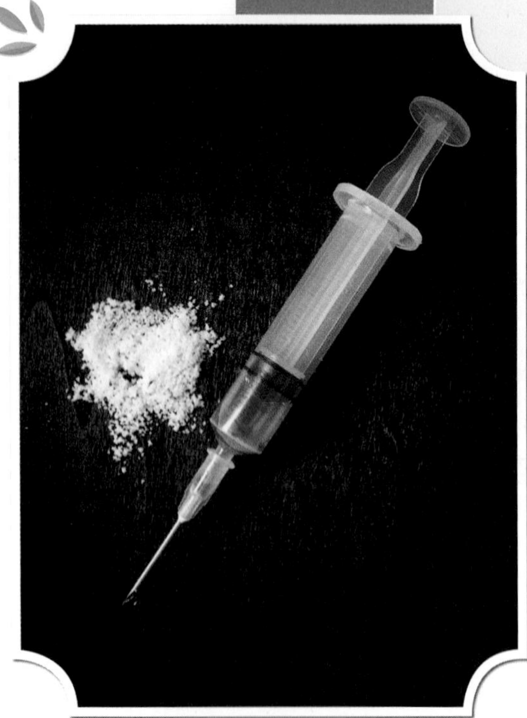

Where to get help	• The Health Service Executive (HSE) treatment centres, e.g. Aiséirí centres • Narcotics Anonymous
Government action on drugs	• It is illegal to possess, buy and sell drugs in Ireland • The HSE offers drug treatment programmes • Legislation on drug driving was introduced in April 2017, which allows Gardaí to do roadside drug testing

The Health Promotion Unit

- This organisation is run by the Department of Health.
- It provides information to the public on all health matters, e.g. immunisation, drugs, smoking, alcohol, nutrition and medical conditions.
- It also runs national campaigns on issues such as healthy eating.
- It is involved in promoting a healthy lifestyle for all.

Further Investigation

To find out more about health issues, visit the following websites:
www.healthpromotion.ie
www.spunout.ie

Revision Questions

1. List the steps to good health.
2. List four benefits of exercise.
3. Discuss why it is important for teenagers to have hobbies.
4. Why is it important to have a positive mental attitude?
5. List some factors that contribute to good mental health.
6. What should a teenager do if they are stressed or anxious?

Use your workbook to revise this chapter •

Summary

- **To stay fit and healthy**, eat a balanced diet, get sufficient rest and sleep, and take regular exercise.
- **Good health starts in childhood** with immunisation against disease, developmental checks and establishing healthy eating habits.
- **Maintain good personal hygiene** and take precautions against illness.
- Having a positive attitude to life leads to **good mental health**.
- Balance getting enough rest and sleep with taking **regular exercise** to reduce stress. Regular exercise improves fitness, health and muscle tone. Aerobic exercise reduces the risk of heart disease. Taking up leisure activities also reduces stress, relieves boredom and keeps you active.
- **Avoid unhealthy habits**, e.g. smoking, alcohol and drugs.

02 HEALTHY EATING

Learning Outcomes 1.1, 1.8, 1.9, 1.15, 1.16, 2.4

What I Will Learn

- to explain what food is
- to state the functions of food
- to discuss why it is important to develop healthy eating habits in childhood
- to recognise the relationship between healthy eating and making good food choices
- to identify the factors that affect personal food choices

Key Words

✓Food
✓Lifestyle
✓Growth
✓Repair
✓Heat
✓Energy
✓Regulate
✓Protect
✓Senses
✓Nutrition
✓Malnutrition

What is food?

Food is any solid or liquid that provides the body with nutrients.

Food is necessary:

- For **growth** and **repair** of body cells
- To provide **heat** and **energy** for the body
- To **regulate** and **protect** the body

Don't Forget!
Good food choices are linked to good health.

We also eat food because we:

- feel hungry
- like the flavours and smells of different foods
- like eating with others
- enjoy celebrating special events with meals

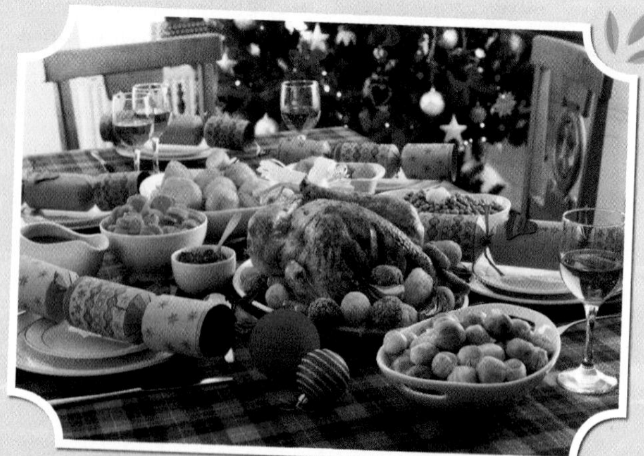

Food choices

You are what you eat. Everything that you eat and drink affects how your body works. Your body's needs vary at different stages of your life, and your nutritional needs vary according to how you live your life.

Most foods will keep us alive, but in order to keep the body healthy we must choose nutritious foods. Eating a wide variety of food helps us maintain good health. Bad food choices lead to bad health – many diseases such as cancer, diabetes, heart disease and dental decay are associated with an unhealthy diet.

Good food choices

Bad food choices

Revision Toolkit

Use the following mnemonic to help you remember the factors affecting food choices:

CAN SAM Cook **H**ealthily?

Culture
Availability
Nutritional awareness
Senses
A person's eating habits
Marketing and advertising
Cost
Health status

Factors affecting food choices

The types of food eaten varies from country to country and within particular countries. Many factors affect our choice of foods. These include:

Culture

The country we live in and the group or race of people we belong to influence what we eat. In Ireland, bread and potatoes are **staple foods**. Different countries have their own food culture and eat certain types of food, e.g. Italians eat a lot of pasta, and Chinese people eat a lot of rice.

Religious beliefs also have an influence on food choices, e.g. Hindus are often vegetarians, and Muslims don't eat pork. Due to immigration and travel, many world cuisine restaurants have opened in Ireland, e.g. Thai, Indian and Lebanese. Television and the internet have also given us greater exposure to a wide variety of cooking techniques and recipes.

A **staple food** is a food that is plentiful and is a main part of the diet in a particular country. It is usually cheap and readily available.

Classroom-Based Assessment

This activity is linked to CBA2.

Discovery Learning

Investigate a country of your choice under the following headings:

- Location (what continent?)
- Flag
- Language/s spoken
- An interesting fact about the country
- The foods associated with that country

Present your project in a creative way to the rest of the class (five minutes max).

Further Investigation

Do you want to find out more about foods in season? Visit **www.bestinseason.ie** and click on 'What's in Season' on the left-hand side of the home page.

Availability

Nowadays, a wider variety of different foods are more readily available due to improvements in technology and transportation. This makes food available all year round, including canned and frozen food. However, different foods are more available at certain times of the year when they are **in season**, e.g. Brussels sprouts at Christmas. People living in rural areas may not have access to all available foods and therefore may have a more limited choice.

In season refers to the time of year when a given type of food is at its peak. This is usually the time when the item is the cheapest, the freshest and most flavoursome.

Nutritional awareness

People today tend to be more health-conscious. They read food labels and make healthier food choices, e.g. buying food that is fresh, high in fibre, and low in sugar, salt and fat. Many food companies now place specific nutritional information on the front of food packets to make it easier for consumers to make healthy food choices.

More people know about nutrition and health these days because of the work of the Health Promotion Unit and Bord Bia, school subjects like Home Economics, Well-being and Science, as well as television programmes like RTÉ's 'Operation Transformation'.

A nutritional information label

Malnutrition means bad nutrition. It is an incorrect balance of nutrients in the body that can be caused by:

- too much food (obesity)
- too little food (starvation)
- a lack of certain nutrients (deficiency diseases)

Sensory aspects

We use our **senses** when eating – they help us decide whether we like or dislike food.

Sight: When food is well presented and looks attractive, it makes us want to eat it.

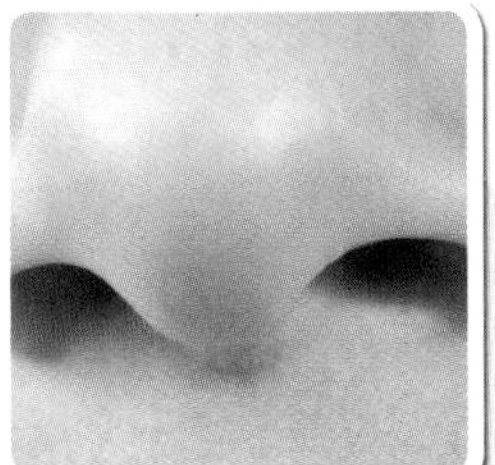

Smell: There are cells in our nose that pick up the odours of food. These make our mouths water and stimulate our digestive juices.

Touch: We use our hands when preparing food and our tongue when eating. They sense the food's temperature (i.e. hot or cold) and texture (e.g. smooth, crunchy, soft or lumpy).

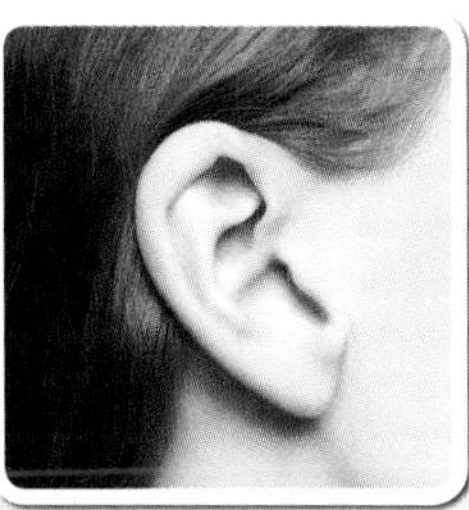

Hearing: We use our ears to hear the sounds associated with food and determine their freshness, e.g. the crunch of crisps, the sizzle of sausages.

Taste: Cells on the tongue, called taste buds, help us experience different flavours: bitter, sour, salty and sweet.

Did You Know?

Butterflies have taste buds on their tongues and on their feet!

Further Investigation

Do you know how the taste buds work? To find out more, go to YouTube and watch the video 'How Do Taste Buds Work?' (1:48).

Discovery Learning

Use your senses to identify a variety of foodstuffs. Work in pairs to identify foods by touch, taste, sight, hearing and smell.

Eating patterns

Lifestyle: This affects eating patterns, which, in turn, affect food choices. Busy lifestyles affect the food we choose to eat. People often choose to cook convenience meals, which are ready to eat and require little preparation, or to eat fast food or takeaways, or to eat out in restaurants. The type of work someone does and the hours they work also influence meal times and their choice of food, for example, family members on different schedules eat at separate times, leading to fewer family meals. Other influencing factors include a person's leisure pursuits and their moral or religious beliefs.

Marketing and advertising: Marketing strategies and advertising influence our food choices. The ways in which food products are marketed and advertised have been shown to influence what we choose to buy. Advertising campaigns aim to increase awareness of a product with a specific target market in mind. The different advertising media used include television, radio, the internet, billboards and magazines. Marketing strategies influence our food choices with clever supermarket layouts, e.g. luxuries at eye level, special promotions and tasting sessions.

Discovery Learning

Watch the following advertisements on YouTube:
'Adventures in Imagination: M&S Food – TV Ad 2014' (1:00)
'M&S Food: Taste of the British Isles – TV Ad 2015' (0:40)
How do these advertisements appeal to our senses and make us want to eat the food?

Discovery Learning

Choose 10 ingredients that you would use at home, then visit your local supermarket or go online and find out the price of each ingredient.

Classroom-Based Assessment

This activity is linked to CBA2 and the Practical Food Skills examination. Working out the cost of a meal is an important skill.

Cost: The price of food affects our food choices. It influences where we shop and the range of foods we can buy. Wealthy people can afford to regularly eat out and travel abroad, both of which enable them to widen their experiences of different foods. Families on a limited budget must buy cheaper foods and fewer luxury food items. However, it is possible to eat nourishing food on a limited budget, e.g. buying vegetables that are in season and buying minced beef instead of fillet steak.

Health status: A person's state of health will influence what foods they eat. Special dietary needs must be taken into consideration when choosing foods, e.g. a person with high cholesterol should choose low-fat products, while a person with coeliac disease (**see p. 80**) must restrict their gluten intake. Pregnant women, older people and people recovering from illness all have to be aware of their particular health status when choosing food.

Regardless of the factors that influence our food choices, it is important that we eat food that keeps us healthy and nourished. It is therefore important to understand nutrition properly.

Revision Questions

1. Why do we eat food?
2. Give three examples of poor food choices.
3. Name some foods that are good for us but that are not very expensive.
4. List five factors that influence our food choices.
5. Explain how a person's religious beliefs might affect their food choices.
6. Name three diseases associated with poor health.
7. How do parents influence their children's food choices and eating patterns?
8. Which senses affect our food choices the most?

Summary

- We need to eat to stay alive, for **growth and repair** of body cells, to provide **heat** and **energy** for the body and to **regulate** and **protect** the body.
- We also eat because we feel hungry, to experience the different flavours and smells of foods, and because we like eating with others and celebrating special events.
- The factors that affect food choices include culture, availability, nutritional awareness, senses, a person's eating habits, marketing and advertising, cost and health status.

Section 2: Nutrition Know-How

03 NUTRITION

Learning Outcomes 1.9, 1.10, 1.11, 1.12, 1.13, 1.14, 1.18, 1.19, 2.4, 2.5, 2.10

What I Will Learn

- to explain what a nutrient is
- to identify the nutrients
- to differentiate between macronutrients and micronutrients
- to state the sources of each nutrient
- to describe the composition of each nutrient
- to classify each nutrient
- to explain the function of each nutrient
- to state the effects of deficiency diseases
- to describe the effects of overconsumption of certain nutrients on the body
- to explain what Reference Intake means

Key Words

✓ Nutrients
✓ Protein
✓ Fats
✓ Carbohydrates
✓ Protein
✓ Minerals
✓ Vitamins
✓ Water
✓ Energy

Don't Forget!
If you come across a word you do not understand, use a dictionary/thesaurus to help you find the meaning.

A **constituent** is a part of a whole. For example, ingredients are constituents of a recipe.

Nutrition is the study of food. **Food** is any solid or liquid that provides the body with nutrients.

All food is made from chemical substances called **nutrients**, which can be digested and used by the body to make it function properly.

There are six **constituents** found in food, five of which are **nutrients**.

1. Proteins
2. Carbohydrates
3. Fats
4. Vitamins
5. Minerals
6. Water (this is a constituent that is necessary for the body to function correctly, although not a nutrient itself)

Nutrients: The chemical substances that make up food, e.g. protein.

Elements: Individual chemicals, e.g. carbon.

Constituent: Part of a whole.

Composition of nutrients: Refers to the structure of each nutrient, i.e. how the elements are arranged.

Composition of food: The amount of each nutrient in a food.

Sources: Foods that supply a nutrient.

Function: A job a nutrient has in the body.

Reference Intake (RI): The average daily intake level of a nutrient that is sufficient to meet the nutritional requirements of 97.5% of people in a specific age group to stay healthy and prevent disease.

Deficiency diseases: Diseases caused by lack of a nutrient.

Molecules: The smallest units of a nutrient, e.g. glucose.

Classification: Grouping together.

Macro: Large.

Micro: Tiny.

Nutrients are **classified** into two groups, according to their size and the amount the body requires.

Macronutrients	Micronutrients
Proteins, carbohydrates and fats (needed by the body in large amounts)	Vitamins and minerals (needed by the body in small amounts)

Most foods contain several nutrients, and are considered very nutritious, e.g. milk. However, no single food contains all the nutrients in the correct proportion for the body's needs. As a result, we must eat a good variety of foods every day in order to stay healthy.

We need the **macronutrients protein**, **carbohydrates** and **fats** in large amounts. They must be broken down by the body during digestion. The **micronutrients vitamins** and **minerals** are needed in smaller amounts and need no digestion (**digestion, see p. 46**).

Revision Questions

1. What is a nutrient?
2. List the five nutrients contained in food.
3. What is the other essential constituent in food?

Protein

Key Words

- ✓ Amino acid
- ✓ Essential
- ✓ Biological
- ✓ Enzyme
- ✓ Hormone

An **enzyme** is a chemical catalyst that speeds up or slows down a reaction without being changed or used up in the reaction itself.

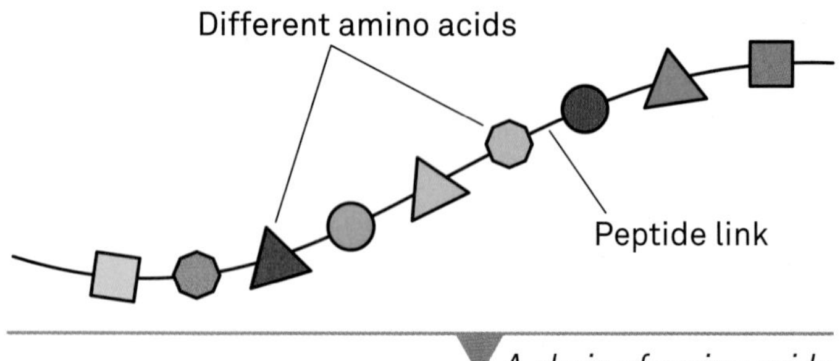

A chain of amino acids

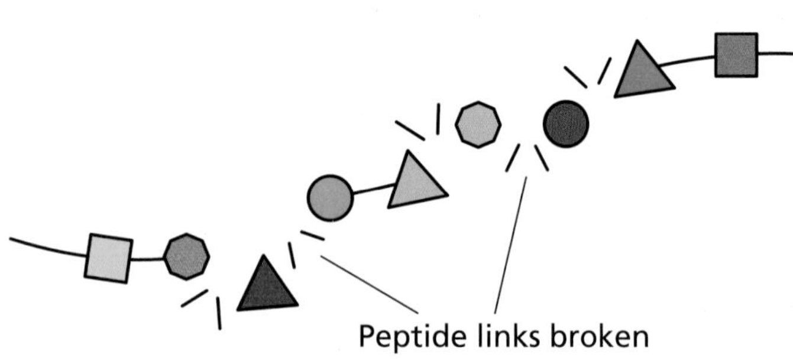

A protein chain being broken down during digestion

Protein is the most important nutrient. It is essential for every body cell.

Composition of proteins

- Proteins are made up of the four **elements** carbon (C), hydrogen (H), oxygen (O) and nitrogen (N).
- Proteins are the only nutrient to contain **nitrogen**, which is necessary for the growth of new cells.
- Each protein is made up of a chain of smaller units called **amino acids**.
- Protein is made up of a chain of amino acids joined together by **peptide links**.

During digestion, these peptide links are broken apart by **enzymes**, freeing each amino acid so that it can easily be absorbed into the bloodstream to keep the body nourished.

Revision Toolkit

Use the following mnemonic to help you remember the elements in protein:

Ciara Has One Nephew
Carbon Hydrogen Oxygen Nitrogen

Classification and sources of proteins

Proteins are classified according to their **source** or **quality**.

The body can break down amino acids in a protein chain and manufacture new proteins from some of them. However, some amino acids cannot be made by the body and must be taken into the body in the foods that we eat. These are called **essential amino acids**.

High biological value (HBV) proteins contain most of the essential amino acids and usually come from animal sources. **Low biological value (LBV)** proteins contain fewer essential amino acids and usually come from plant sources.

It is important to get your protein from both **plant** and **animal** sources.

Plant foods are a valuable source of protein. It is very important to eat plenty of plant or vegetable sources of protein because they are healthier, have more fibre, less fat, and are cheaper to produce (**see vegetarian diets, p. 68**).

Meat alternatives

There are many different high-protein meat alternatives on the market today, including:

- **Textured vegetable protein (TVP)**, which is made from soya beans. TVP is high in protein and calcium, but is low in fat, so is an excellent meat alternative. It is available in steak or minced form.
- **Mycoprotein** (e.g. Quorn) is made from edible fungi. It is available as a cooking ingredient and as a range of ready meals.

Quorn

Did You Know?

Though they come from a plant source, soya beans are HBV. TVP and mycoprotein products like Quorn are also HBV.

Source	Animal	Vegetable
Quality	High biological value (HBV) or 1st class protein	Low biological value (LBV) or 2nd class protein
Examples	Meat, fish, eggs, milk, cheese, yoghurt, soya beans, TVP and Quorn	Peas, beans, cereals, nuts, bread, pasta and breakfast cereals

Functions of proteins

- Growth of body cells (skin, blood, tissues and bone)
- Repair of damaged cells (cuts)
- Produce heat (temperature control)
- Provide energy (ability to work)
- Produce important body chemicals such as enzymes, hormones and antibodies

Protein deficiency symptoms

- Poor or stunted growth
- Slow healing
- Poor general health
- Imbalance of hormones and enzymes
- The body is open to infection and disease as fewer antibodies are produced

Reference Intake (RI) of proteins

Adults need approximately 1 g of protein per 1 kg of body weight daily. Children and teenagers need more because they are growing.

Further Investigation

Find out more about plant foods as a source of protein by going to **www.care2.com** and searching for 'Best Protein Alternatives to Meat Besides Tofu' (**see vegetarian diets, p. 68**).

Revision Questions

1. Explain the following terms: (a) amino acid, (b) essential amino acids and (c) high biological value.
2. Classify protein and give four sources in each class.
3. Explain the importance of protein in the diet of (a) a pregnant woman, (b) children and (c) an older person.

Carbohydrates

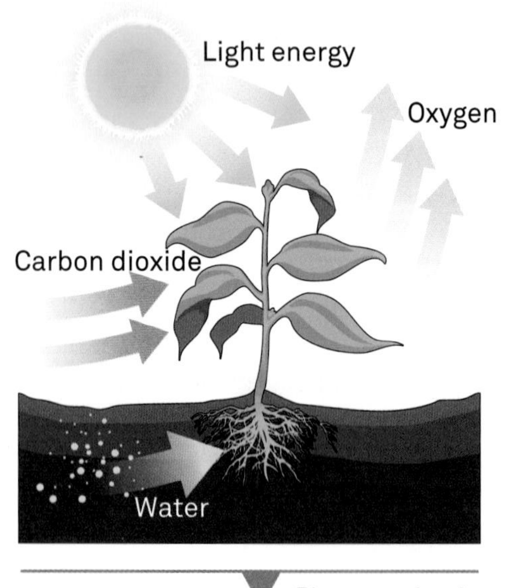

Photosynthesis

Key Words

✓ Photosynthesis	✓ Fibre
✓ Source	✓ Starch
✓ Glucose	✓ Vegetable
✓ Sugar	✓ Constipation

Carbohydrates are found in plant foods only and are the most plentiful nutrient. Plants can manufacture their own food by a process called **photosynthesis**.

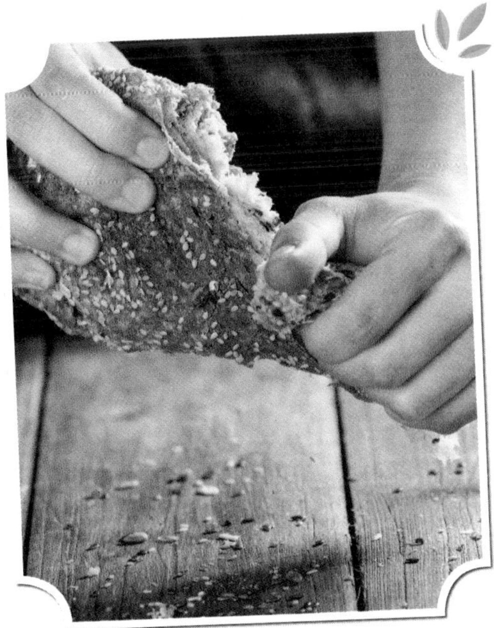

Composition of carbohydrates

Carbohydrates are made up of the elements carbon (C), hydrogen (H) and oxygen (O). These elements combine to form **simple sugar molecules, e.g. glucose**. When several sugar molecules join together they form long chains of starch. During digestion, the starch is broken into individual sugar molecules.

Further Investigation

Find out more about photosynthesis by going to YouTube and watching the video 'Photosynthesis | Photosynthesis in plants | Photosynthesis – Biology Basics for children | elearnin' (4:52).

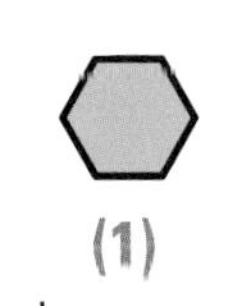

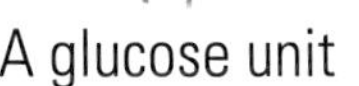

(1)
A glucose unit

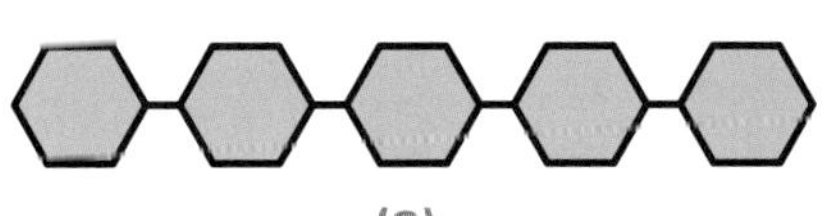

(2)
Starch

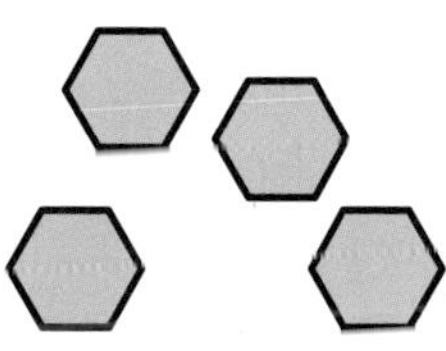

(3)
Starch after digestion

Digestion of carbohydrates

Classification and sources of carbohydrates

Carbohydrates are categorised into three groups.

Sugars	Starch	Dietary fibre

Sugar, honey, cakes, biscuits, jam, fruit, sweets and soft drinks	Cereals, pasta, flour, bread and potatoes	Whole cereals, oatmeal, wholemeal bread, outer skins of fruit and vegetables

Functions of carbohydrates

- Supply heat and provide energy (sugar and starch)
- Excess carbohydrate is stored as fat (adipose tissue)
- Insulate the body
- Dietary fibre moves waste materials through the intestines
- Dietary fibre prevents bowel disease

Don't Forget!
To stay healthy, try to increase your fibre intake and decrease your sugar intake.

Carbohydrate deficiency symptoms

- Poor general health
- Leaves a person open to infection and disease
- Constipation

Carbohydrate deficiency is rare, except for fibre.

Sugar

It is not a good idea to eat too many foods that are high in sugar, as they provide '**empty kilocalories**'. This means that they only contain sugar and are lacking in any nutritional value, e.g. some soft drinks. Many processed foods like ready meals, cakes and confectionery contain high levels of added sugars and can be high in calories. Cutting down on these will help maintain a healthy weight, as too much sugar leads to obesity and tooth decay. Sugar and sugary foods are included on the top shelf of the food pyramid (**see p. 54**) and need to be limited.

0% • Vitamin E 25% • Thiamin 25% • Riboflav
25% • Pantothenic Acid 25% • Phosphorus 20
num 35%
DGE (CORN SYRUP, INVERT SUGAR, PEANUT BUTTER [PEANUT
ROB SEED GUM, BETA-CAROTENE), CHOCOLATE FLAVORED C
A FLAVOR), CORN SYRUP, ACACIA GUM, FRUCTOSE SYRUP, PE
PHOSPHATE, SALT, **VITAMIN AND MINERAL BLEND** (CALCIU
ROUS FUMARATE, PYRIDOXINE HYDROCHLORIDE, VITAMIN A PA
LAMIN).
ES EGGS, TREE NUTS AND WHEAT.

Hidden sugars

Many foods contain 'hidden sugars'. These foods may not taste sweet but may contain a lot of sugar, e.g. crisps or savoury sauces like tomato ketchup.

Remember, added sugars can be called by their chemical names – sucrose, glucose, maltose, fructose, dextrose – and are also in syrups and honey, so always check the nutrition label on the back or side of packaged foods because they could contain more sugar than you think.

Did You Know?

EU guidelines on nutrition labels tell you if a food or drink is high or low in sugar:

- High is more than 15 g of total sugars per 100 g
- Low is 5 g or less of total sugars per 100 g

If you are trying to cut down on sugar, you should limit your consumption of foods that have more than 5 g/100 g.

How to reduce your sugar intake

- Replace sugary snacks with healthier choices, e.g. nuts and fruit.
- Don't add sugar when cooking.
- Use fruit juices instead of syrups in desserts.
- Drink fruit juices or water instead of fizzy drinks.
- Use low sugar products, but be careful to check labels as many diet products use artificial sweeteners that can be more harmful than sugar, e.g. aspartame.
- Use NutraSweet/Canderel instead of sugar.
- Avoid sweets, biscuits, cakes and desserts.

Dietary fibre

- Dietary fibre is also known as **cellulose** or **roughage**.
- Fibre-rich foods are cheap and plentiful.
- Processed, convenience and refined foods are low in fibre.
- Fibre absorbs water and makes us feel full.
- Fibre-rich foods provide vitamin B, which helps release energy in the body.
- Fibre is not digested – it passes unaffected through the body. However, it is very important in the diet as it helps with the digestion of other nutrients by helping to push the food through the intestines by a process known as **peristalsis** (**see p. 49**) This prevents constipation, diverticulosis and haemorrhoids.

Key Terms

Refined foods are processed foods that lack many of their original nutrients. They generally add many calories to your diet when compared to the amount of nutrients they contribute.

How to increase your dietary fibre intake

- Eat less **refined foods**, e.g. wholegrain bread, pasta, breakfast cereals and brown bread instead of white bread.
- Keep the skins on fruit and vegetables wherever possible, e.g. wedges and baked potatoes.
- Eat raw fruit and vegetables.
- Eat high-fibre breakfast cereals, e.g. Bran Flakes, Shredded Wheat and Weetabix.
- Add bran, fruit, nuts or seeds to homemade bread or breakfast cereals.

Reference Intake (RI) of carbohydrates

It is recommended that we eat 24–35 g of fibre every day, but on average we eat only 15–20 g.

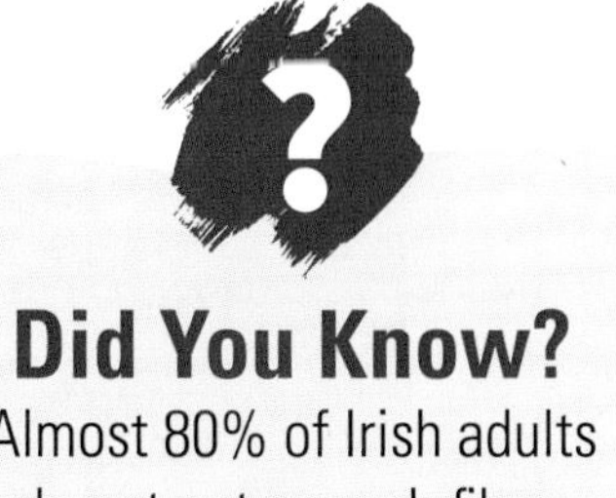

Did You Know?

Almost 80% of Irish adults do not eat enough fibre.

Further Investigation

Find out more about peristalsis by going to YouTube and watching the video '3D Medical Animation – Peristalsis in Large Intestine/Bowel || ABP' (0:33).

Revision Questions

1. Name the basic unit of a carbohydrate.
2. Classify carbohydrates and name two sources of each type.
3. Name two functions of dietary fibre.
4. Explain the terms: (a) hidden sugars and (b) empty kilocalories.
5. Suggest three ways of decreasing sugar in the diet.
6. Suggest three ways of increasing dietary fibre in the diet.

Fats (lipids)

Key Words

✓ Fat
✓ Oil
✓ Lipids
✓ Glycerol
✓ Carbon
✓ Hydrogen
✓ Oxygen
✓ Insulate
✓ Adipose
✓ Saturated
✓ Unsaturated

Fats, also called **lipids**, are the main source of energy in the diet.

- They are called **fats** when solid at room temperature, e.g. butter.
- They are called **oils** when liquid at room temperature, e.g. olive oil.

Did You Know?

Fat cells live for an average of 10 years. Once a fat cell dies, the body makes a brand new one to take its place. Fat cells die at the rate of 150 per second.

Too much fat in the diet can lead to obesity, coronary heart disease, stroke, high blood pressure and some forms of cancer.

Composition of fats

Fats are made up of the elements carbon (C), hydrogen (H) and oxygen (O). These are arranged to form **glycerol and fatty acids**.

These link together to form an E-shape. They contain more carbon than all the other nutrients.

During digestion, the glycerol is separated from the fatty acids.

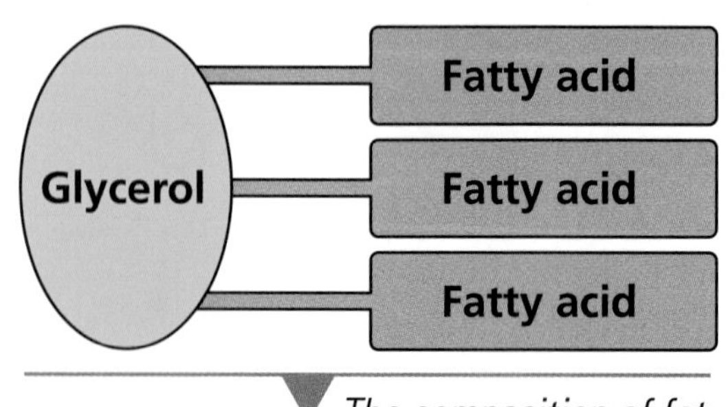

The composition of fat

Classification and sources of fat

Fats are classified in three ways, according to source, degree of saturation and form.

Source	**Animal**	**Vegetable** 
Degree of saturation	Saturated	Unsaturated 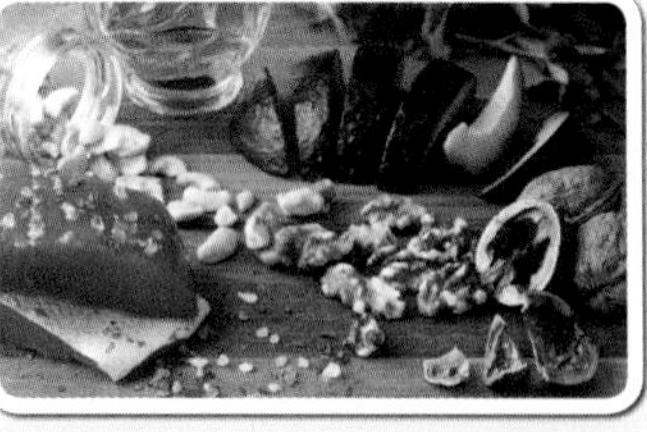
Form	Fat	Oil 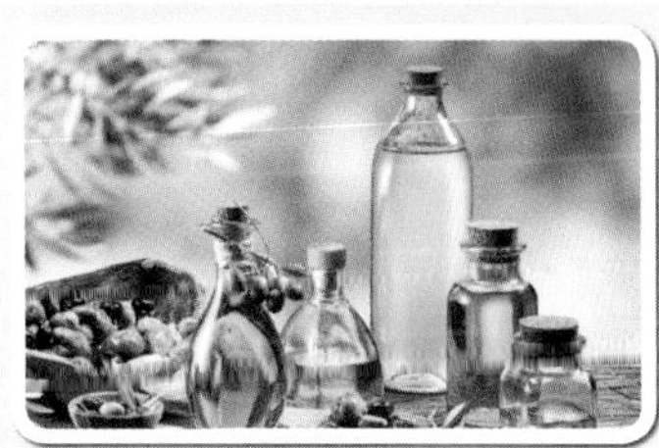
Examples	Meat fat (e.g. lard, suet, dripping), egg yolks, full-fat cheese, cream, butter and hard margarines	Vegetable oils (e.g. corn, olive, rapeseed), oily fish, cereals, nuts and soft spreads (e.g. Flora, Golden Olive)

Did You Know?

Fish contains unsaturated fat even though it is from an animal source. These fats are omega oils, which help the brain and nervous system, and help lower cholesterol in the blood, so they are good for you.

Functions of fats

- Fats give us a concentrated source of heat and energy.
- Excess fat is stored as body fat, known as **adipose tissue**. This insulates the body and prevents heat loss.
- Layers of fat protect delicate organs, e.g. kidneys.
- They delay hunger as they fill you up for longer.
- Fats also add flavour to the diet.

Fat deficiency symptoms

These are rare. We have more problems associated with excess fat, especially saturated and **hydrogenated fats**. These are:

- Poor general health
- Obesity
- Heart disease
- High blood pressure
- Strokes
- Some forms of cancer

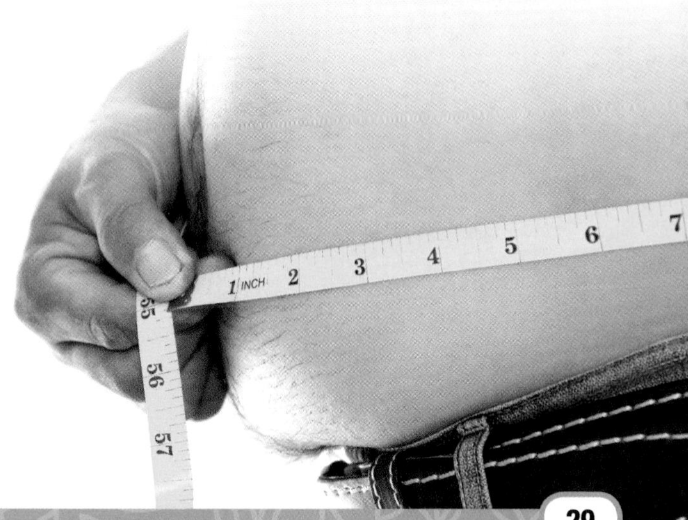

Hydrogenated fats are hardened vegetable oils (margarine) used in processed foods like biscuits, cakes and pastries.

Benefits of unsaturated fats in the diet

- Some unsaturated fats help to reduce cholesterol in the blood.
- Omega-3 and omega-6 reduce the risk of heart disease. They are also associated with improved brain function.
- Good sources include oily fish, seeds and nuts.

How to reduce your fat intake

- Use fat-free or reduced-fat products, e.g. low-fat milk and yoghurt.
- Substitute vegetable fats for animal fats.
- Use polyunsaturated fats, e.g. Flora, which help lower cholesterol.
- Use fat-free and low-fat cooking methods, e.g. steaming, grilling and stir-frying.
- Avoid fatty snack foods like crisps and chips.
- Avoid oil/butter-based dressings and sauces.

Reference Intake (RI) of fats

Keep to 30% (or less) of our total energy intake for a day.

Further Investigation

Do you want to find out more about how cholesterol build-up can affect your health? Watch the video 'Cholesterol animation | Heart disease risk factors' (1:13) on YouTube.

Revision Questions

1. Outline the composition and classification of fat.
2. Outline four functions of fat in the diet.
3. Suggest two ways of reducing fat in the diet.
4. Explain the term 'adipose tissue'.

Micronutrients

The two micronutrients are **vitamins** and **minerals**.

Key Words

✓ Vitamins
✓ Recommended
✓ Daily
✓ Folic
✓ Allowance
✓ Fortified
✓ Rickets
✓ Scurvy

Vitamins

Vitamins are needed in very small amounts by the body, yet they are essential for good health. The main source of vitamins is food but some are made by the body. A deficiency disease may develop if a vitamin is missing from the diet. Vitamins are available as food supplements, but a good mixed diet should provide all the vitamins needed by the body.

Classification

Vitamins are classified into **fat-soluble** (A, D, E and K) and **water-soluble** (B and C) vitamins.

- **Fat-soluble vitamins** dissolve in fat, so can be stored in the fatty tissue of the body. It is possible to have too much of vitamins A and D in your diet – they can build up and have harmful effects on the body. This condition is known as **hypervitaminosis**.
- **Water-soluble vitamins** dissolve in water and are not stored in the body, but are removed in the urine, so they must be consumed daily through food.

Fat-soluble vitamins

Vitamin	Sources	Functions	Deficiencies
Vitamin A	• **Pure vitamin A** comes from animal sources: oily fish, fish liver oils, liver, kidneys, eggs and margarine • **Carotene** comes from plant sources: carrots, peppers, dark green vegetables, e.g. spinach	• Good eyesight • Healthy lining tissue in nose, mouth and throat • Growth and development • Healthy eyes, skin and hair	• Night blindness • Lining in tissues becomes dry and irritated • Retarded growth • Dry, scaly skin
Vitamin D	• Oily fish, cod liver oils, tinned salmon and sardines, margarine, butter, cheese and eggs • Sunlight on the skin	• Healthy bones and teeth (helps the body absorb calcium) • Prevents rickets	• Rickets – a bone disease in children • Tooth decay • Osteoporosis and osteomalacia
Vitamin E	• Seeds, nuts, cereals, margarine and eggs	• Protects against heart disease • Healthy red blood cells and skin • Natural antioxidant (prevents damage in cells) • Helps wounds to heal	• Rare • Anaemia in newborn babies
Vitamin K	• Green vegetables, milk and cheese • Made in the body by bacteria in the digestive tract	• Normal blood clotting • Works with calcium in the bones	• Blood will not clot normally (very rare)

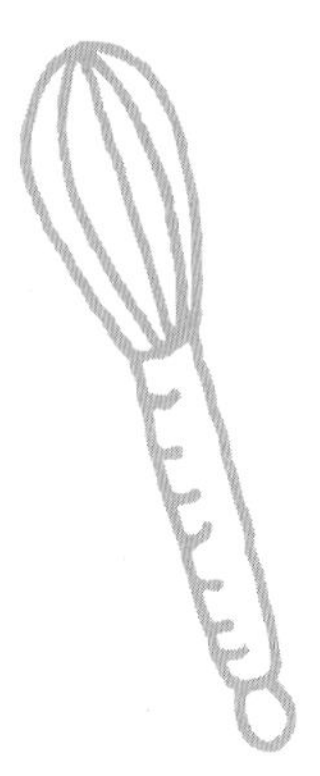

Reference Intake (RI) of fat-soluble vitamins

Vitamin A	Children: 400–500 μg Teenagers: 500–600 μg Adults: 600–700 μg Pregnant and breastfeeding women: 950 μg
Vitamin D	Children: 10 μg Teenagers: 15 μg Adults: 10 μg

Water-soluble vitamins

Water-soluble vitamins are easily destroyed by heating and overcooking.

Vitamin	Sources	Functions	Deficiencies
Vitamin B group There are many vitamins in this group. They share similar features but differ in their chemical structure.	• Meat, fish, eggs, milk, cereals, nuts, flour, yeast and pulse vegetables	• Controls the release of energy from food • Maintains a healthy nervous system • Needed for growth	• Retarded growth • Tiredness • Beriberi (a nerve disease) • Pellagra (a disease of the skin and tongue) • Neural tube defects such as spina bifida in newborn babies.
Folate/folic acid	• Wholemeal bread, leafy greens, red/orange/yellow fruit and vegetables • Fortified cereal products	• Particularly important during pregnancy to prevent neural tube defects.	*Spina bifida*
Vitamin C	• Fruit and vegetables, e.g. blackcurrants, citrus fruits and red berries, • Green leafy vegetables, tomatoes and new potatoes	• General good health • Healthy gums, skin and blood vessels • Healing of cuts and wounds • Helps absorb iron into the body	• Scurvy (symptoms include joint pain, weakness and gum disease) • Delayed healing of wounds • Anaemia (because iron is not absorbed)

Discovery Learning

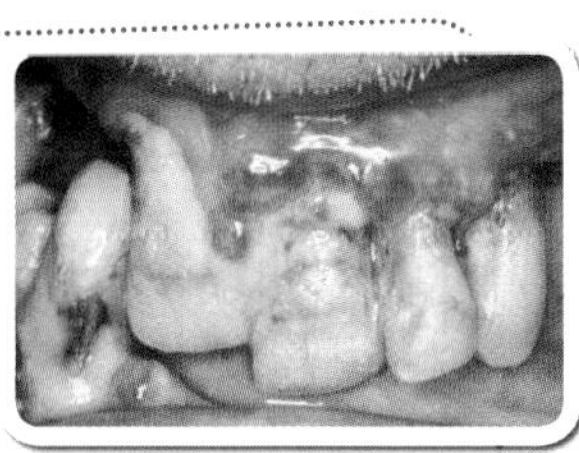

Scurvy is a disease caused by a lack of vitamin C. It was common in the past among sailors due to lack of fresh fruit and vegetables on board ships. The symptoms include bleeding under the skin, swollen spongy gums and loose teeth. Find out more about scurvy, by going to ***www.the-pirate-ship.com***, clicking on 'Explore the Pirate Ship' on the right-hand side of the home page, and then clicking on 'Scurvy Facts' in the list provided. Afterwards, list three things you have learned. Present them in a creative way.

Did You Know?

On food labels, vitamin C is also called ascorbic acid. It is a natural **preservative** and an **antioxidant**. Find out the meaning of each highlighted word.

Reference Intake (RI) of water-soluble vitamins

Vitamin C	Children: 45 mg Teenagers and adults: 60 mg Pregnant and breastfeeding women: 80 mg
Folic acid	Children: 200 μg Teenagers and adults: 300 μg Pregnant women: 500 μg Breastfeeding women: 400 μg

Don't Forget!
Vitamins are Vital for good health.

Revision Questions

1. List (a) the fat-soluble vitamins and (b) the water-soluble vitamins.
2. Describe the sources, functions and effects of a deficiency of vitamin A and C.
3. Explain why the water-soluble vitamins cannot be stored in the body.
4. Write a note on folic acid.

Minerals

Like vitamins, minerals are only needed in small amounts, but they are essential for good health. They work with other nutrients to prevent diseases and help the body function properly.

- **Major minerals** are measured in milligrams, e.g. calcium, phosphorus, sodium and potassium.
- **Trace elements** are minerals that the body needs in much smaller amounts and are measured in micrograms, e.g. iron, zinc, fluoride and iodine.

Key Words

✓ Mineral
✓ Trace
✓ Calcium
✓ Iron
✓ Fluoride
✓ Sodium
✓ Iodine
✓ Phosphorus
✓ Osteoporosis
✓ Anaemia
✓ Offal

Nutritional surveys, e.g. SLÁN 2007, show that calcium and iron are the minerals that are particularly lacking in many people's diets. The latest healthy eating guidelines (**see p. 56**) encourage us to choose foods that are high in these minerals.

Be Numerate

In the kitchen, we use grams and kilograms to measure our ingredients. Minerals are measured in much smaller units:

- Milligrams: A unit of mass equal to one thousandth of a gram
- Micrograms: A unit of mass equal to one millionth of a gram

Did You Know?

Some minerals need certain vitamins present so they can work efficiently in the body. Can you find out which vitamin works with iron and calcium?

Mineral	Sources	Functions	Deficiencies
Calcium	Milk, cheese, dairy products, green vegetables, hard water, fortified white flour and tinned fish	• Healthy bones and teeth • Needed for clotting blood • Transmission of nerve pulses	• Rickets – a bone disease in children • Osteomalacia in adults • Osteoporosis in adults • Tooth decay

Calcium combines with phosphorus to make bones and teeth hard and strong. These minerals also need vitamin D to be present so they can be absorbed by the body properly to prevent rickets, osteomalacia and osteoporosis.

Rickets

Rickets is a disease that occurs in children. It leads to deformed bones as a result of insufficient calcium and vitamin D in the diet. The symptoms include bow legs, a deformed spine, bones that fracture easily and a flattening of the skull in infants. This condition can be corrected by introducing a diet rich in calcium and vitamin D. Rickets rarely occurs in the Western world because of improved diets and health. Osteomalacia is the adult version of rickets.

Osteoporosis (brittle bone disease)

As a natural part of ageing, bones lose calcium and become thinner. In some people, the bones become porous and fragile, breaking very easily. This is much more common in women, partly due to the fact that women's bones are thinner than men's, and due to calcium loss during pregnancy. While little can be done once it occurs, we can help to prevent it by:

- eating foods rich in calcium and vitamin D from an early age
- avoiding smoking
- taking regular exercise from an early age

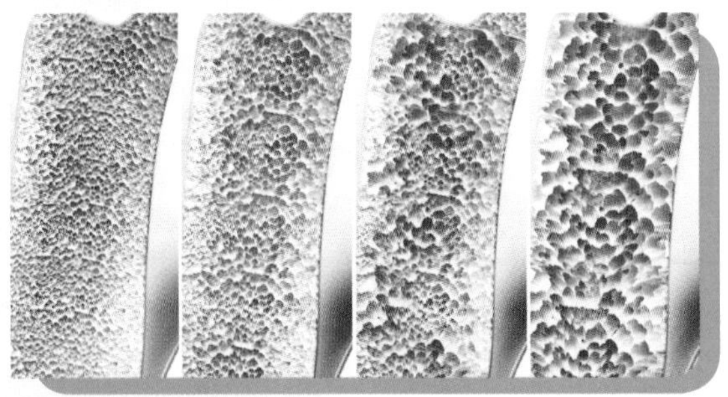

A healthy bone *A bone with osteoporosis*

Further Investigation

To find out more about rickets and osteoporosis go to **www.study.com** and search for 'Osteomalacia and Rickets: Causes and Symptoms'.

Mineral	Sources	Functions	Deficiencies
Iron	Red meat, offal, liver, kidneys, fortified breakfast cereals, eggs, raisins, pulse and dark green vegetables	Necessary to form haemoglobin in the red blood cells, which carry oxygen around the body to give us energy	• Poor concentration • Tiredness and a lack of energy • Anaemia

Anaemia

Anaemia is a condition that results from a shortage of iron in the diet. Since iron is used to make haemoglobin, it means that not enough is being produced in the body. It may also develop as a result of menstruation or severe blood loss, so iron is particularly important in the diet of women and teenage girls.

Symptoms: Tiredness, dizziness, headaches, paleness, shortness of breath and loss of appetite.

Further Investigation

To learn more about anaemia, go to YouTube and search for the video 'Anaemia' (1:14).

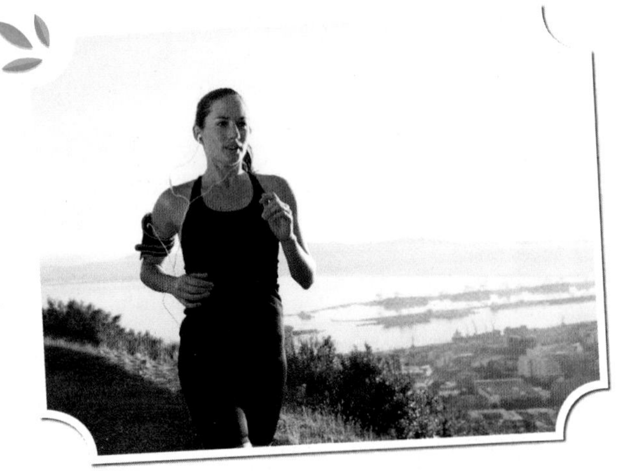

It is very important to eat foods that are rich in vitamin C in order to absorb iron. Toddlers, children, teenagers and women, especially when pregnant, need a good intake of iron. Women need extra iron due to menstruation, and during pregnancy they need it for the unborn baby. Athletes and vegetarians are at risk of developing iron deficiency.

How to increase iron and calcium

- Eat more red meats and offal.
- Eat more green vegetables, e.g. broccoli and cabbage.
- Eat more vitamin C for absorption (citrus fruits and blackcurrants).
- Drink more milk and eat more dairy products.
- Eat more oily fish and nuts.
- Eat more vitamin D for absorption (eggs and greens).

Other important minerals

Mineral	Sources	Functions	Deficiencies
Phosphorus	Found in most foods, especially cheese, oatmeal, liver, poultry, fish and eggs	Helps calcium to form teeth and bones.	Unlikely, as found in most foods.
Iodine	Sea fish, seaweed, whole cereals and iodised salt, eggs, cheese, butter, pulses and vegetables	Necessary for the thyroid gland, which controls metabolism.	• Goitre – enlargement of the thyroid gland • Slowdown of metabolism • Weight gain and tiredness

Did You Know?
Phosphorus works with calcium and vitamin D.

Did You Know?
Iodine is added to salt to make up for the lack of iodine levels in soils in some areas.

Mineral	Sources	Functions	Deficiencies
Fluoride	Fish eaten with bones, tea and drinking water	Healthy teeth	Tooth decay
Potassium	Found in most foods including meat, fish, fruit, vegetables, seeds, nuts and milk	• Healthy cell formation • Maintains the body's fluid balance	Unlikely as in most foods
Sodium	All salty foods including bacon, snack foods, butter, stock cubes, instant sauces and cheese	• Controls water balance in the body • Improves the functioning of cells, muscles and tissues	Muscular cramps
Zinc	Cereals, offal, meat, milk, cheese, oysters and pulse vegetables	• Controls enzymes, aids general health, fights infection, heals wounds • Healthy skin • Helps growth by metabolising macronutrients	• Loss of appetite • Skin disorders • Slow growth • Dry, flaky skin

Did You Know?
A cup of dried fruit each day improves potassium intake.

Did You Know?
Too much salt in the diet raises blood pressure and can lead to strokes, coronary heart disease and kidney disease.

Be Numerate

To convert sodium to salt, multiply amount of sodium by 2.5.

Did You Know?
80% of the salt intake in the average Irish person's diet comes from processed foods.

How to reduce salt intake

- Remove salt from the kitchen table.
- Do not add salt when cooking.
- Avoid processed foods, as they are very high in salt.
- Use spices and herbs to flavour food instead.
- Use a low-sodium alternative, e.g. LoSalt.
- Drink plenty of water.

Reference Intake (RI) of minerals

Calcium	1200 mg	**Potassium**	3.5 g
Iron	10–14 mg	**Sodium**	1.6 g
Iodine	130 µg	**Zinc**	7–9 g
Phosphorus	None		

Retaining vitamins and minerals

Micronutrients are easily destroyed by careless food preparation and cooking. It is important to follow some simple guidelines in order to retain maximum nourishment.

- Eat all foods as fresh as possible.
- Eat fruit and vegetables raw if possible.
- Avoid peeling or soaking fruit and vegetables.
- Use the least possible amount of cooking water and avoid overcooking.
- Never add bread soda when cooking green vegetables.
- Antibiotics and smoking can have a damaging effect on certain vitamins, so supplements may be needed.
- Serve food immediately; avoid keeping it warm for long periods of time.

Fortified foods are **foods** or **food products** to which extra nutrients have been added to replace nutrients that are lost during manufacturing and storage.

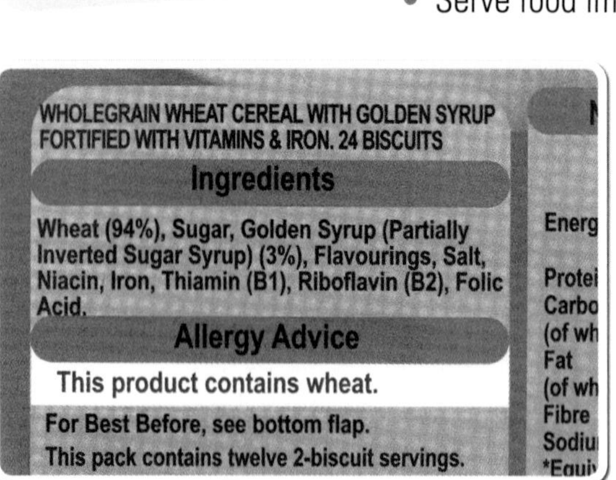
WHOLEGRAIN WHEAT CEREAL WITH GOLDEN SYRUP FORTIFIED WITH VITAMINS & IRON. 24 BISCUITS

Ingredients

Wheat (94%), Sugar, Golden Syrup (Partially Inverted Sugar Syrup) (3%), Flavourings, Salt, Niacin, Iron, Thiamin (B1), Riboflavin (B2), Folic Acid.

Allergy Advice

This product contains wheat.

For Best Before, see bottom flap.
This pack contains twelve 2-biscuit servings.

Revision Questions

1. Name six minerals needed by the body.
2. What is a trace mineral? Identify two of them.
3. How much sodium should be consumed per day?
4. Write an informative note on (a) scurvy (b) osteoporosis.

Water

Key Words

- ✓ Evaporation
- ✓ Perspiration
- ✓ Dehydration
- ✓ Properties

Water is essential for life. The human body is about 70% water – it is the main constituent of every cell. The amount of water in the body is carefully controlled. The body loses on average 2–2.5 litres of water daily through perspiration and as urine via the kidneys. This loss must be replaced or the body will become **dehydrated**. Dehydration is common when severe food poisoning causes prolonged vomiting and diarrhoea. This is particularly dangerous for babies.

If water and salts are not replaced, death may occur.

Key Terms

Dehydration occurs when the body loses more than 2% of its normal volume of water. This can occur after a long period of vomiting or diarrhoea or if too much alcohol is consumed. Symptoms include bad breath, headache, cramps, low blood pressure, dizziness, dry and itchy skin, rapid heart rate and tingling in the fingers and toes. To prevent dehydration, drink eight glasses of water every day.

Composition of water

The elements in water are hydrogen and oxygen (H_2O) in the ratio 2:1.

Properties of water

- Water boils at 100°C and freezes at 0°C.
- It evaporates easily at 100°C and changes into a vapour (steam).
- It is colourless, odourless and tasteless.
- It dissolves salt (creating brine) and sugar (creating syrup).

Solid

Liquid

Gas

Sources of water

Water is found in both food and drinks.

Food	Most foods contain water, except for solid fats (e.g. butter) and dried foods (e.g. flour). Fruit and vegetables contain up to 90% water.
Drinks	Water, tea, coffee, milk, juices, soft drinks and fruit juices.

Did You Know?

The water evaporated from dried foods such as fruit and vegetables is replaced during soaking. This is known as rehydrating. For example, marrowfat peas are dried out naturally in the field and packaged. They are then soaked before cooking.

Functions of water

- Quenches thirst.
- Essential for all body fluids, tissues and cells.
- Transports oxygen, nutrients and hormones around the body.
- Assists the digestion and absorption of food.
- Regulates body temperature (through perspiration).
- Helps remove waste from the body (kidneys filter urine from the blood).
- Source of minerals and vitamins.

Did You Know?

True mineral waters come from natural springs. Many bottled waters are ordinary water to which carbon dioxide has been added. Many drinks contain substances such as caffeine, flavourings, sweeteners and sugar, so always check the labels.

Revision Toolkit

Use the mnemonic below to help you remember your food nutrients and constituents:

Fred **C**an't **P**lay **M**onopoly **V**ery **W**ell

Fats, **C**arbohydrates, **P**rotein, **M**inerals, **V**itamins, **W**ater

Revision Questions

1. Outline why water is important in the diet.
2. Suggest three ways of increasing water intake, besides drinking it.
3. Explain what dehydration is and how to prevent it.
4. Describe four properties of water.

Energy

Key Words

- ✓ Energy
- ✓ Burn
- ✓ Input
- ✓ Balance
- ✓ Output
- ✓ Calories
- ✓ Kilojoules
- ✓ Basal metabolic rate

Energy is the ability to do work and to perform any task. We need energy for each body function, as well as for sleeping, resting and other activities. Every single cell in the body requires a constant supply of energy.

Food is the fuel that supplies energy to the body. Much like petrol in a car, the food is **burned** in the body cells and, in the process, heat and energy are released and allow the body to work. Because oxygen is needed to burn the food, this process is known as **oxidation**.

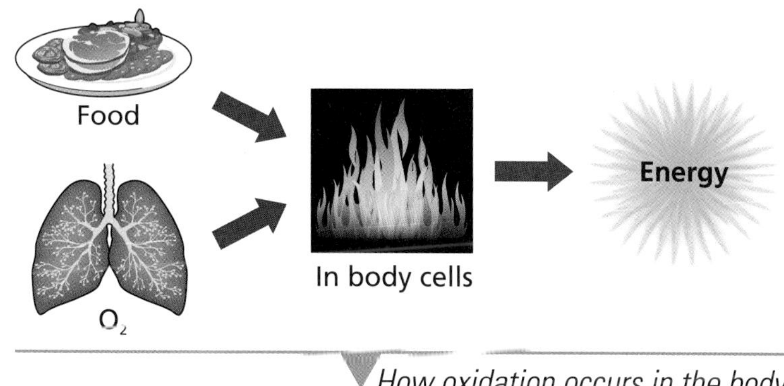

How oxidation occurs in the body

Energy requirements

The body needs a basic amount of energy to stay alive, and to keep vital organs such as the heart and digestive system working. The **basal metabolic rate (BMR)** is the minimum amount of energy needed to keep the body's organs working. Extra energy is needed for any activities we do, such as walking, swimming or running. The more active the body, the more energy is used.

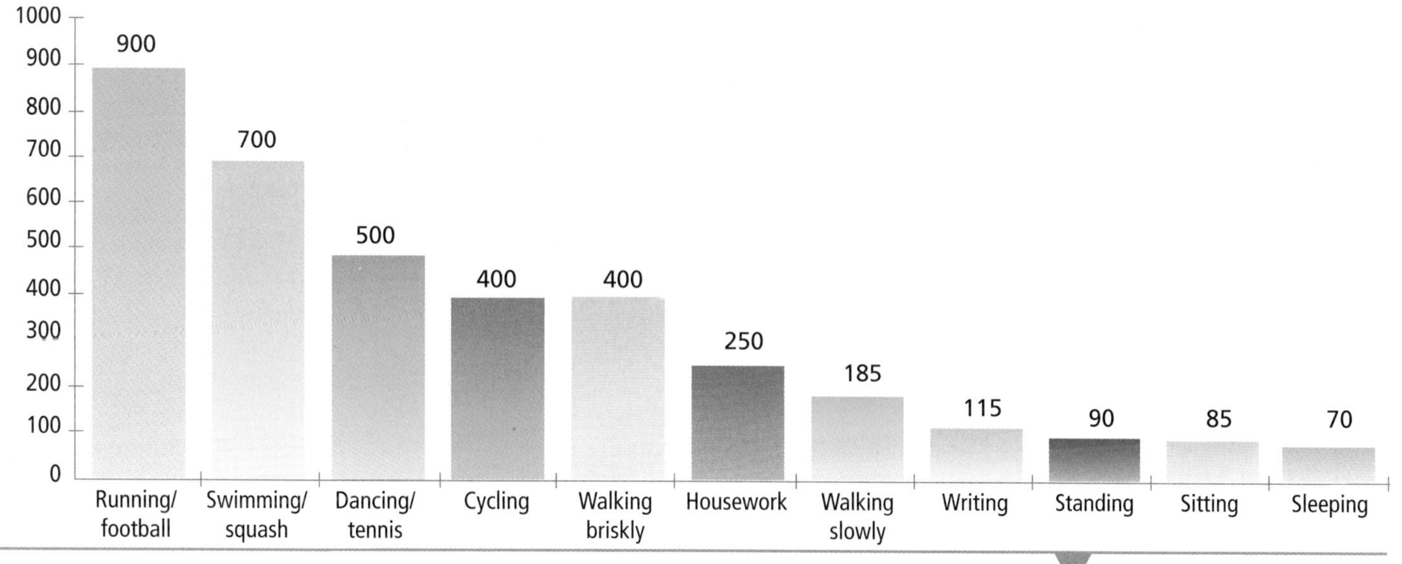

Kilocalorie use per hour

- If we eat **more energy foods than we need**, the energy produced is converted into fat and stored as adipose tissue.
- If we eat **too few energy foods**, we can suffer from deficiency disorders.
- If we eat a **balanced diet**, energy intake will be equal to energy output.

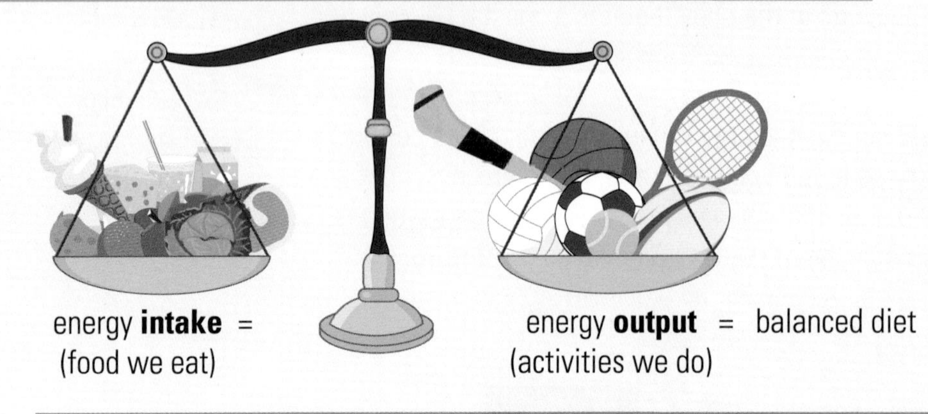

Balancing energy intake and output

As a general guideline, at least 55% of our energy should be sourced from carbohydrates (including fibre), and no more than 30% from fats and 15% from proteins.

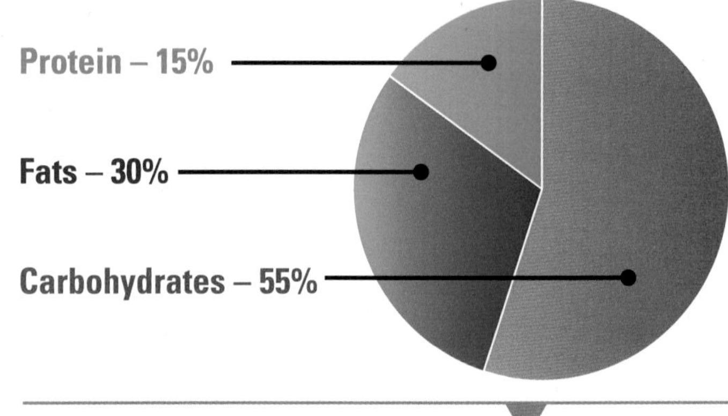

Energy intake

Be Numerate: Measuring Energy

The energy content of food is measured in two ways: in kilocalories (kcal) and kilojoules (kJ).

- A kilocalorie is the amount of heat needed to raise the temperature of a litre of water by 1°C.
- 1 kilocalorie = 4.2 kilojoules, e.g. if a yoghurt contains 90 kilocalories (kcal) it contains 378 kilojoules (kJ) (90 kcal x 4.2 kJ).

The energy content of food

The amount of energy in a food depends on the nutrients the food contains. So, it follows that foods that are high in kilocalories are 'fattening', while foods containing large amounts of water, like fruit and vegetables, are low in kilocalories.

Vitamins, minerals and water supply little or no energy. It would take a long time to work out the amount of nutrients and energy provided by foods, so food tables have been compiled to provide us with this information. The nutrients and kilocalories in a food may be shown by unit (e.g. in one egg) or by weight (e.g. per 100 g).

- 1 gram of protein produces 4 kcal (17 kJ)
- 1 gram of lipids produces 9 kcal (37 kJ)
- 1 gram of carbohydrates produces 4 kcal (17 kJ)

Food packaging provides nutritional information about a product. This simplifies the planning of meals and caters for all ages and dietary needs. It also helps those with special requirements and allergies to avoid certain food additives.

Functions of energy

- To keep vital organs such as the heart and lungs working.
- For muscle movement and daily activities (running, dressing, writing).
- For normal nerve function.
- For cell activity and growth of cells in children, teenagers and pregnant women.
- To maintain correct body temperature (37°C).
- Extra energy is needed in colder climates.

Factors that influence energy requirements

Activity levels – active people use more energy than less active people.

Size – smaller people use less energy than larger people.

Gender – females require less energy than males as they have a lower muscle ratio.

Age – a child or adolescent needs more energy for their size than an adult.

Pregnancy – extra energy is needed for growth during pregnancy and for breastfeeding.

Climate – in cold climates more energy is needed to keep warm.

Discovery Learning

Try and come up with a mnemonic to remember the factors that influence energy requirements. Share your ideas with the rest of your class.

Estimated average daily energy needs (in kilocalories)

Age group	Daily requirements for sedentary to active (kcals per day)	Age group	Daily requirements for sedentary to active (kcals per day)
Babies 0–1	800	Women (sedentary)	2,100
Toddlers 1–4	1,000–1,400	Men (active)	3,500
Children 5–7	1,800	Women (active)	2,500
Girls 9–18	2,300	Men (older)	2,250
Boys 12–15	2,800	Women (older)	2,000
Boys 15–18	3,000	Pregnant women	2,400
Men (sedentary)	2,700	Breastfeeding women	2,700

Revision Questions

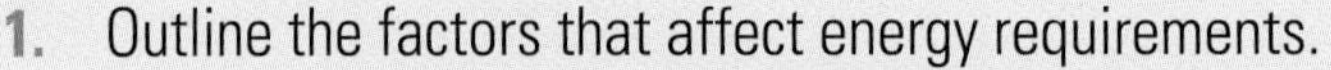

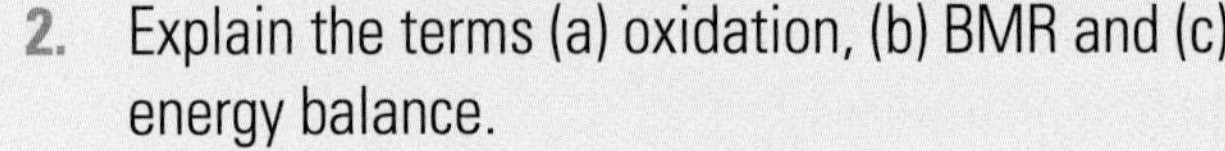

1. Outline the factors that affect energy requirements.
2. Explain the terms (a) oxidation, (b) BMR and (c) energy balance.

Summary

- **Nutrition** is the study of food. There are six nutrients found in food: protein, carbohydrates, fats, vitamins, minerals and water. All food is made up of one or a combination of nutrients.
- **Protein** is made up of carbon, hydrogen, oxygen and nitrogen, organised into units called **amino acids**. Proteins are needed for growth and repair. The best sources are meat, fish, eggs, dairy foods, soys **(HBV proteins)**; peas, beans and cereals **(LBV proteins)**.
- **Carbohydrates** consist of carbon, hydrogen and oxygen, organised into simple sugar units. They are classified as sugar (jam, sweets and biscuits), starch (potatoes, pasta, rice) and fibre (wholegrain cereals, vegetables). We should reduce our sugar intake and increase fibre in our diets.
- **Fats** are made up of carbon, hydrogen and oxygen. They consist of **fatty acids and glycerol**. They are classified into **saturated fats** (meat, dairy) and **unsaturated fats** (fish, vegetable oils, nuts and cereals). Eating too much fat can lead to many health problems, e.g. heart disease, high blood pressure and strokes. However, some fats, e.g. omega oils, are particularly good for you.

- **Vitamins** are divided in two types: **fat-soluble (A, D, E and K)** and **water-soluble (B and C)**. Each vitamin has a job to do (function) in the body and if you do not get enough, deficiency diseases can occur. Hypervitaminosis can occur if there is a build-up of vitamin A or D.
- **Minerals** are classified as **major** (calcium, phosphorus, sodium and potassium) and **trace** (iron, zinc, fluoride and iodine), which may not be needed in as large amounts but are still very important to prevent deficiency diseases. Calcium is needed for healthy bones and teeth. Sources include milk, cheese, green vegetables and tinned fish – too little results in rickets and osteoporosis. Iron is needed to produce haemoglobin; it is sourced from offal, red meat, green vegetables and eggs. An iron deficiency could result in anaemia.
- **Water** is in all drinks and most foods. It carries nutrients, oxygen, heat and waste around the body. Water **boils** at 100°C, **freezes** at 0°C and **evaporates** at temperatures above 100°C. If you do not have enough water you can become **dehydrated**.
- **Energy** is the ability to do work. It is measured in kilocalories or kilojoules. Oxidation means using the food in the body to produce energy. The **basal metabolic rate (BMR)** is the least amount of energy needed to stay alive. The amount of energy a person needs depends on their age, size, gender and activity levels.

04 DIGESTION

Learning Outcomes 1.9, 1.10, 1.11

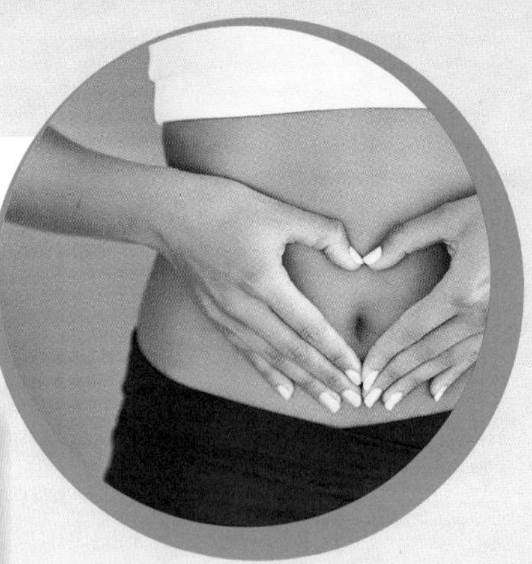

What I Will Learn

- to describe the basic structure of the digestive system
- to explain the basic functions of the digestive system

Key Words

✓ Enzyme	✓ Oesophagus	✓ Pepsin	✓ Bile
✓ Physical	✓ Gastric juice	✓ Peristalsis	✓ Duodenum
✓ Chemical	✓ Chyme	✓ Pancreas	✓ Villi
✓ Alimentary canal	✓ Hydrochloric acid	✓ Pancreatic juice	✓ Colon
✓ Amylase	✓ Diaphragm	✓ Liver	✓ Absorption
✓ Saliva	✓ Abdomen	✓ Gall bladder	✓ Faeces

Food provides the energy and nutrients that the body needs to stay alive and keep healthy.

Before the body can make use of food, the macronutrients (protein, carbohydrates and fats) must be broken down to release the individual components – this breaking-down process is called digestion.

The micronutrients (vitamins and minerals) do not need to be digested and can be used by the body as they are. Water is absorbed into the bloodstream. Fibre is not digested – it absorbs water and is used to push waste materials from the body in the form of faeces. Once nutrients have been digested, they are absorbed into the bloodstream and taken into the cells where they can be used.

During digestion, food goes through both **physical** (or mechanical) and **chemical** changes.

Physical or mechanical changes

- The food is **chewed** and broken down into smaller pieces by the teeth.
- It is **mixed** with saliva in the mouth to form a ball by the tongue.
- Once swallowed, food is **churned** in the stomach and broken down further, while fat **melts**.

Chemical changes

- The digestive juices in the stomach contain chemicals called **enzymes**, which help to convert the foods into simpler substances so they can be absorbed into the bloodstream:
  1. **Proteins** are broken down into **amino acids**.
  2. **Carbohydrates** are broken into **simple sugars**.
  3. **Fats** are broken down into **fatty acids** and **glycerol**.
- Each enzyme works on a specific nutrient, e.g. the enzyme in saliva only acts on starch – it has no effect on proteins or fats.

The digestive system

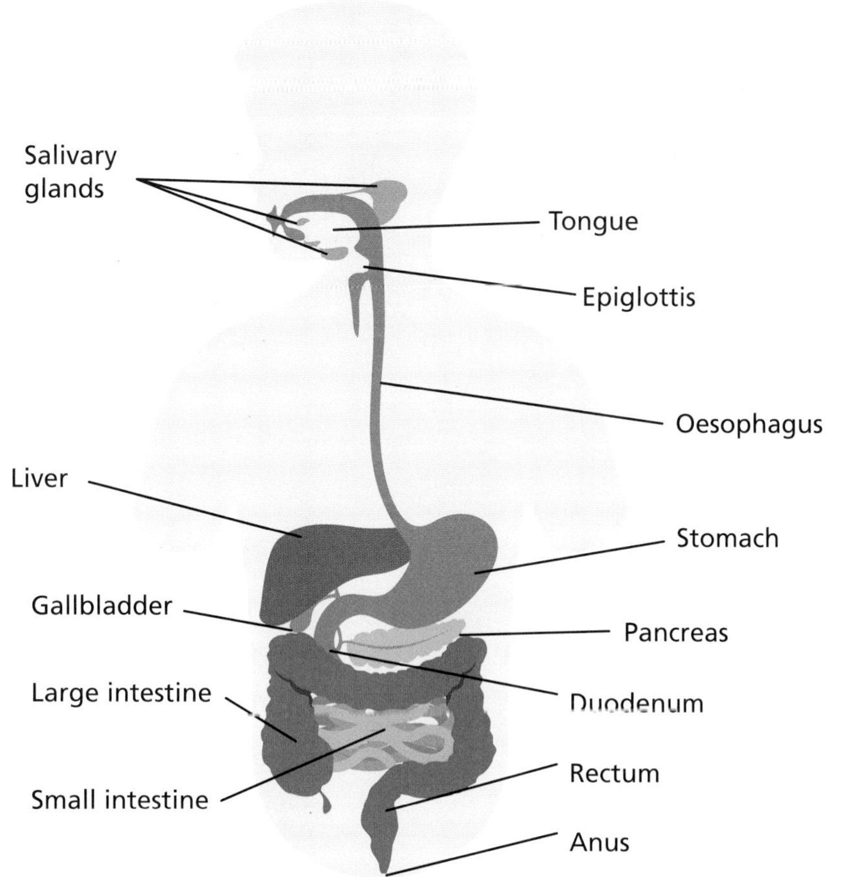

The digestive system

Discovery Learning

Find the epiglottis in the diagram of the digestive system. Find out what its function is and share your findings with the class.

The digestive system is like a tube – this is known as the digestive tract or the alimentary canal. Food enters the tube in the mouth and waste leaves the body through the rectum and anus.

Discovery Learning

Saliva in the mouth contains an enzyme. Can you find out what it is called and explain what it does?

The mouth

In the mouth, the teeth and jaws crush and grind the food into small particles and mix them with saliva from the salivary glands, making it easier to swallow.

Teeth

There are four different types of teeth in the mouth and each has a different job.

1. Incisors are for cutting and chopping food.
2. Canines are for cutting and tearing food.
3. Premolars are for crushing and grinding food.
4. Molars are for grinding and mashing food.

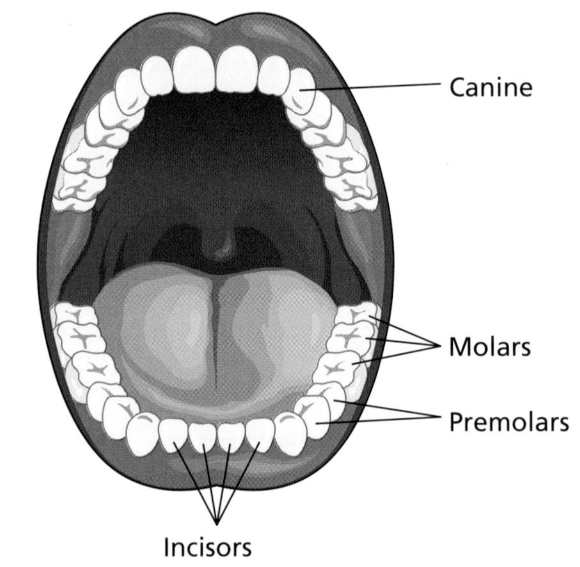

Teeth

The chewed food is then swallowed and moves into the oesophagus.

The oesophagus

The food passes down the oesophagus, which is a tube that connects the mouth to the stomach. The oesophagus is about 25 cm long. The food is squeezed along the oesophagus by a process called **peristalsis**. It takes about three to six seconds for food to go from the mouth to the stomach.

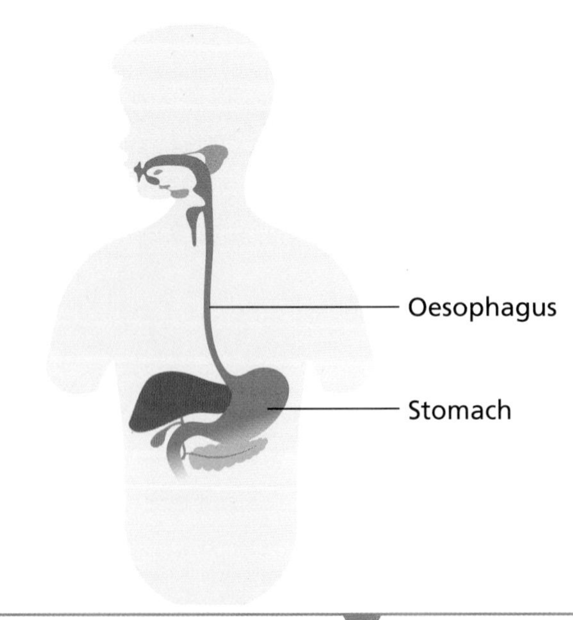

The oesophagus

Peristalsis is the muscular action of the digestive system. It occurs in the oesophagus and the intestine.

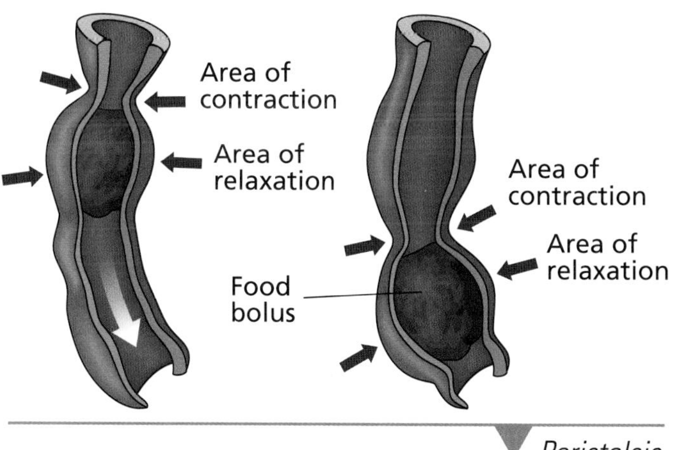

Peristalsis

Further Investigation

Learn more about peristalsis by watching the following videos on YouTube:
'Through the Esophagus [US spelling of oesophagus] The Function of Peristalsis' (1:41)
'3D Medical Animation – Peristalsis in Large Intestine /Bowel' (0:33)

Discovery Learning

Have you ever heard of 'heartburn'? Did you know that it has nothing to do with your heart? Find out what heartburn is and its connection to digestion. Share your findings with the class.

The stomach

The stomach is a pouch-shaped bag with thick, muscular walls. It is situated in the top left-hand side of the abdomen under the diaphragm. It is similar to a mixing tank that churns the food into a liquid called **chyme**.

- The stomach lining contains cells which produce a liquid called **gastric juice**. The gastric juice contains the enzyme **pepsin** and an acid called **hydrochloric acid**, which pepsin needs to work effectively. This acid also kills most of the bacteria present in food.
- Fat melts because of the heat in the stomach, making the digestion of fat easier. The rhythmic churning of the stomach mixes the food with the gastric juice.
- Food usually stays in the stomach for one to four hours, but liquids may pass through in a few minutes.

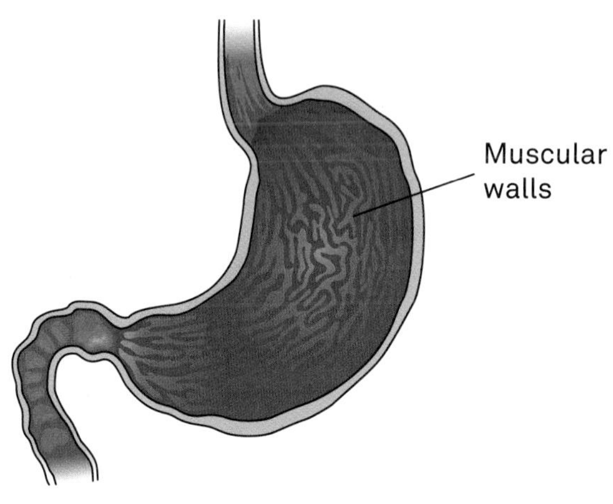

The stomach

Discovery Learning

In the stomach the enzyme pepsin mixes with hydrochloric acid. Can you find out what this enzyme does to protein in the stomach?

The small intestine

The small intestine is a tube about six metres long that joins the stomach to the large intestine. It is coiled up in the centre of the abdomen.

- Chyme passes into the duodenum from the stomach, where two digestive juices – **bile** and **pancreatic juice** – flow into the chyme.
- Bile is produced by the liver and stored in the **gall bladder**. It breaks the fat down into tiny droplets.
- The pancreatic juice contains three enzymes that help break down the starch, fat and protein.

Discovery Learning

Can you find out what enzyme is in bile and explain how it works? In pancreatic juices there are three enzymes – can you name them and explain what each does?

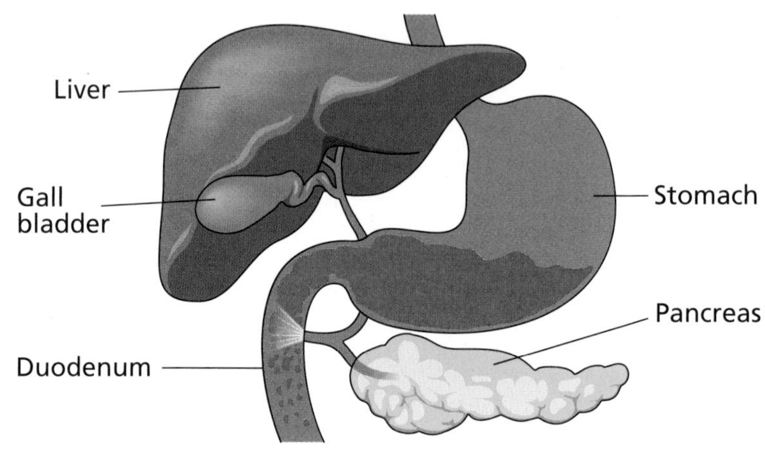

Food being broken down in the small intestine

The chyme is pushed along the small intestine by the action of peristalsis. Intestinal juice produced in the walls of the small intestine completes the breakdown of proteins, fats and carbohydrates.

Absorption

- These juices are then able to enter the intestinal wall by **absorption**, where the soluble, digested food passes into the bloodstream.
- The lining of the small intestine is folded and has little finger-like projections called villi, which increase the area for absorption. The surface is only one cell thick, which speeds up the absorption of nutrients.
- These nutrients are carried by the blood to all the cells of the body, where they are used to provide energy and make new cells.
- The remaining materials then pass into the large intestine.

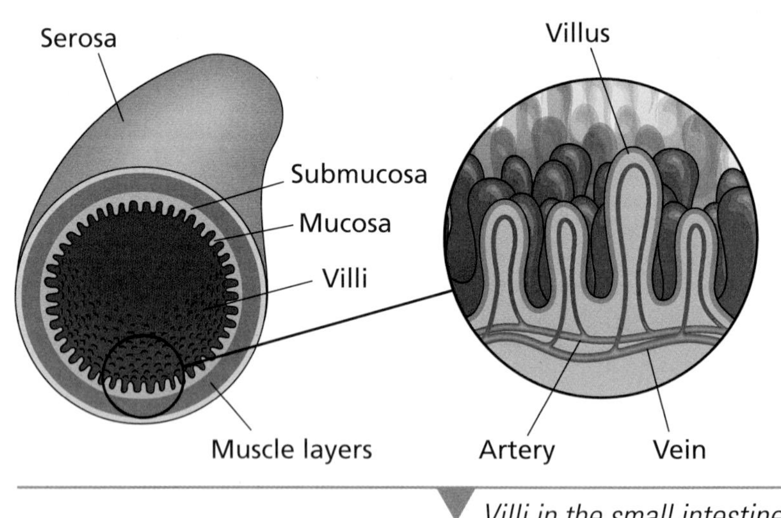

Villi in the small intestine

The large intestine

- The large intestine is a two-metre long tube that is inhabited by bacteria.
- It is a continuation of the small intestine. It passes up along the right-hand side of the abdomen across the top and down the left-hand side, where the last few centimetres are called the **rectum**.
- Some remaining nutrients are absorbed and vitamins B and K are manufactured.
- Water is absorbed into the bloodstream making the waste food – now called **faeces** – more solid.
- Faeces is pushed through the intestine by peristalsis into the rectum, where strong muscles push it out of the body through the anus.

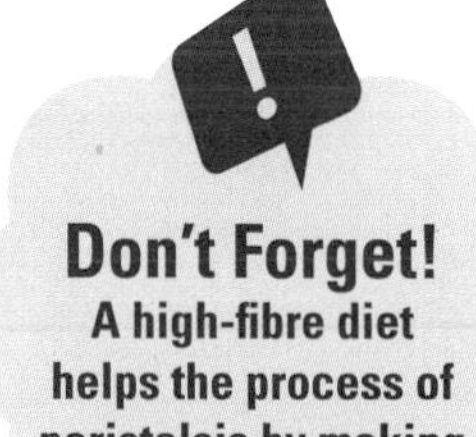

Don't Forget!
A high-fibre diet helps the process of peristalsis by making the waste bulkier.

Further Investigation

To learn more about digestion watch the video 'New GCSE BBC Bitesize – Digestion' (3:43) on YouTube or go to **kidshealth.org**, click on 'for Kids' on the home page, and then search for 'Digestion' and click on the article 'Your Digestive System'.

Revision Questions

1. Describe two physical changes and two chemical changes that occur during digestion.
2. State the function of each of the following parts of the digestive system: (i) the mouth, (ii) the stomach and (iii) the small intestine.
3. Explain how digested food is absorbed into the bloodstream.
4. Outline the functions of the large intestine.

Summary

- **Digestion** is the breakdown of nutrients into simpler substances that can be absorbed into the bloodstream and used by the body to keep us alive and healthy.
- Food is broken down in the mouth and mixed with saliva, so **starch** is changed to **maltose**.
- The food is squeezed along the **oesophagus** by a process called **peristalsis**, with continued action by saliva.
- In the **stomach**, food is churned into **chyme** and fats melt. Proteins are converted to peptides by gastric juices. Bacteria are killed by hydrochloric acid.
- The food then moves into the small intestine, where bile splits the fat into fatty acids and glycerol. **Pancreatic juices** change peptides to amino acids, and starch into sugars, while working with bile to break down fats. Intestinal juices complete the digestion of macronutrients, which are **absorbed** through the villi.
- In the **large intestine**, the remaining nutrients are **absorbed**. Water is absorbed. Waste is then excreted (**faeces**). Vitamins B and K are manufactured.

05 BALANCED EATING

Learning Outcomes 1.1, 1.2, 1.3, 1.4, 1.5, 1.6, 1.9, 1.10, 1.12, 1.17, 1.18, 1.19, 2.10

What I Will Learn

- to describe the healthy eating guidelines
- to relate the food pyramid to meal planning
- to use food composition tables

Key Words

✓ Balanced diet
✓ Food pyramid
✓ Serving
✓ Portion
✓ Composition
✓ Healthy
✓ Supplements

Nutritional research has shown that the type and amount of food a person eats has a huge impact on their health and general well-being. A balanced diet, combined with exercise, helps to ensure good health and reduce the risk of diet-related diseases. But what exactly is a balanced healthy diet?

Healthy eating means getting the correct amount of nutrients – protein, fat, carbohydrates, vitamins and minerals – you need to maintain good health. It is important to follow the healthy eating guidelines (**see p. 56**) and use the food pyramid (**see p. 54**) to plan meals, to ensure your diet is balanced and nutritious.

Diet: The food a person eats.
Balanced diet: A diet containing all of the nutrients in the correct proportions to meet a person's needs.

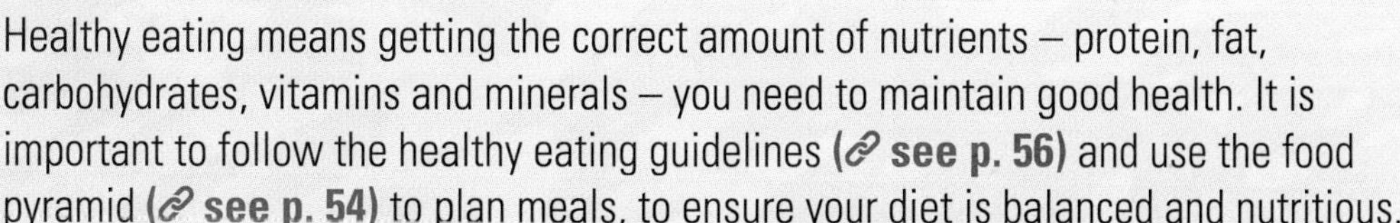

The food pyramid

To have a balanced diet you need to combine several different types of foods from each of the main food groups in the right amounts so your body gets all the nutrients and maintains a healthy weight. Foods that contain the same types of nutrients are grouped together on each level of the food pyramid.

The food pyramid

Not needed for good health

Foods and drinks high in fat, sugar and salt

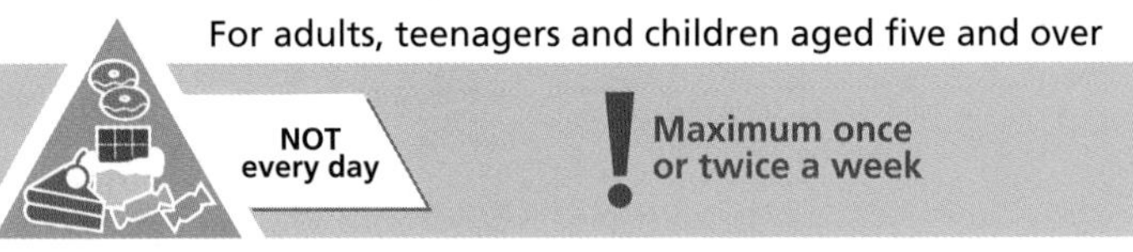

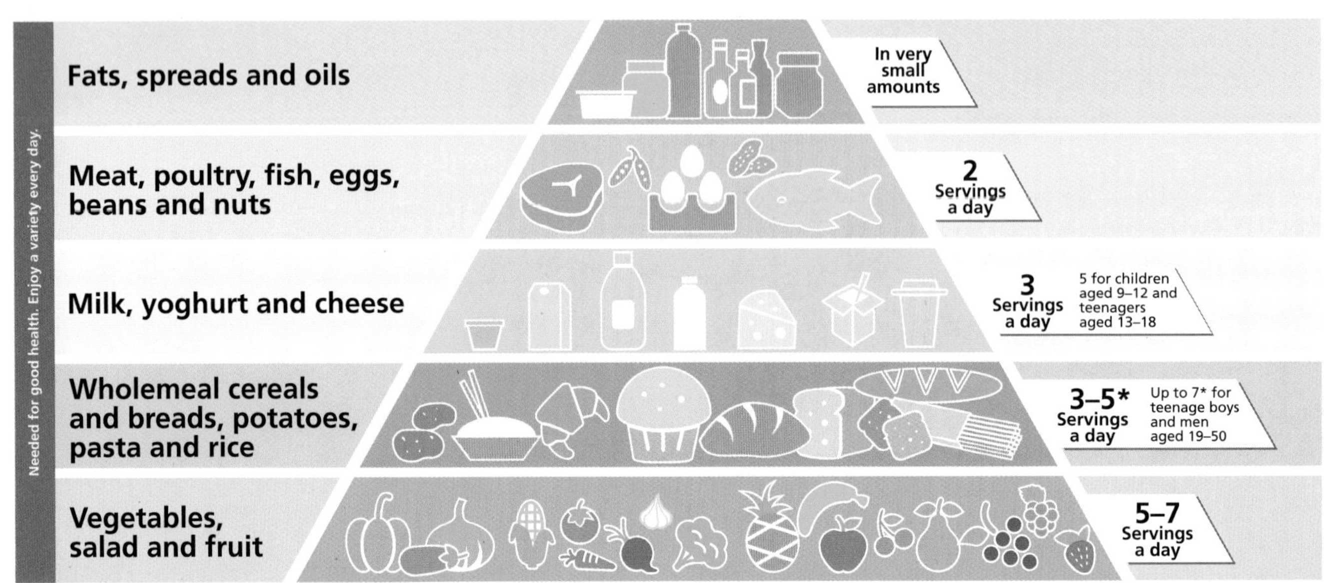

***Daily servings guide – wholemeal cereals and breads, potatoes, pasta and rice**

Active	Child (5–12)	Teenager (13–18)	Adult (19–50)	Adult (51+)
	3–4	4	4–5	3–4
	3–5	5–7	5–7	4–5

Inactive	Teenager (13–18)	Adult (19–50)	Adult (51+)
	4	3–4	3
	4–5	4–6	4

8 **Drink at least 8 cups of fluid a day – water is best**

Get Active!
To maintain a healthy weight, adults need at least 30 minutes a day of moderate activity 5 days a week (or 150 minutes a week); children need to be active at a moderate to vigorous level for at least 60 minutes every day.

There is no guideline for inactive children as it is essential that all children are active.
*Source: Department of Health, December 2016.

The food pyramid

Food groups on the food pyramid

Vegetables, salad and fruit

Wholemeal cereals and breads, potatoes, pasta and rice

Milk, yoghurt and cheese

Meat, poultry, fish, eggs, beans and nuts

Fats, spreads and oils

Foods and drinks high in fat, sugar and salt

The food pyramid is designed to make healthy eating easier:

- Foods that contain the same type of nutrients are grouped together on each of the shelves. This gives a choice of different foods from which to choose a healthy diet.
- Using the food pyramid can guide you to get the right balance of nutritious foods within your calorie range.
- It has been shown that we take in too many calories from foods and drinks high in fat, sugar and salt (found on the top shelf of the food pyramid). These provide a lot of calories with little nutrients, so limiting these is essential for healthy eating.

Further Investigation

To find out more about each food group and the new food pyramid, go to **www.safefood.eu**, click on 'Healthy Eating' at the top of the home page, then click on 'The Food Pyramid and the Eatwell Guide', and then on 'The Food Pyramid (ROI)'.

Did You Know?

Food supplements are concentrated sources of nutrients taken as a dietary top-up. They include fish oils, which have been shown to benefit heart health, minerals like iron to prevent anaemia and a whole list of vitamins from A to K. Supplements contain higher amounts of nutrients than are found in most foods.

If you eat a varied and balanced diet there is usually no need to take any food supplements – you'll get everything you need from your food. The one exception to this is folic acid. All women of child-bearing age who could become pregnant should take a supplement of 400 µg (micrograms) folic acid each day. If a woman does become pregnant, she should continue to take the supplement during the first 12 weeks of pregnancy. Do you know why?

Healthy eating guidelines

- Eat a **wide variety** of foods from the five healthy food groups and follow the food pyramid.
- Limit food and drinks from the top shelf of the food pyramid. These are rich in calories, fat, sugar and salt, so remember: **NOT too MUCH and NOT too OFTEN**.
- Keep an eye on your **serving sizes** – choose smaller serving sizes.
- Plain wholemeal breads, cereals, potatoes, pasta and rice provide the best calories for a healthy weight. Base your meals on these simple foods and include plenty of vegetables, salad and fruit.
- Eat **plenty** of different coloured **vegetables**, **salad and fruit** – at least five a day.
- **Low-fat** milk, yoghurt and cheese are the best – choose milk and yoghurt more often than cheese.
- Choose lean meat and poultry; include fish (oily is best) and remember, peas, beans and lentils are good alternatives.
- Use polyunsaturated and monounsaturated spreads and oils sparingly – **reduced fat spreads are the best to use**.
- Choose **healthy cooking methods**, i.e. grill, bake, steam or boil food, instead of frying or deep frying.
- Reduce your **salt** intake – use herbs and spices to flavour foods.
- **Drink** plenty of **water** – between 8 and 10 glasses per day.

Did You Know?

It is recommended that everyone should take a daily vitamin D supplement: 5 μg per day for those aged 5–50 years and 10 μg per day for those aged 51 years and over.

Revision Questions

1. Define a 'balanced diet'.
2. Name the five healthy food groups and give three examples of foods from each group.
3. From which two groups should we get most of our food? Explain why.
4. Name three diseases associated with an unhealthy diet.
5. List the healthy eating guidelines.
6. Write a day's menu for a family following the healthy eating guidelines and using the food pyramid.

Planning balanced diets

What I Will Learn

- to use the food pyramid and healthy eating guidelines to plan balanced diets
- to describe the nutritional needs and dietary requirements of each age group
- to plan balanced menus for all age groups

Key Words

✓ Weaning
✓ Sedentary
✓ Manual
✓ Convalescent
✓ Invalid

Don't Forget!
We should aim to include three out of the four main food groups in each meal for all individuals.

A well-balanced diet contains all the nutrients in the correct proportions for each individual. This is achieved by eating a wide variety of foods, chosen from all the bottom five food groups in the food pyramid. Dietary requirements depend on the **life stage** of the individual.

Classroom-Based Assessment

Remember food groups when choosing menus for CBA2 and the Practical Food Skills examination.

Babies

1. Babies should be breastfed if possible for the first few months of life because:
   - It helps the mother and baby bond.
   - The milk is always at the correct temperature.
   - Breast milk is properly balanced, as it has all the nutrients in the correct proportions to suit a baby's needs.
   - There is less chance of the baby becoming overweight, as breast milk contains less fat than formula milk.

- Breast milk contains antibodies, hormones and enzymes which are passed onto the baby to help build resistance to diseases, so they are less likely to suffer from allergies, gastric upset, respiratory problems and insulin-dependent diabetes.

2. If dried formula milk is used, follow the measurement and preparation instructions carefully.
3. It is extremely important to prepare milk formula hygienically. As babies are so young, it is easier to upset their digestive systems or give them food poisoning.
4. Milk remains an important part of a baby's diet, but solid foods can be introduced at around 4–6 months. This is called **weaning**.
5. All solids must be mashed up or liquidised at first, so the baby learns to swallow. Each new food should be introduced slowly (one new food at a time), so that the baby will get used to a variety of tastes and food intolerances can be recognised.
6. Babies are usually born with sufficient iron to last them six months. It is recommended that their first solids include cereals with a bland flavour that is similar to milk but that also contain iron, e.g. ground rice or semolina.

7. Babies need vitamin C. Serve juice in a cup or on a spoon, never in a bottle because it rots teeth. Sieved/puréed fruit and vegetables also provide vitamin C.
8. Avoid using too many convenience baby foods. They are expensive and the baby will get used to their taste and texture and may refuse home-cooked foods.
9. Do not add sugar or salt to baby foods as they are unnecessary in the diet. Exclude tea, coffee, fatty, fried or spicy foods and honey from the diet of babies under one year.
10. Crunchy foods such as rusks and apples help to soothe teething problems and strengthen gums.
11. By the time the baby is one year old, they should be eating many of the same foods as the rest of the family.

Children

Childhood is a very important time in terms of growth and development. It is at this stage that eating habits are established. The diet of children should be highly nutritious and balanced.

Did You Know?

One in four children in Ireland is overweight or obese. Obese children are likely to become obese adults. Many parents find it difficult to recognise that their child's weight is not healthy.

1. Children should be encouraged to eat a wide variety of healthy foods based on the food pyramid.
2. Meals should be based on regular family meals, to encourage healthy eating patterns and to provide good parental example. Portions should be small and attractively served – experts recommend three small meals and two to three healthy snacks a day. Avoid using desserts, chocolate or sweets as treats or rewards, and discourage 'faddy' (fussy) eating.
3. Important nutrients for children include:
   - **Protein** for growth
   - **Carbohydrates** for energy
   - Small amounts of **fibre** to prevent constipation
   - **Calcium**, **vitamins A** and **D** for healthy teeth and bones
   - **Iron** to prevent anaemia
4. Children should be given full-fat milk and other dairy products until they are at least two years old to make sure they get enough vitamins A and D.
5. Fruit and vegetables are important to supply vitamins, minerals and fibre. They add bulk to the diet but are low in fat.
6. Encourage children to drink water rather than fruit juices and fizzy drinks to prevent dehydration.
7. Sweet treats and snack foods high in salt and fat should be limited and only eaten after meals to reduce the risk of childhood obesity.
8. A healthy breakfast, including foods from three of the four main food groups, is important for children.

Did You Know?

Seven out of ten parents said they know their own eating habits have a huge influence on their children's likes and dislikes. Yet, in the same research, only one in ten parents said they would change their own eating habits to help their children.

Teenagers

1. Protein foods are needed for growth and hormone development in teenagers.
2. Active teenagers can include a lot of high-energy foods (carbohydrates) in their diet. However, inactive teenagers will become overweight on a high-energy diet.
3. High-fibre energy foods, e.g. cereals (preferably wholegrain), should be chosen, as they prevent bowel disorders and constipation.
4. Teenagers should avoid eating too much junk food or snacks – these are high in sugar but supply few other nutrients.
5. Fried foods or high-fat foods should be kept to a minimum as they can cause weight problems and tend to aggravate acne and other skin problems.
6. Drinks, particularly water, help keep the skin clear. Fruit and vegetables supply fibre and vitamin C, which also help to keep the skin in good condition.
7. Calcium and vitamins A and D are important for the development

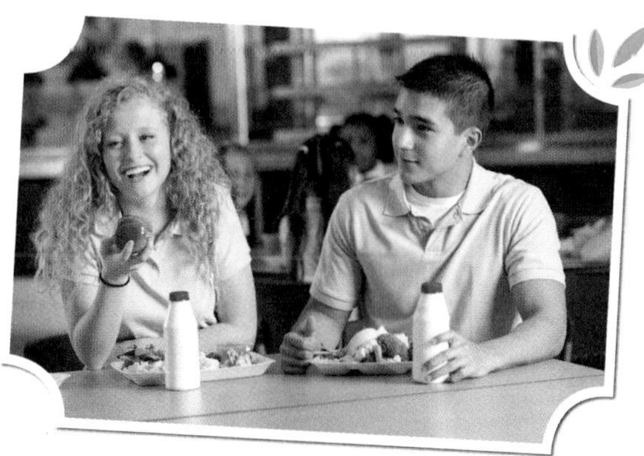

of healthy bones and teeth and help to prevent osteoporosis in later life.

8. Iron and vitamin C are particularly important in the diet of teenage girls (because of menstruation) to prevent the development of anaemia.
9. Teenagers who wish to become vegetarian or vegan must be very careful that they are eating balanced, nutritious diets.
10. Teenagers have busy schedules with school and exams; they can also worry about their physical appearance and they may have a lot of peer pressure – all of which can affect their food choices.

Adults

1. All adults should eat a well-balanced diet that includes a variety of foods. Energy intake varies according to the gender, body size and activity levels of the individual (**factors that influence energy requirements, see p. 41**).
2. A good supply of protein is essential to repair body cells and maintain good health – include a good mix of animal and vegetable proteins. Vegetarians, vegans and people over 40 with a family history of bowel cancer should make sure they get sufficient protein from plant sources and meat alternatives. A plentiful supply of vitamin B ensures the release of energy from food.
3. Keep fat intake low – reduce animal fat and replace it with low-fat dairy products or vegetable oils to help reduce cholesterol and supply omega fatty acids.
4. Carbohydrate foods are needed for energy; the diet should be high in starches and fibre and low in sugars to reduce the risk of obesity and diabetes. A high-fibre diet is recommended to aid digestion and avoid constipation.
5. Salt intake should be reduced because salt is associated with high blood pressure.
6. It is important that women in particular eat enough calcium-rich foods in order to reduce the risk of bone disease.
7. Iron is also of importance to women to avoid becoming anaemic. Vitamin C is needed to help absorb iron.
8. Keep alcohol consumption to a minimum, as it is a source of empty kilocalories.
9. Balance energy intake with activity. As people age (over 25), their calorie requirements reduce unless a person is very active.

Sedentary workers: Adults who are not very active need to reduce their kilocalorie intake to prevent weight gain. Alcohol and foods that are high in fat and sugar should be restricted. Exercise helps to control weight.

Manual workers: These lead a more active lifestyle so they can afford to eat a higher-energy diet, but it is advisable to choose energy foods that are high in fibre and restrict those high in sugar or fat.

Pregnant and breastfeeding women

1. During pregnancy, the baby depends on the mother for its nutrients and health. A failure to follow a healthy diet may cause deficiency diseases in mother and baby. While it is not necessary to 'eat for two', it is important to eat a well-balanced and nutritious diet.
2. Energy intake should be increased slightly, but a pregnant woman should avoid excessive weight gain.
3. Protein is very important for the growth of the foetus. Calcium, phosphorus and vitamins A and D are essential for healthy bone and teeth development in the baby, and to reduce the risk of bone disease in the mother.
4. Fruit, vegetables and wholemeal cereals supply fibre and vitamins B and C.
5. Intake of fluids, such as water and low-sugar fruit juices, should be increased to prevent constipation.
6. Iron is necessary to prevent anaemia and may need to be supplemented by iron tablets.
7. Folic acid should be taken to reduce the risk of neural tube defects in newborn babies.
8. Pregnant women should avoid:
   - Strong tea and coffee
   - Rich, spicy or fatty foods
   - Soft cheeses, pâté, cook-chill foods and prepared salad because of the risk of listeria
   - Soft cooked or raw eggs, e.g. mayonnaise, because of the risk of salmonella
   - Liver and shellfish
   - Alcohol, smoking and drugs of any type, unless on prescription

Discovery Learning

Using books or going online, find out the following:

- How many kilocalories should a pregnant woman eat on a daily basis?
- What is an acceptable weight gain during pregnancy?
- Why should a pregnant woman avoid rich, spicy or fatty foods?

Older people

1. Older people could have problems that affect their diets. They may:
   - Live on low incomes.
   - Experience a loss of appetite or interest in food or have poor digestion. This may result in a poor diet, e.g. buying less variety of fresh foods and more convenience foods, which can lead to malnutrition.
   - Have poor general health or physical disabilities such as arthritis, poor mobility, weak eyesight and dental problems, which could interfere with shopping for, preparing, cooking and eating food.
   - Have reduced mental capacity, which could affect an older person's ability to ensure a healthy diet. Loneliness can also lead to a lack of interest in cooking for one person.
   - Difficulties when shopping, e.g. they are less mobile, live too far from the shops, or are unable to carry heavy shopping bags
2. Older people should eat three balanced meals every day. This can be difficult as many have small appetites. They should follow the healthy eating guidelines and eat less sugar, salt and fat, while eating fibre and drinking plenty of water.
3. A supply of protein is important to help replace worn-out body cells and to maintain good health, so choose easy-to-digest proteins like white fish and chicken.
4. As many older people are less active, they should reduce their intake of high-energy food or they risk becoming overweight. Choosing low-fat alternatives will also help prevent excessive weight gain.
5. High-fibre foods are necessary to aid digestion and prevent constipation. Drinks like water and milk are important for the same reason.
6. Dairy foods are essential for calcium and vitamins A and D. These nutrients help to keep bones and teeth healthy and to prevent osteoporosis.
7. Meat, including offal, is a good source of iron, which helps to prevent anaemia. Vitamin C – found mainly in fruit and vegetables – helps iron absorption and protects against colds, flu and other infections.
8. Spicy foods can be hard to digest.

Ways to prevent malnutrition in an older person:
- Buy specialised kitchen gadgets, e.g. tap turners, jar openers and electrical can openers.
- Use services such as Meals on Wheels and Home Help.
- Use home delivery services from shops, e.g. SuperValu and Tesco.
- Have emergency supplies always in store, e.g. dried and tinned foods.

Invalids and convalescents

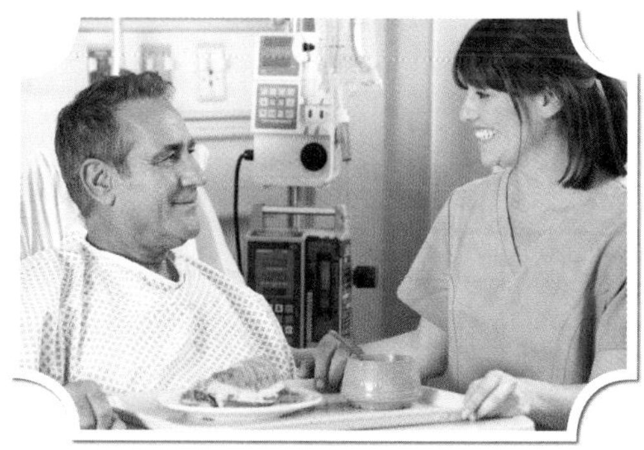

Invalids and convalescents are people who are sick or recovering from illness. They need a nourishing diet to help restore them to good health. They may have a very poor appetite at first, so it is essential that the foods they eat contain the important nutrients without being too bulky. The following are guidelines for invalids and convalescents.

1. Follow doctor's orders.
2. Choose foods that are easy to digest and lightly seasoned.
3. Avoid spicy, fatty foods and coffee.
4. Serve small, attractive portions that are easy to eat, and remove any leftovers when the meal is finished.
5. Boiling, steaming, stewing and grilling are better methods of cooking food for invalids than frying or roasting.
6. Meals should be prepared under strict hygienic conditions.
7. Use good-quality fresh foods – avoid using leftovers or reheated foods.
8. Eat protein-rich foods to repair and replace body cells lost during the illness.
9. Energy intake should be reduced during convalescence as energy expenditure is low.
10. Fibre is important to prevent constipation, which is more likely due to inactivity.
11. Vitamins – especially vitamin C – help the body to return to health and build up resistance to further infection.
12. Minerals – especially iron – are important if there has been any blood loss to prevent the patient from becoming run down or anaemic.
13. Fluids are always important in the diet but are particularly important if the person has a fever or high temperature. Water helps to replace the fluids lost through perspiration and to prevent the body from becoming dehydrated. This is a condition that can be especially dangerous in the case of babies or very young children.

Invalid: A person who has been affected by a disease or medical disorder over a long period of time.
Convalescent: A person who is recovering from an illness.

Discovery Learning

Devise a day's menu for each age group, using the correct menu format, while keeping in mind the healthy eating guidelines for a balanced diet. Meal planning guidelines should also be considered. Be ready to justify and explain your choices.

Classroom-Based Assessment

Menu-writing can be linked to CBA2.

Revision Questions

Use your workbook to revise this chapter

1. What guidelines should be followed when feeding babies?
2. How would you encourage a child to develop healthy eating habits?
3. Suggest three healthy lunches for school-going children.
4. Why is healthy eating important for a teenager?
5. Write up a day's menu for (i) a manual and (ii) a sedentary worker. Explain why they are different.
6. What nutrients are important in the diet of a pregnant woman?
7. List foods that a pregnant woman should avoid and give reasons why.
8. Compile a set of guidelines for feeding a person recovering from an illness.

Summary

- **Balanced diets** can be planned using the food pyramid and following the healthy eating guidelines.
- **Babies** should be breastfed if possible and weaned between four and six months. The first foods include cereals, fruit and vegetables. Avoid using convenience foods or adding salt or sugar to homemade foods.
- **Children** should eat a wide variety of fresh foods in child-sized portions. Include protein, calcium, iron and vitamins A and D, and avoid sweet and high-fat treats. Adults should lead by example by eating well.
- **Teenagers** need a variety of fresh foods from a diet rich in protein, vitamins and minerals, especially calcium and iron. The amount of energy food required depends on their activity levels. Discourage snacking on foods high in sugar and fat.
- **Adults** need a varied diet that is high in fibre, unsaturated fats, calcium and iron, while avoiding excess salt, sugar, saturated fat and alcohol. The amount of energy required depends on their activity levels.
- **Pregnant and breastfeeding women** need a diet high in protein, calcium, folic acid and vitamins A and D for the healthy development of the foetus. Water, fibre and B-group vitamins are also important.
- **Older people** need a varied diet containing protein, fibre, vitamins, minerals and water to maintain good health. They should keep active, reduce high-energy food and choose low-fat food to avoid weight gain.
- **Invalids and convalescents** need a nourishing, low-energy diet to help them with their illnesses. They need protein for repair, and vitamin C, iron and water are very important to aid recovery and to prevent weight gain.

06 SPECIAL DIETS

Learning Outcomes 1.1, 1.2, 1.3, 1.4, 1.5, 1.6, 1.7, 1.8, 1.9, 1.10, 1.13, 1.14, 1.17, 1.18, 1.19

What I Will Learn

- to describe the nutritional needs and dietary requirements of each special diet
- to plan balanced menus for all special diets
- to explain the nutritional choices I made
- to list the causes and health risks associated with each condition
- to compile a set of dietary guidelines for each dietary condition

Key Words

✓ Obesity
✓ Anorexia
✓ Bulimia
✓ Refined foods
✓ Vegan
✓ Lacto-vegetarian
✓ Quorn
✓ Textured vegetable protein
✓ Tofu
✓ Coronary heart disease
✓ Stroke
✓ Cholesterol
✓ Coeliac disease
✓ Gluten
✓ Diabetes
✓ Insulin
✓ Dental disease
✓ Osteoporosis
✓ Food intolerance
✓ Allergy

Special diets

People with diet-related diseases or conditions require a modified or special diet.

Obesity

Obesity means being 20% or more above the normal weight for your height and build. Obesity is sometimes the result of a hormone imbalance, in which case it must be medically treated. More often, it results from overeating – when the amount of energy taken into the body is more than the amount of energy used up.

Did You Know?

According to the Healthy Ireland Survey 2015, 37% of the population in Ireland are overweight and a further 23% are obese.

Classroom-Based Assessment

This section is linked to CBA2 and the Practical Food Skills examination.

Why do people become overweight?

- **Overeating**: If a person's calorie intake is excessive, weight gain can result.
- **Lack of regular exercise or no exercise at all**: Sedentary lifestyles and an increase in portion sizes also contribute.
- **Unhealthy eating patterns** are often established from an early age, e.g. consuming large portion sizes, skipping meals and eating late at night.
- **Poor nutritional knowledge** can lead to poor food choices and an overuse of convenience foods.
- **Low income**: Buying cheaper foods that are high in sugar, salt and saturated fats but low in fibre.
- **Busy lifestyles** can lead to an overuse of convenience foods at home and regularly eating fast foods instead of making healthy, home-cooked meals.
- **Emotional reasons**: 'Comfort eating', possibly due to boredom or stress.
- **Hormonal imbalance**, i.e. in the thyroid gland, can cause weight gain.
- **Some medications**, in particular anti-depressants, can lead to weight gain.

Health problems associated with obesity

- Heart disease
- High blood pressure
- Stroke
- Varicose veins
- Diabetes
- Gout and arthritis (joint pain)
- Liver disease and gall stones
- Low self-esteem
- Problems in surgery and childbirth
- Shorter life expectancy

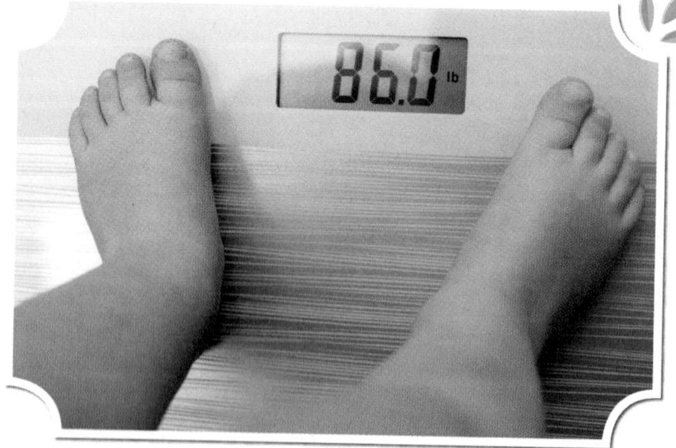

Treatment

Obesity can be treated by **cutting down** on energy intake, i.e. eating a healthy, low kilocalorie diet and **increasing** daily exercise and activity levels. Combining both will speed up weight loss.

Top tips for weight reduction

- Enjoy a wide **variety** of fresh, nutritious foods from all five food groups every day.
- Establish a pattern of eating **regular**, balanced meals.
- Do not exclude any nutrient, but **reduce portion** sizes if necessary.
- **Eat** plenty of **fruit and vegetables**, as they are low in fat and make great snacks. Include different types and colours and pulses, e.g. peas and beans.
- **Avoid** refined carbohydrates or sugar-rich foods. **Increase your intake** of **high-fibre** foods such as wholemeal bread, wholegrain cereals, rice, pasta, noodles, polenta, couscous, oats, quinoa and barley.
- **Avoid** foods high in **saturated fats** such as fatty red meat and butter. Choose lean meats and poultry, fish, eggs, tofu, nuts and seeds.
- **Avoid** convenience foods and keep **takeaways** to a minimum.
- **Read labels carefully** to check for sugar and fat content.
- **Drink** at least eight glasses of **water** a day. It keeps you hydrated but can also fill you up, reducing hunger.
- **Avoid alcohol**.
- **Choose low-fat/sugar alternatives**, e.g. low-fat cheese and yoghurt.
- **Change** your **cooking methods**: Grill and steam foods and avoid fried foods.
- Use a **smaller plate** – it is easier to fill.
- **Do not skip meals**.
- Always **sit down to eat**.
- **Take regular exercise** and do not eat between meals.

Did You Know?

Extreme weight loss can be harmful to the body, so quick-loss and fad diets should be avoided. A slow weekly loss of 1 kg is much more beneficial and sustainable. It is important to consult a doctor before commencing with any dietary plan. Many people find it beneficial to join a slimming club or group for support and motivation, e.g. Slimming World.

Eating disorders

In modern society, there is an emphasis on being slim. It is important to maintain a healthy weight, but sometimes losing weight can become an obsession. This can lead to eating disorders.

Further Investigation

Bodywhys is an organisation that provides counselling and information on eating. To learn more about eating disorders, visit **www.bodywhys.ie**.

Anorexia nervosa

This is a psychological condition where a person refuses to eat enough to maintain a healthy body weight. Anorexia can affect both males and females of all ages, but is more common in teenage girls and young women. Anorexics may see themselves as fat even though they may be very underweight. This condition requires professional treatment, as it can result in death from starvation.

Bulimia nervosa

This often involves 'binge eating', followed by vomiting. Sometimes laxatives are used to eliminate (get rid of) food. People who suffer from bulimia are not always thin and they may be older than anorexia sufferers. Treatment can take the form of counselling and help from support groups such as Bodywhys.

Did You Know?

The Department of Health estimates that:

- Up to 200,000 people in Ireland may be affected by eating disorders.
- An estimated 400 new cases emerge each year, and approximately 80 deaths occur annually.

Source: Bodywhys website, 2017

Revision Questions

1. Outline the causes of obesity.
2. Plan a one-day menu for an obese person.
3. Compile a set of healthy living guidelines for a person who is overweight.

• Use your workbook to revise this chapter •

Classroom-Based Assessment

This section is linked to CBA2 and the Practical Food Skills examination.

Vegetarian diets

A **vegetarian** is a person who does not eat meat, fish or poultry.

There are two main types of vegetarians:

- **Vegans** (strict vegetarians) **do not eat any animal products**, e.g. meat, fish or dairy products. Their diet is composed entirely of plant foods, e.g. fruit, vegetables, nuts and cereals.
- **Lacto-vegetarians do not eat meat, fish or poultry but do eat animal products**, e.g. milk, cheese and eggs. This is not as limiting as a vegan diet.

Discovery Learning

Go online or use books to find out the following:

- What supplements should vegans take in their diets? Explain why.
- What other types of vegetarians are there?

Why do people become vegetarian?

People become vegetarian for many reasons:

- They object to the killing of animals for food for **moral or ethical reasons**, or they disapprove of the methods or practices involved in the rearing of animals for food, e.g. battery hens, calves reared in cages for veal.
- They consider it a **healthier option**. Vegetarians are less likely to be overweight or suffer from heart disease or bowel disorders.
- Some **religions** such as Buddhism might encourage vegetarianism, as they do not like to kill animals. Other religions like Hinduism, Islam and Judaism place restrictions on the consumption of certain meat or animal products, e.g. Hindus do not eat beef and Jews do not eat pork.
- Vegetables and cereals are easier and cheaper to produce, so they are not as **environmentally wasteful**.
- Some people do **not like the look, smell or taste of meat**. Plant foods offer a variety of colour and texture to food.

Vegetarians should consult the food pyramid for advice on alternatives to animal products when planning meals.

Discovery Learning

A vegetarian diet often lacks protein. Find out what you can about the following meat substitutes:

- TVP (textured vegetable protein)
- Tofu
- Quorn

Suggest three other high-protein substitutes.

Classroom-Based Assessment

This section is linked to CBA2 and the Practical Food Skills examination.

Guidelines for planning a vegetarian diet

- A good knowledge of nutrition is needed to ensure a balanced diet.
- Read labels and check for the vegetarian symbols.
- Include vegetable protein foods such as pulse vegetables, cereals and nuts.
- Use unprocessed cereals and grains for extra vitamins and fibre (higher in vitamin B).
- Use vegetable stock only.
- Use vegetable fats or oils, as many margarines contain animal products (always read the labels).
- Use soya milk/products as a substitute for dairy products.
- Shop around for new vegetarian products on the market.

Further Investigation

If a young person is planning to become a vegetarian, it is a good idea to visit **www.safefood.eu** and **www.indi.ie** to get up-to-date information and advice on food choices.

Revision Questions

1. State three reasons why a teenager would become a vegetarian.
2. List three advantages of becoming a vegetarian.

Classroom-Based Assessment

This section is linked to CBA2 and the Practical Food Skills examination.

Low-salt diets

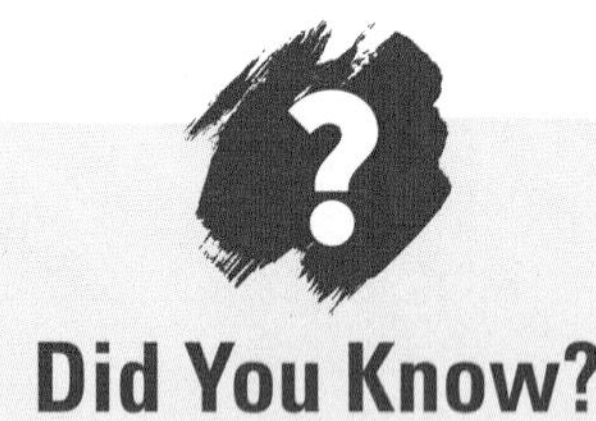

Did You Know?

A low-salt food has 0.1 g of salt per 100 g of food.

- Salt controls the amount of fluid in the body. We require about 2 g of salt each day. However, most people eat up to 10 times that amount.
- Salt is added to food for flavour or as a preservative.
- A reduction in salt could prevent many health problems, including high blood pressure (hypertension), coronary heart disease, stroke, fluid retention and kidney damage.
- Salt is labelled on foods as salt (NaCl) or sodium (Na), so always check labels to see if there is salt present.

Health problems associated with salt

- High blood pressure (hypertension)
- Coronary heart disease
- Stroke
- Fluid retention
- Kidney damage

Salt is present naturally in foods such as meat, fish and eggs, but we add extra salt to our diets by:

- Using processed foods containing salt, e.g. packet soups, stock cubes, packet and tinned foods, snack foods, sauces, breakfast cereals and many sweet foods
- Adding salt during cooking
- Using salt at the table
- Eating cured foods, e.g. bacon and ham

Be Numerate

To convert sodium to salt, multiply by 2.5.

Did You Know?

Salt for human consumption is produced in the following forms: unrefined salt (such as sea salt), refined salt (table salt) and iodised salt. Salt is a crystalline solid that is white, pale pink or light grey in colour. It is normally obtained from sea water or rock deposits.

Did You Know?

About 70% of the salt we eat comes from processed foods, fast food, canteen and restaurant food. About 20% is added at home, in cooking or at the table. Only 10% occurs naturally in food (Irish Heart Foundation, 2017).

Salty foods to avoid

Snack foods

Processed meats

Stock cubes

Tinned foods

Butter, margarine and cheese

Packet foods

Guidelines for reducing salt

- Parents should avoid **adding salt to children's food** or giving them salty snack foods.
- **Use herbs and spices** instead of salt during cooking.
- Make use of **salt substitutes**, e.g. LoSalt, and low-salt foods.
- Keep **salt off the table** and always taste food before adding salt.
- **Avoid convenience, processed and snack** foods. **Change to low-salt** versions.
- **Read labels carefully:** Look out for the chemical name for salt (sodium chloride) and the symbol NaCl. Some food additives, e.g. monosodium glutamate and sodium sulfite, are also high in salt.

Classroom-Based Assessment

This section is linked to CBA2 and the Practical Food Skills examination.

Further Investigation

To learn more about salt in the diet, visit the Irish Heart Foundation's website **www.irishhealth.ie**. Click on 'Your Health' on the home page, then click on 'Ways to Live Better' and then on 'Managing Salt Intake'.

Revision Questions

1. What are the risks of a high-salt diet?
2. Explain how to reduce salt in the diet.

Classroom-Based Assessment

This section is linked to CBA2 and the Practical Food Skills examination.

Low-fat/low-cholesterol diets

- Fat is an essential part of our diet (can you remember why?).
- It is recommended the average person reduce their fat intake to remain healthy.
- There are healthy and unhealthy sources of fat, so we need to be aware of the types of fat we are eating, as well as the amount we consume.

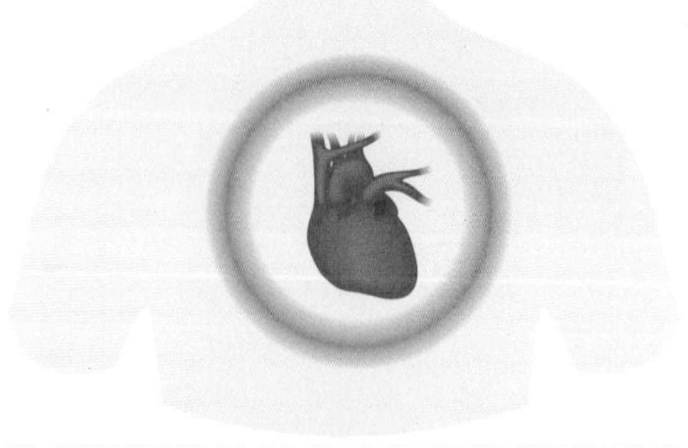

The location of the heart in the body

Associated health problems of a high-cholesterol diet

A high-cholesterol diet can lead to obesity, cardiovascular diseases, e.g. coronary heart disease, stroke and high blood pressure. It can also aggravate diseases like diabetes and cancer.

- The heart pumps blood around the body to carry oxygen to every cell in the body. The cells that make up the walls of the heart need a separate supply of blood.

- This blood is carried by a special artery called the coronary artery, which branches off from the aorta.
- If these blood vessels get blocked, a person will suffer from coronary heart disease.

Coronary heart disease

This occurs when the arteries of the heart become blocked with a substance called **cholesterol**. Cholesterol is a fatty substance that clings to the walls of the arteries. This causes the arteries to become narrower, which puts more pressure on the heart as it has to pump the blood through smaller vessels. This can result in high blood pressure, heart disease or strokes.

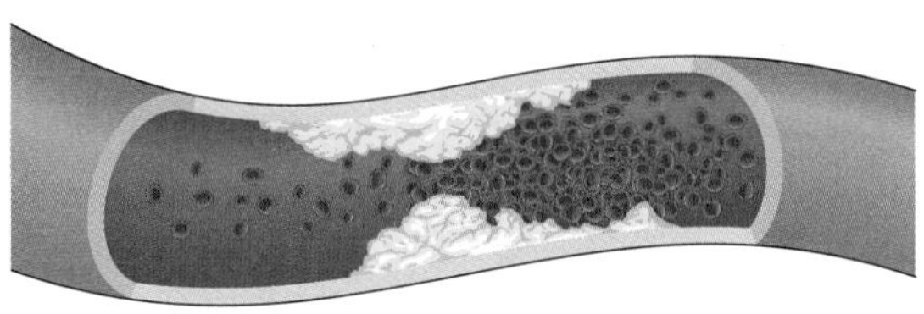

Arteries blocked with cholesterol

Did You Know?

According to the Health Service Executive (HSE), approximately 10,000 people die each year from cardiovascular diseases. These include coronary heart disease (CHD), stroke and other circulatory diseases.

Heart disease can develop over many years and is usually very advanced by the time people experience any symptoms. However, it is preventable! Up to 80% of the incidence of heart disease can be prevented through reducing cholesterol levels, lowering blood pressure and quitting smoking.

Causes of heart disease

- A history of heart disease in your family (heredity)
- Being overweight or having a diet high in saturated fat
- Lack of exercise
- Smoking
- Stress
- Too much alcohol

How to reduce the risk of heart disease

- Have a low-fat/low-cholesterol diet
- Avoid becoming overweight
- Do not smoke
- Avoid stress
- Take lots of exercise
- Do not drink alcohol excessively

Guidelines for reducing fat intake

- Avoid high-fat sauces such as cream or cheese sauces
- Avoid pastries and cakes
- Choose low-fat dairy products
- Choose low-fat unsaturated spreads
- Grill, steam, bake or microwave instead of frying
- Eat lean meat, fish or poultry without the skins to supply protein
- Trim excess fat from meat and cut down on red meat
- Avoid fatty snack foods
- Increase the intake of fruit and vegetables in the diet
- Substitute low-cholesterol foods for high-cholesterol ones (see the table below)

Further Investigation

To learn more about reducing cholesterol in the diet, visit the Irish Heart Foundation's website **www.irisheart.ie**, click on 'Your Health' at the top of the home page, then click on 'Ways to Live Better', and then on 'Cholesterol'. To learn more about coronary heart disease (CHD), go to **www.hse.ie**, click on 'Health A–Z' on the home page, and search for coronary heart disease. To watch an animation on coronary heart disease, go to YouTube and search for 'Coronary Heart Disease Animation' (2:03).

High-cholesterol foods	Low-cholesterol foods
Butter	Unsaturated spreads
Hard margarine	Oils
Suet	White and oily fish
Lard	Chicken, turkey
Dripping	Pulse vegetables
Fat meats (e.g. bacon, sausage, pâté)	Cottage cheese
Cheese	Low-fat yoghurt
Cream	Fruit and vegetables
Eggs, particularly yolks	High-fibre cereals

Revision Questions

1. What are the risks of a high-cholesterol diet?
2. List five risk factors associated with coronary heart disease.
3. Suggest three ways coronary heart disease can be prevented.

Classroom-Based Assessment

This section is linked to CBA2 and the Practical Food Skills examination.

High-fibre diets

- Dietary fibre (cellulose) is only found in plant foods.
- When plant foods are processed, the fibre is removed, so refined or processed foods contain very little fibre.
- Fibre is not digested, but it helps to move food along the intestines by creating bulk.

Benefits of a high-fibre diet

- Fibre absorbs water, which makes food bulky inside the body.
- This causes peristalsis (**see p. 49**) in the intestine, which moves the food along quickly.
- Fibre prevents constipation.
- It also prevents any poisonous chemicals from building up in the body.
- Fibre does not contain calories but it gives a feeling of fullness; it is therefore useful in weight-reducing diets.

Health problems associated with a low-fibre intake

- Constipation occurs when faeces (waste) becomes lodged in the bowel.
- Bowel diseases, e.g. inflammatory bowel disease and diverticulosis, are caused when hard faeces becomes lodged in the bowel wall. This can lead to bowel cancer.
- Piles (swollen blood vessels) occur in the anus as a result of hard waste matter passing through.

Guidelines to increase fibre intake

(Carbohydrates, see p. 24)

- Choose whole cereals such as wholemeal bread, wholegrain rice and whole wheat pasta, instead of refined cereals.
- Eat high-fibre breakfast cereals (can you name some?).
- Leave the skins on fruit and vegetables, where possible.
- Eat whole fruits instead of fruit juices.
- Include pulse vegetables in the diet.
- Substitute fresh or dried fruit for processed snack foods.
- Drink plenty of water. Fibre absorbs water so extra is needed by the body.

Did You Know?

Bran is the outer layer of the cereal grain. It is an important source of fibre. However, large amounts of fibre can reduce the amount of iron absorbed from our food, so children and pregnant women should avoid eating too much bran.

Revision Questions

1. What is a refined food?
2. Explain how fibre prevents constipation and other bowel disorders.

Classroom-Based Assessment

This section is linked to CBA2 and the Practical Food Skills examination.

Diabetes

Diabetes is a chronic disease that is on the increase worldwide. There is no cure for diabetes, but it can be managed.

- Diabetes is a condition in which the body does not produce enough, or properly respond to, insulin, a hormone produced in the pancreas.
- Insulin enables cells to absorb glucose in order to turn it into energy.
- In people with diabetes, the body either doesn't respond properly to its own insulin, doesn't make enough insulin, or both. This causes glucose to accumulate in the blood, often leading to various health complications.

Did You Know?

In 2013, the International Diabetes Federation estimated that by 2020 there will be 233,000 in Ireland living with diabetes.

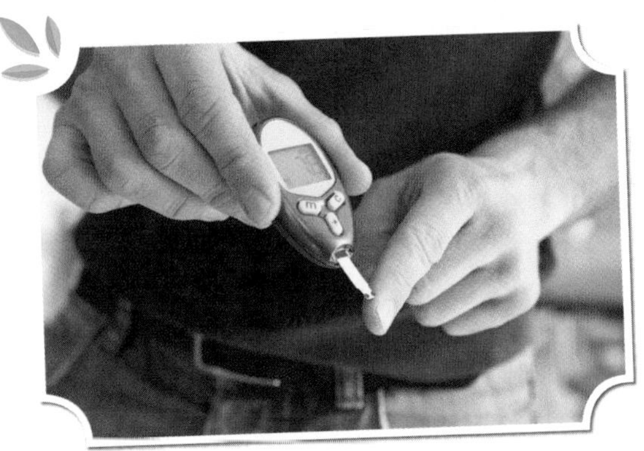
A blood sugar monitor

The two types of diabetes

Type 1: Insulin dependent

- Usually occurs in children or young adults.
- The **pancreas** does not produce enough insulin, so daily insulin injections are needed to regulate blood sugar levels and keep the body healthy.
- Glucose is excreted by the kidneys, leaving little in the body for energy production.
- If the blood sugar level rises or falls, the sufferer may become weak and lapse into a coma.

Type 2: Non-insulin dependent

- Usually occurs in adults over the age of 40; it is common in old age.
- With this type of diabetes, the person makes some insulin but it does not work satisfactorily.
- Usually associated with being overweight, it can be controlled by weight loss and diet. However, in some cases tablets are required to help the person's own insulin to work, or additional insulin may be required.
- The symptoms include excessive thirst and frequent urination.

Risk factors

Some people are more at risk of developing diabetes than others. The known risk factors include:

- A family history of diabetes
- Being overweight (80% of people with diabetes are overweight)
- Age (the likelihood of developing diabetes increases with age)
- Lack of physical exercise
- Having had diabetes during pregnancy or having given birth to a large baby

Dietary guidelines to control diabetes

Mild diabetes may be treated by doing the following:

- Following a low-sugar diet (see p. 79)
- Eating high-fibre and starchy foods
- Eating regularly and never missing a meal or snack
- Reaching and maintaining the ideal weight
- Exercising regularly to balance blood sugar levels

Some artificial sweeteners can be used instead of sugar. Diabetic products are available but can be expensive.

Further Investigation
To learn more about diabetes in Ireland, visit **www.diabetes.ie**.

Revision Questions

1. What is diabetes?
2. Describe the two different types of diabetes and explain how they differ.
3. List the ways diabetes can be controlled.

Classroom-Based Assessment

This section is linked to CBA2 and the Practical Food Skills examination.

Dental diseases

Healthy teeth and gums are important because:

- They help digest food properly
- They enhance your general appearance
- They enable you to speak clearly

Bad teeth can cause problems such as stomach upsets and bad breath.

The structure of a tooth

Functions of teeth

(For more information on teeth, see p. 48)

- **Incisors:** Bite food
- **Canines:** Cut and tear food
- **Molars and pre-molars:** Grind food

Dental diseases

The two main forms of dental diseases are:

1. **Dental caries** – the decay of the enamel of teeth, leading to tooth decay.
2. **Periodontal disease** – affects the gums and tissues surrounding the teeth.

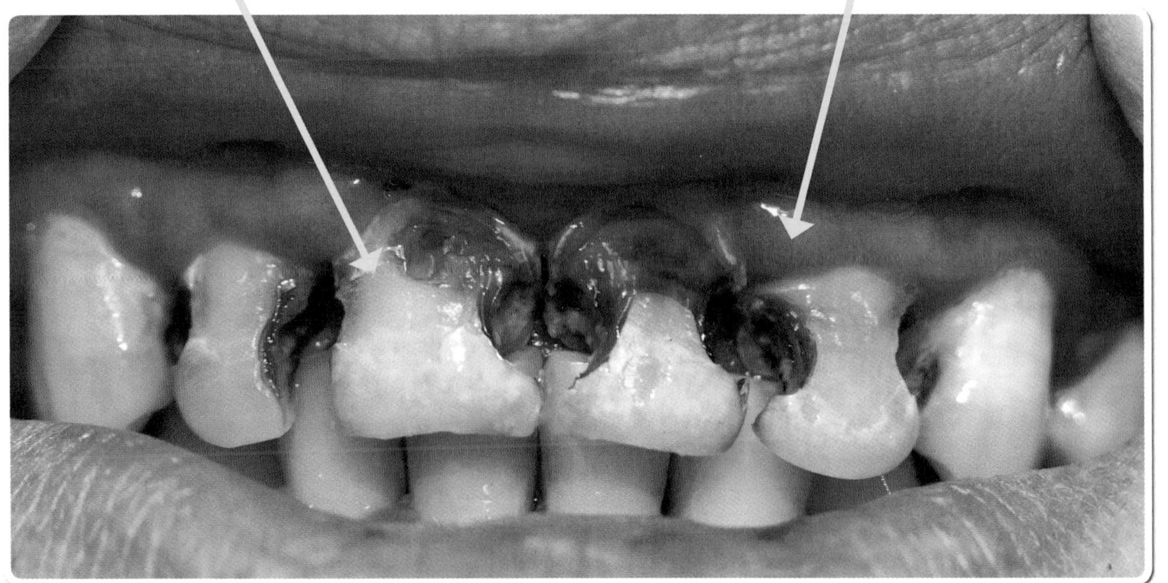

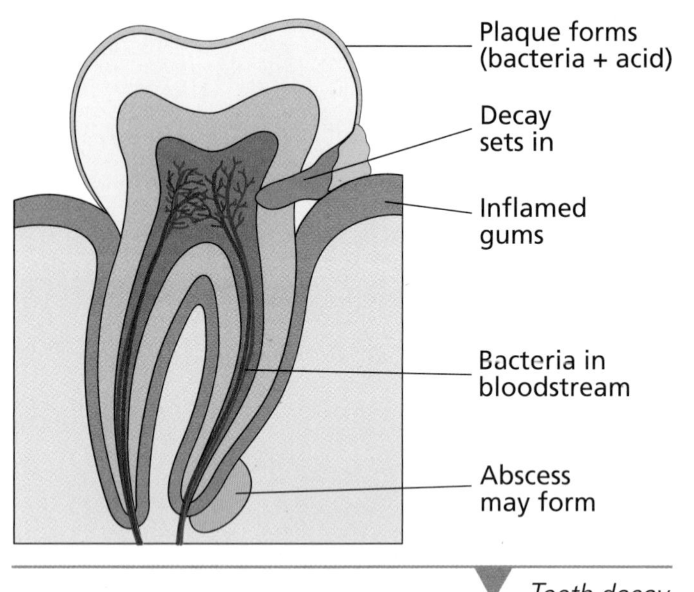

Tooth decay

Plaque

Tooth decay is caused by plaque, which forms a sticky film on the teeth between brushings. Plaque consists of bacteria and acid, which is formed by the breakdown of food, especially sugar, in the mouth.

If plaque is not removed, it gradually breaks through the enamel on the tooth until it reaches the softer dentine, which decays quickly. Toothaches will occur when the nerves in the pulp cavity become exposed. If plaque builds up and hardens on the teeth (tartar), it can lead to gum disease. If the gums become infected an abscess may occur – this is a painful swelling that contains pus.

Guidelines to prevent cavities and gum disease

- **Avoid** sugar.
- **Sealant** may be applied to the biting surface of the molars in childhood (on permanent teeth) to prevent the onset of dental caries (decay).
- **Increase the resistance of the tooth** by brushing at least twice a day.
- Remove bacteria by using a **mouthwash**.
- **Floss** regularly to remove lodged food from between teeth.
- **Visit a dentist** at least twice a year.
- **Use artificial sweeteners** instead of sugar, but be careful to check labels, as many diet products use artificial sweeteners that can be more harmful than sugar, e.g. aspartame.
- Drink **fluoridated water** instead of fizzy drinks.

Did You Know?

Water fluoridation is the controlled addition of fluoride to a public water supply to reduce tooth decay. Fluoride hardens tooth enamel by combining with the calcium phosphate in the teeth.

Further Investigation

To learn more about teeth care, watch the video 'How to brush your teeth? Learn in 4 simple steps!' (4:53) on YouTube.

Classroom-Based Assessment

This section is linked to CBA2 and the Practical Food Skills examination.

Low-sugar diets

Sugar is a source of energy in the diet, but has no other nutrients, so it is filled with 'empty calories' (see p. 26). Many people have a 'sweet tooth', meaning they like the taste of sweet foods. Food manufacturers add sugar to many foods to encourage people to eat them – it is even found in savoury foods. Sugar is the main cause of tooth decay, as it produces the most acid in the mouth. The more often sugar is eaten, the more acid that attacks the teeth, increasing the risk of decay.

Associated health problems of a high-sugar diet

These include diabetes, tooth decay, malnutrition and weight problems, including obesity.

Foods with a high sugar content (junk food): Fizzy drinks, sweets, sweet snacks, drinks sweetened with sugar, sugary breakfast cereals, cakes, biscuits and convenience sauces.

Guidelines for reducing sugar in the diet

- Avoid sugar-rich foods, i.e. junk food.
- Reduce the amount of sugar added during food preparation and cooking.
- Use artificial sweeteners instead of sugar to sweeten foods.
- Eat healthier, low-sugar snacks.
- Read food labels – check for hidden sugar (glucose, fructose, sucrose and honey are all forms of sugar).

Discovery Learning

Learn more about dental diseases using books, magazines or by going online. Present your findings to the class in a creative way.

Revision Questions

1. Describe two problems associated with a high-sugar diet.
2. Suggest ways to reduce sugar in the diet.

Classroom-Based Assessment

This section is linked to CBA2 and the Practical Food Skills exam.

Food allergies and intolerances

Many people suffer from food allergies and food intolerances, but what is the difference between them?

Did You Know?

There are 14 allergens that must be declared if used as an ingredient in pre-packed and loose foods. All menus and labels need to include allergen advice (see p. 99). Learn more by visiting **www.fsai.ie** and searching for 'Allergens'.

Food allergies

When someone has a food allergy, their immune system sees the food as hostile and the body's defence mechanism springs into action. This produces a range of symptoms, which can vary from mild itching to severe breathing difficulties, or even shock. These symptoms usually happen immediately after eating the food.

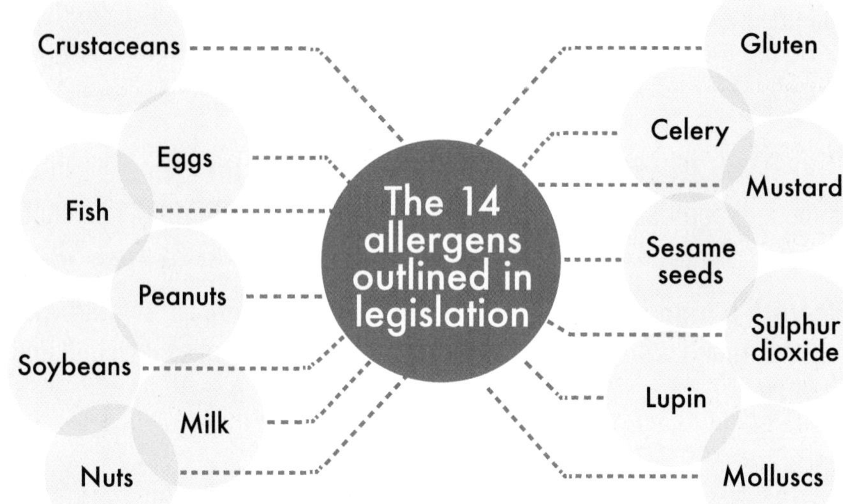

Food allergens

Classroom-Based Assessment

This section is linked to CBA2 and the Practical Food Skills examination.

Food intolerances

When someone is intolerant to a food, the immune system is usually not involved. Symptoms take much longer to develop and are generally not life-threatening. However, a food intolerance can adversely affect long-term health. The symptoms of an intolerance to food include diarrhoea, bloating, upset stomach and weight loss. Lethargy or anaemia can occur, as well as migraine headaches and psychological effects such as confusion and even depression. However, these usually manifest over longer periods of time, along with a variety of other symptoms that can result from poor nutrition. The most common food intolerances include coeliac disease, lactose intolerance and an intolerance to monosodium glutamate (MSG).

Coeliac disease

Gluten is a protein found in wheat, wheat products and some other cereals.

- Coeliac disease is an intolerance to a protein substance called **gluten** which is present in wheat. When a coeliac eats gluten it causes damage to the villi in the small intestine. This prevents nutrients being absorbed properly.
- Symptoms include weight loss, diarrhoea and stomach pain.
- Long-term problems include anaemia and osteoporosis.
- All foods containing gluten must be excluded from a coeliac diet.

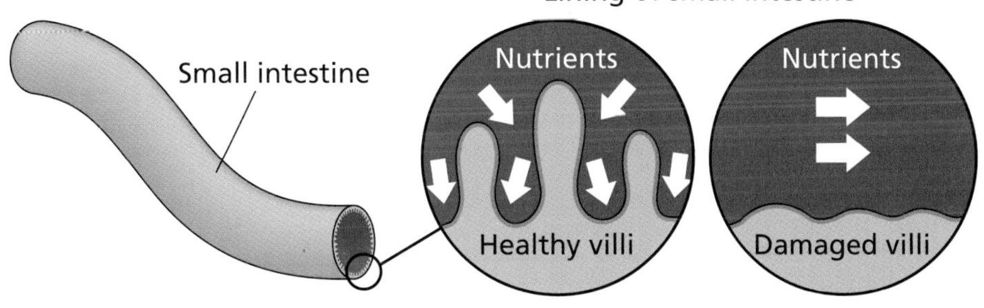

Gluten-free food

The gluten-free symbol is used on the labels of foods that do not contain gluten. It means that the food is suitable for those on a coeliac diet.

Treatment of coeliac disease

- People with coeliac disease must eat a gluten-free diet.
- All foods that contain gluten must be excluded from the diet, e.g. glutenous bread, pasta, cakes and biscuits.
- Any foods that contain flour or breadcrumbs must also be excluded, e.g. fish fingers, packet soups and burgers.
- Special gluten-free products are available, e.g. gluten free flour, bread, pasta and biscuits.
- Cereals such as maize (corn) and rice can be used, as well as products made from these, e.g. cornflour.
- The diet must be based on naturally gluten-free foods like vegetables, eggs and fish.

Further Investigation

To learn more about coeliac disease, visit **www.coeliac.ie**, where the Coeliac Society of Ireland provides an up-to-date list of gluten-free foods and much more information.

Lactose intolerance

Lactose is a natural sugar found in milk and dairy products.

A person with lactose intolerance cannot digest lactose. It cannot be absorbed in the large intestine, resulting in symptoms such as cramps and diarrhoea.

Causes of lactose intolerance

Lactose intolerance occurs when the small intestine does not make enough of an enzyme called lactase. The body needs lactase to break down, or digest, lactose. A big challenge for people who are lactose intolerant is learning how to eat to avoid discomfort and to get enough calcium for healthy bones.

Further Investigation

To find out more about lactose intolerance, visit **www.alpro.com** or **www.avonmore.ie**.

Revision Questions

1. Differentiate between a food allergy and a food intolerance.
2. Why do restaurants and shops have to identify allergens in food?
3. How does coeliac disease affect the body?
4. What foods have to be avoided by coeliacs?
5. What is lactose intolerance?

• Use your workbook to revise this chapter

Summary

- **Obesity** is a major problem among Irish people of all ages. It is treated by a balanced, low-calorie diet and an increase in exercise. Obesity increases the risk of **coronary heart disease (CHD)**, diabetes, chest infections and low self-esteem. Reduce foods that are high in fat and sugar, convenience foods and alcohol. Increase fruit and vegetables, low-fat and high-fibre foods. Eating disorders like anorexia and bulimia need medical and psychological treatment.
- **Vegetarians: Vegans** (strict vegetarians) do not eat meat, fish, poultry or any animal products. **Lacto-vegetarians** do not eat meat, fish or poultry, but do eat animal products. People choose to follow a vegetarian diet for a number of reasons, e.g. moral, health and religious. A vegetarian diet is a healthy one as it is low in fat and high in fibre, but vegetarians must be careful to get enough iron and protein by eating plenty of dark green vegetables, nuts, beans and high-protein meat substitutes.
- Too much **salt** in a diet can lead to high blood pressure, CHD and strokes. Foods high in salts include cured meats like bacon and convenience foods like packet soup. Cut down on salt by avoiding it; do not put it on the table and avoid convenience foods. Use spices and herbs to add flavour to food instead.
- **Cholesterol** is a type of fat that builds up on the walls of the arteries, causing a blockage that leads to high blood pressure and CHD. A **stroke** occurs if the blockage is in the brain. Ireland has a very high rate of CHD. To prevent CHD, avoid saturated fats, fried and junk foods, being overweight, smoking, stress and consuming too much alcohol. Choose foods that are low in fat like chicken and fish; eat plenty of fruit and vegetables and drink lots of water.
- **Fibre** is needed in the diet for a healthy digestive system. A high-fibre diet rich in cellulose helps keep the bowel functioning correctly, so include plenty of wholegrain cereals, fruit and vegetables.

- **Diabetes** occurs when the pancreas does not produce any or enough insulin to meet the body's needs. Insulin regulates the amount of sugar in the blood. There are two types of diabetes: **type 1 is insulin dependent** and is more common in children and teenagers; **type 2 is non-insulin dependent** and occurs most often in overweight older people. Diabetics must try to maintain a healthy weight, eat regular meals and maintain a low-sugar diet.
- **Dental caries** is the decay of the enamel of teeth, leading to tooth decay and cavities.
- **Periodontal disease** affects the gums and tissues surrounding the teeth. This is mainly caused by too much sugar in the diet.
- A **high-sugar diet** can cause obesity and tooth decay. Avoid sugary drinks and foods, use artificial sweeteners and snack on fruit. Read food labels and be careful of hidden sugars; glucose, fructose and sucrose are all sugars.
- **A food allergy** is an adverse reaction by the immune system to a food. The reaction is almost immediate and the symptoms can range from mild itching to shock. When someone is **intolerant to a food**, the immune system is not involved and symptoms take much longer to develop, but are not usually life-threatening. However, a food intolerance may have an adverse effect on long-term health.
- **Coeliac disease** is an inability to digest **gluten**, which is a protein found in wheat. People who suffer from coeliac disease must only eat gluten-free food. They must avoid bread, biscuits and some breakfast cereals. Gluten-free products are available in most supermarkets; look for the gluten-free symbol and carefully read all food labels when buying a product for the first time.
- **Lactose intolerance** is an inability to digest lactose, a type of natural sugar found in milk and dairy products. It can result in symptoms such as cramps and diarrhoea.

Section 3: Let's Get Cooking!

07 KITCHEN HYGIENE AND SAFETY

Learning Outcomes 1.5, 1.6, 1.7, 1.16, 2.4, 2.7, 2.8

Before cooking, it is important to learn about kitchen hygiene and safety, as well as meal planning, food preparation and cooking methods.

What I Will Learn

- to explain food spoilage
- to identify the causes of food spoilage
- to discuss the conditions needed for bacteria to grow
- to state the causes of food poisoning
- to identify the symptoms of food poisoning
- to prepare a list of guidelines for food handlers
- to compile a set of guidelines for food and kitchen hygiene
- to explain how to care for and clean kitchen equipment
- to prepare a set of guidelines for kitchen safety

Key Words

- ✓ Hygiene
- ✓ Safety
- ✓ Food spoilage
- ✓ Enzymes
- ✓ Micro-organisms
- ✓ Bacteria
- ✓ Yeast
- ✓ Moulds
- ✓ Cross-contamination
- ✓ Contaminate
- ✓ Danger zone
- ✓ Salmonella
- ✓ Staphylococci
- ✓ Listeria
- ✓ Campylobacter
- ✓ Botulism
- ✓ HACCP

Kitchen hygiene and safety involves being careful while preparing and cooking food, in order to protect health and ensure safety.

Food spoilage

Food has a limited life. After a certain time it will go off or spoil. Food spoilage is caused by chemicals called **enzymes** in food, by air or by micro-organisms, e.g. moulds, yeast and bacteria, which are also called germs. Food spoilage occurs more quickly when food is:

- not stored correctly
- prepared in a dirty kitchen
- handled by a person who is careless or unhygienic

Enzymes

- Chemicals that are naturally present in fruit and vegetables.
- Help food to ripen.
- After food has been harvested, enzymes continue to ripen it, eventually causing it to become over-ripe and decay.

The stages of ripening in bananas

Micro-organisms

- Micro-organisms are tiny living organisms called **germs**. They include bacteria, yeasts and moulds.
- They are all around us: in soil, air, water, humans and animals.
- Most micro-organisms are harmless in small amounts, but in large amounts they are dangerous because they cause food poisoning.

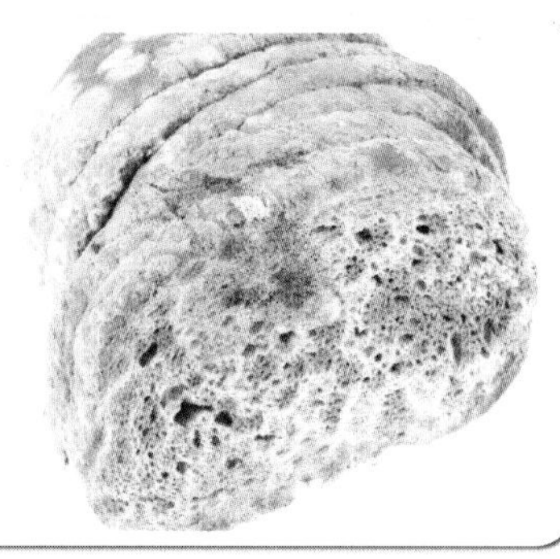

Moulds

In certain conditions, **moulds** form a furry growth on fruit and bread.

Yeasts

Yeasts cause fruit and jam to go off.

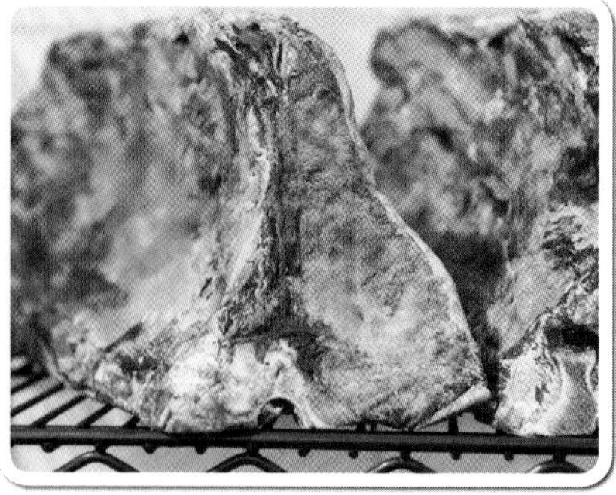

Bacteria

Bacteria cause food poisoning, as well as causing animal foods like meat and fish to spoil.

Discovery Learning

Find out more about moulds, yeast and bacteria, and about how they can be useful to us. Present your findings in a creative way.

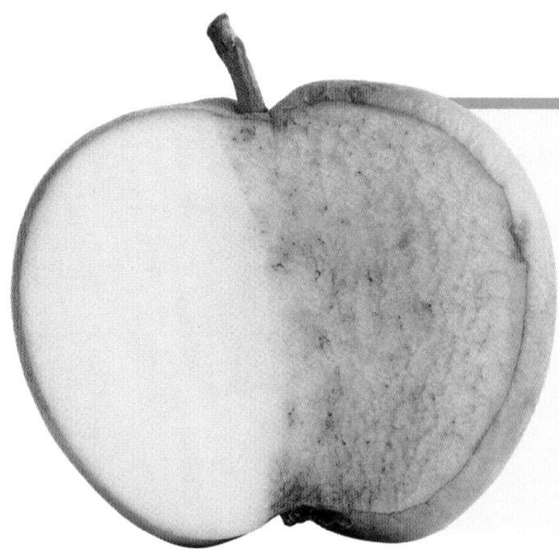

Oxygen in the air causes fats to go off or become **rancid**. This is why unwrapped items like butter develop off flavours. Oxygen also reacts with enzymes, causing discolouration of foods, e.g. apples go brown.

Rancid means fatty food that smells and tastes unpleasant as a result of being old and stale.

Food poisoning

Food poisoning occurs when a person eats or drinks foods that have large numbers of pathogenic (disease-causing) bacteria. When they enter our body, they multiply very quickly and make us sick. Often foods show no signs of spoilage because there is no change in colour, taste or smell.

Symptoms of food poisoning

These include nausea, vomiting, abdominal pains, cramps, diarrhoea and high temperature.

Food-poisoning bacteria

Each of the following bacteria causes food poisoning.

Food-poisoning bacteria

Salmonella

- Found everywhere, but especially in the intestines of humans, birds and animals.
- Poultry, eggs and raw meat are sources of salmonella food poisoning.
- Pets, rats, mice and insects carry salmonella and spread it to our food.
- Can also be spread as a result of carelessness in personal hygiene in the bathroom or kitchen, e.g. not washing hands after going to the toilet.

Staphylococci

- Found mainly in humans, in the nose, mouth, throat, and in cuts and boils.
- Passed from humans to food during food preparation, e.g. sneezing or coughing over food, or through uncovered cuts.

Campylobacter

- Found in raw poultry and meat, unpasteurised milk and untreated water.
- Pets with diarrhoea can also be a source of infection.

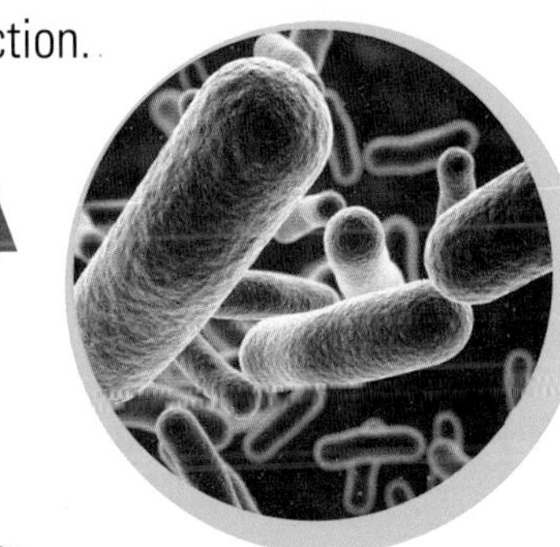

Listeria

- Multiply at lower temperature than most bacteria, e.g. in a fridge, so can be in soft cheese, mayonnaises and pâté.
- Present in soil on unwashed fruit, vegetables and salads.
- Heathy adults are not usually affected by listeria, but they can cause food poisoning and serious side effects in babies, older people and pregnant women.

Clostridium botulinum

- Botulism is an extremely rare but very serious type of food poisoning.
- It can result in paralysis and even death.
- Multiplies in faulty cans of food, so always examine cans before buying – they must not be rusted, leaking or bulging.

E. coli

- Live in the intestines of cattle and sheep and can pass into the food chain through the faeces of these animals.
- Can also contaminate water supplies.

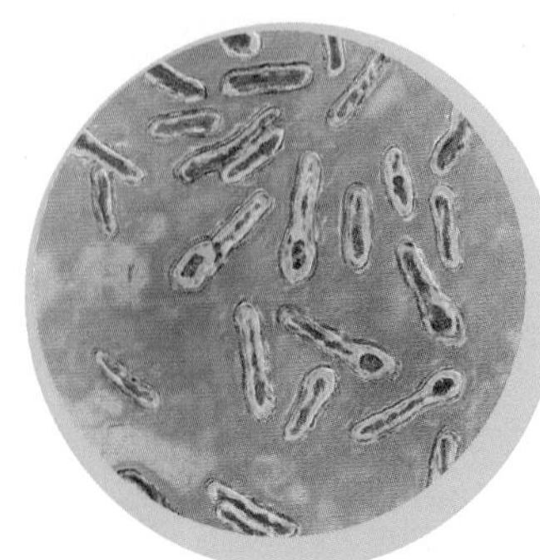

Did You Know?

Campylobacter is the most common cause of bacterial food poisoning in Ireland. Over 2,600 people got food poisoning from campylobacter in Ireland in 2014, up 14% on the previous year when 2,288 cases were reported.
Source: *The Irish Independent*, 2015

Further Investigation

To find out more about food-poisoning bacteria, visit the Food Safety Authority of Ireland (FSAI) website, **www.fsai.ie**. The FSAI has overall responsibility for protecting public health and consumer interests in the area of food safety and hygiene.

Food hygiene

Bacteria are tiny invisible (to the human eye) living cells, which are found everywhere: in the air, water, soil, animals and humans. In small amounts they do little harm – this is known as an acceptable level of contamination. However, in larger amounts, they are dangerous. In the right conditions, they multiply rapidily, causing disease and sometimes death.

Conditions for growth of micro-organisms

Example: Bacteria

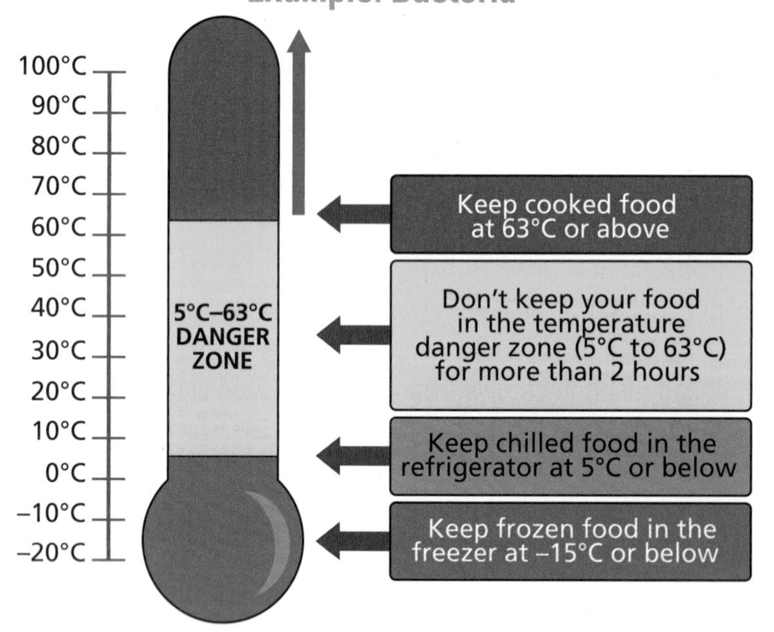

Warmth

- Most micro-organisms grow best at 30–40°C, so a warm kitchen is a suitable place for bacterial growth.
- Our body temperature is 37°C, so bacteria multiply easily in the human body and make us sick.
- Low temperatures such as in a fridge (4°C) slow down the growth, and very low temperatures like freezing inactivates them (0°C or lower) but does not kill them.
- High temperatures used in cooking kill them.
- Disinfectants also kill bacteria.

Did You Know?

Micro-organisms can survive and grow at any temperature between 5°C and 63°C. This is known as the **danger zone**.

Moisture

- All micro-organisms need moisture to grow and multiply. A lot of moisture is created in a kitchen during cooking and washing up – as a result, surfaces can be damp and therefore suitable for micro-organisms to thrive.
- Most foods contain moisture, so bacteria can grow on these.
- Bacteria don't grow on dried foods such as flour.

Food

- All micro-organisms need food to survive. They feed on food, dirt and dust, so they grow well in a kitchen.
- They grow and multiply quickly in protein foods like raw meat, fish and poultry, and in liquid foods like milk and custard. A lot of care needs to be taken when storing, preparing and cooking these foods.

Oxygen

- Micro-organisms need air to grow and multiply, so food should be tightly wrapped to exclude air.
- Some can survive without air, e.g. in canned or bottled foods.

Time

- Micro-organisms multiply quickly, so store food correctly and use it up while it is fresh.
- A single micro-organism becomes two micro-organisms every 20 minutes.

Don't Forget!

To avoid food contamination and food poisoning, food should be kept:

- **in cool, dry storage areas, e.g. the fridge**
- **clean and covered**
- **in a well-ventilated kitchen to remove moisture**

How food becomes infected with bacteria

1. Careless and unhygienic people

For example, not washing hands, especially after using the toilet, not covering cuts, or coughing and sneezing over food.

2. Dirt and grease

Dirty preparation areas, equipment, utensils and kitchen cloths all provide food for bacteria to multiply.

3. Bacteria are carried and transferred to food by:

- Household **pets**, e.g. dogs and cats
- **Insects** like flies and cockroaches
- **Vermin**, e.g. mice and rats

Did You Know?
Flies feed on dirt and waste. They pick up bacteria on the hairs on their legs and land on uncovered food. They vomit and excrete on the food as they eat.

4. **Cross-contamination**

This is the transfer of bacteria from raw to cooked food. This can occur when bacteria are transferred to food from a food handler, or from dirty equipment or surfaces, e.g. if raw chicken is prepared on the same surface as salad, bacteria can cross from the raw chicken to the salad, which can result in food poisoning. To reduce the risk of cross-contamination, food premises use colour-coded equipment, e.g. chopping boards and knives.

7.4

Hygiene in food preparation

Food hygiene guidelines relate to the **food handler**, the **food** itself and the **kitchen** where the food is prepared.

Food handlers

Humans carry bacteria in their nose, throat, skin and intestines. Bacteria can be transferred to food unless basic personal hygiene rules are followed.

Tips for good personal hygiene

- Tie back or cover your hair.
- Do not touch your face or hair while cooking.
- Never cough, sneeze or smoke over food.
- People who are sick should not handle food as they can spread infection.
- Remove jewellery.
- Wear a clean apron.

- Wash hands before handling food.
- Cover cuts and sores with a waterproof dressing.
- Keep nails short and clean.
- Handle food as little as possible – use tongs or wear gloves.
- Taste food with a clean spoon each time. Never lick your fingers.
- Never wear open-toe shoes in the kitchen (**why?**).

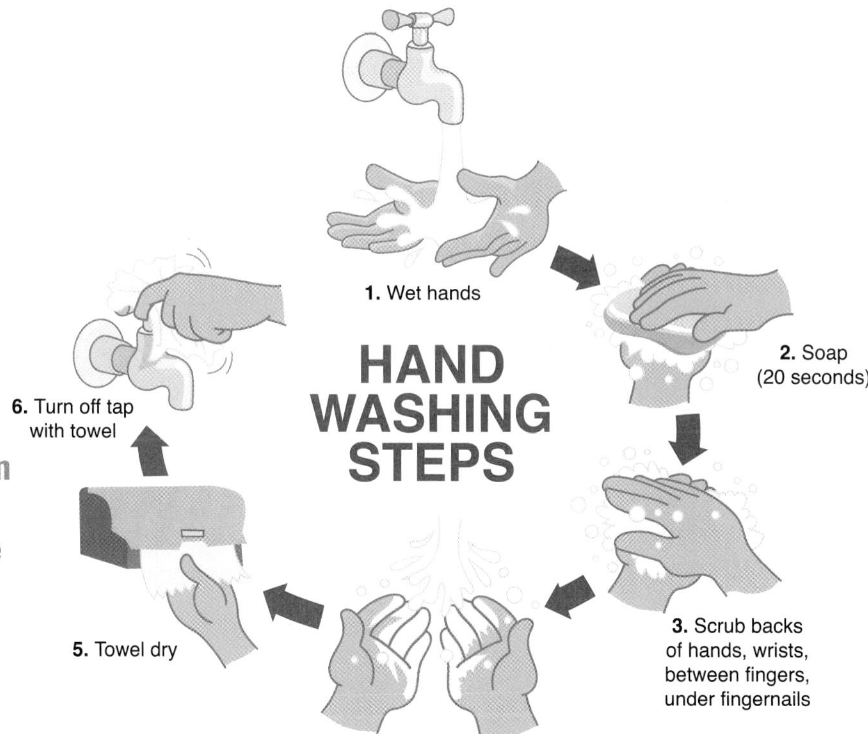

Tips for hygienic food preparation

- Use the freshest ingredients.
- Be aware of 'sell by' (guideline) or 'use by' (deadline) dates.
- Keep all food clean and covered.
- Prepare food on a clean work surface, using clean equipment.
- Cool leftovers quickly. Cover and store them in the fridge. Reheat thoroughly.
- Check the fridge every day and use up leftovers and check for expiry dates.
- Put perishable foods in the fridge and frozen foods in the freezer as soon as possible after buying them.
- Always keep raw meat and fish separate from food that will not be cooked.
- Thaw all frozen meat or poultry fully in the fridge before cooking thoroughly.

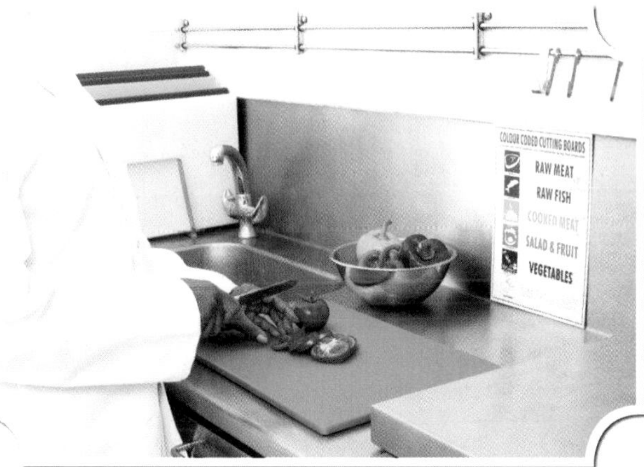

Keeping the kitchen clean

A kitchen should be well designed with easy-to-clean surfaces. As bacteria grow best in dark, warm and moist conditions, the kitchen should be bright, well-lit and ventilated.

- All surfaces like counters, tables and floors should be cleaned and disinfected regularly.
- All equipment should be washed after use in hot, soapy water, rinsed, dried and stored in clean, dry cupboards.
- Keep cooker, fridge and sink clean. Disinfect sink regularly.
- Make sure all kitchen cloths are clean as they are a breeding ground for bacteria. Use different cloths for each job.

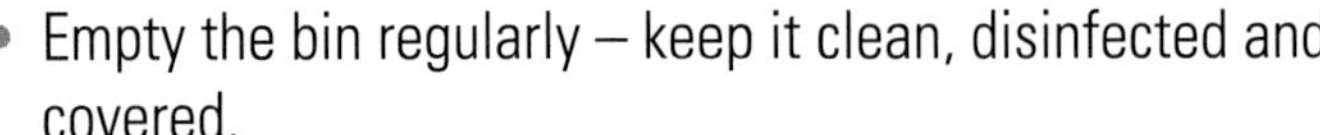

- Empty the bin regularly – keep it clean, disinfected and covered.
- Sweep the floor daily. Mop and disinfect it regularly.
- Never allow pets in the kitchen when food is being prepared.

- Keep the kitchen free from smoke and pests like insects and vermin.

Don't Forget!
Separate raw and cooked foods to prevent cross-contamination.

Care and cleaning of kitchen equipment

Kitchen utensils are made from a range of materials. A high standard of hygiene is essential to avoid contaminating food with dirty equipment.

Material	Care and cleaning
Metals: For example, stainless steel and aluminium. Used in cutlery, saucepans and baking trays. 	• Soak if necessary. • Wash in hot, soapy water. • Rinse and dry thoroughly. **Top Tip:** Never use abrasives or sharp utensils, i.e. knives or metal implements, on non-stick cookware.
Delph and glass: For example, plates, jars, glasses and casserole dishes. 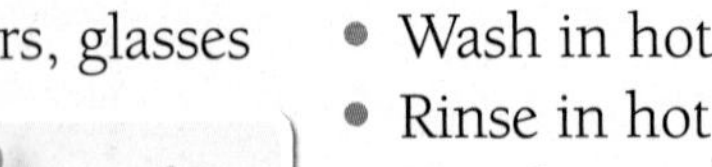	• Soak if necessary. • Wash in hot, soapy water. • Rinse in hot water. • Dry thoroughly. **Top Tip:** Pyrex (heat-resistant glass) should not be put on direct heat (e.g. a hot cooker hob) or subjected to sudden changes in temperature (e.g. pouring boiling water into it) because it could shatter.
Wood: For example, chopping boards, wooden spoons and bread bins. 	• Remove food particles. • Wash in warm, soapy water. • Using a brush scrub, cleaning along the grain of wood. • Rinse in warm water. • Dry thoroughly. **Top Tip:** Wooden utensils cannot be washed in a dishwasher, as the higher temperatures can warp and damage the wood.
Plastic: For example, bowls, spatulas and measuring jugs. 	• Wash in hot, soapy water. • Rinse in warm water. • Dry thoroughly. **Top Tip:** Be careful not to expose plastic to excessive heat, as it will melt.

Did You Know?

A non-stick coating, e.g. Teflon™, can be applied to metal cookware, which allows food to brown without sticking to the pan.

Hygiene in food preparation

Further Investigation

Find out more about HACCP by visiting the Food Safety Authority website, **www.fsai.ie**, clicking on 'Food Businesses', on the top of the home page, and then clicking on 'HACCP' on the left-hand side of the page.

Anyone involved in the food industry must be extremely conscious of food hygiene and safety. **Hazard Analysis and Critical Control Points (HACCP)** is an international food safety system that helps to prevent the contamination of food. It works by identifying potential risks in advance and then putting systems in place to minimise their risk. All Irish food businesses are required by law to take steps to make sure their food is safe using the HACCP system.

Safety rules in the kitchen

- Wipe up spills as they occur.
- Close all cupboard doors and drawers.
- Never run in the kitchen.
- Turn all handles of saucepans inwards on the cooker.
- Turn off cooker rings when not in use.
- Always use oven gloves when handling hot dishes.
- Never handle electrical appliances with wet hands.
- Take care using sharp implements, e.g. knives and mixer blades.
- If something breaks, carefully sweep it up and wrap any broken glass or delph in newspaper before placing it in the bin.

Revision Questions

1. What is meant by food spoilage?
2. What causes food to spoil?
3. Outline the conditions needed for bacteria to grow.
4. State the causes of food poisoning.
5. List the symptoms of food poisoning.
6. Compile a set of guidelines for:
   (a) food handlers
   (b) preparing food
   (c) kitchen hygiene
7. Explain how to care for and clean kitchen equipment.
8. Discuss how to store foods correctly.
9. Draw up a set of guidelines for kitchen safety.

Summary

- Food has a limited shelf life; after a certain time, it will go off or spoil. **Food spoilage** is caused by chemicals called **enzymes** in food. It is also caused by air or by **micro-organisms**, e.g. moulds, yeast and bacteria, which are also called germs. Micro-organisms need food, warmth, moisture, oxygen and time to grow and multiply.
- **Food poisoning** occurs when bacteria multiply to unacceptable levels on food. Bacteria can be introduced to food by **careless and unhygienic people, dirty equipment and surfaces, by pets, vermin and insects,** or through **cross-contamination**. Food-poisoning bacteria that cause infections in humans include salmonella, staphylococci, campylobacter, listeria and E. coli. **Symptoms** of food poisoning include nausea, vomiting and diarrhoea.
- **Food hygiene tips:**
  1. **Food handlers** should be hygienic, wear an apron, tie back or cover hair and remove all jewellery. Do not touch the face or hair, and never cough or sneeze over food. A person who is ill should not cook as it can spread infection. Cover cuts and sores with a waterproof dressing and handle food as little as possible – use tongs or wear gloves.
  2. **Food preparation:** Use fresh ingredients and be aware of expiry dates. Keep food clean and covered. Separate raw and cooked foods, store food correctly, thaw properly and cook thoroughly.
  3. **Working in the kitchen:** Clean and disinfect kitchen surfaces, sinks and floors regularly. Clean equipment and wash cloths regularly. Empty the bin regularly; keep it clean, disinfected and covered. Keep the kitchen free from smoke, pets and pests like insects and vermin.
- All Irish food businesses are required by law to use **HACCP**. This is an international food safety system that helps to prevent the contamination of food. It identifies potential risks and puts systems in place to minimise risk.
- **Care and cleaning of kitchen equipment:** Kitchen equipment can be made from metal, wood, plastic, delph or glass. All kitchen equipment need to be washed, rinsed and dried carefully to prevent cross-contamination.
- **Safety in the kitchen:** Wipe up spills, close all cupboards and drawers, do not run in the kitchen, keep all pot handles facing inwards on the cooker and turn off cooker rings when not in use. Always **use oven gloves** when handling hot dishes. Take care when using sharp items. Never handle electrical appliances with wet hands and always wear proper shoes. If something breaks, carefully sweep it up and wrap any broken glass or delph in newspaper before placing it in the bin.

08 MEAL PLANNING

Learning Outcomes 1.2, 1.3, 1.5, 1.6, 1.7, 1.12, 1.13, 1.14, 1.15, 1.16, 2.7, 2.8, 2.9

What I Will Learn

- to identify the factors that affect meal planning
- to create menus
- to differentiate between à la carte and table d'hôte menus
- to set a table for meals
- to compile a list of shopping guidelines
- to discuss how to store foods correctly
- to cost dishes

Key Words

✓ Table d'hôte
✓ À la carte
✓ Buffet
✓ Appetiser
✓ Accompaniments
✓ Condiments
✓ Garnish
✓ Work plan
✓ Shelf life
✓ Food miles
✓ Fairtrade
✓ Own brand
✓ Premises

Meal planning makes sense! A healthy diet requires a certain amount of planning and organisation. By spending some time planning menus, shopping, preparing and cooking, you work more efficiently and waste less time.

Don't Forget!
Use the food pyramid and think about the healthy eating guidelines when planning meals for a family.

Advantages of weekly meal planning

It is a good idea to plan meals for about one week at a time because:

- It is easier to make meals nutritionally balanced
- It provides a basis for doing the weekly shopping
- It is easier to vary menus from week to week
- Being prepared saves time in the long term. Double up on the cooking, e.g. cook two and freeze one
- Waste is reduced and leftovers can be used up
- Money is saved, food is healthier and there is less need to rely on convenience foods and takeaways

Factors that affect meal planning

- All meals should be **nutritious** and **well balanced** to meet the needs of each individual. For a meal to be balanced, it should include three out of four of the main food groups.
- It is essential to remember the **individual dietary requirements** of the people eating the meal, e.g. a school-going child will have different needs to an adult manual worker, so it is also important to consider **portion sizes**.
- Some individuals may also have **special dietary requirements**, so certain **modifications** may need to be made, e.g. diabetics need to watch their sugar and fat consumption, and a coeliac cannot eat gluten (**see p. 80**).
- **Season and availability**: Some foods are only available fresh at certain times of the year. Foods **in season** are usually cheaper and taste better, e.g. strawberries in the summer or fresh asparagus in April and May. Certain ingredients for international dishes may need to be purchased from specialist shops like an Asian supermarket or a health shop.
- Offer a **variety** of flavours, colours, textures, cooking methods and temperatures to make meals interesting and appealing.

Revision Toolkit
To prepare for CBA2 and the Practical Food Skills examination, practise drawing up menus to suit a variety of people and conditions, following the guidelines for menu planning.

- **Skill and equipment**: The ability of the cook and equipment available will influence the type of meal planned.
- Choose meals that can be produced within the **budget** available, e.g. minced beef is cheaper than steak but equally nutritious.
- The **time** available to prepare, cook and serve meals also influences our choice of dish, e.g. a stew will take a long time to cook while a stir-fry can be ready much more quickly. Labour-saving kitchen **preparation and cooking equipment** may save time.
- **The number of people eating**: The number of people eating will influence the cost, choice and complexity of the dish.
- **Occasion**: Select foods or dishes that are suitable for the occasion, the time of year and the tastes (likes and dislikes) of the people for whom the meal is being prepared. The type of meal also influences choice of dish, e.g. breakfast, lunch or dinner, and if it is a buffet or sit-down meal.

Don't Forget!
Shopping wisely can provide better quality foods at lower prices, e.g. meal deals, three-for-the-price-of-two offers, 50% off today. All major supermarkets put on special offers each week. If you buy in bulk and prepare dishes in advance for the freezer, you can save both money and time, e.g. chicken curry or lasagne.

Meals

In Ireland, we generally eat three meals plus snacks. These are arranged in two ways, depending on when people have their main meal of the day.

Breakfast	**Breakfast**
Lunch	**Lunch (main meal)**
Dinner (main meal)	**Tea**

Snacks are small food items that are eaten between meals. Avoid snacks that are high in sugar, salt or fat. Choose healthy, natural options instead.

Main meals are usually divided into courses.

1. **Starter or appetiser**: This course is made up of tasty but not too filling food or foods. It helps stimulate the digestive juices.
2. **Main course**: A meat, fish or vegetarian dish is central to this course. **Accompaniments**, such as a starch-rich food, e.g. potatoes, pasta or rice, are also served. Accompaniments also include vegetables, salads, sauces or gravy.
3. **Dessert**: This is usually sweet and can be hot or cold. As a savoury option, a **cheeseboard** could be served with crackers and grapes.
4. A meal is usually followed by **tea** or **coffee**.

Menus

- The list of dishes served for a meal is called a menu.
- When eating out in a restaurant, you are given a menu. This can be either a table d'hôte menu or an à la carte menu.
- A **table d'hôte** menu is a set menu that is usually between two and five courses. It offers a smaller selection of foods and a set price is paid for the meal, regardless of how many courses are eaten.
- An **à la carte** menu offers a much larger selection of foods, grouped into courses. Each dish is priced separately and it is usually more expensive overall.

TABLE D'HÔTE MENU

Starters

Potato and leek soup
Served with homemade brown bread

Caesar salad
Cos leaves with bacon, garlic croutons, Parmesan shavings and Caesar dressing

Homemade chicken liver pâté
Served with Melba toast and Cumberland sauce

Barbecue chicken wings
Served with seasonal salad and sour cream dip

Breaded brie
Served on a bed of mixed leaves and red onion marmalade

Main courses

Grilled 10 oz sirloin steak
Served with sautéed onions and mushrooms, French fries and pepper sauce

Poached darne of salmon
Served on a bed of mashed potatoes, with steamed seasonal vegetables and a dill sauce

Chicken and chorizo penne pasta
In a tomato sauce served with Parmesan shavings and rocket

Vegetarian casserole
A Mediterranean one-pot stew with peppers, courgettes, lentils, sweet smoked paprika and thyme

Sticky duck legs
Served with steamed rice, sliced cucumber, chopped chilli and coriander leaves

Desserts

Fruit crumble
Served with custard and vanilla cream

Lemon cheesecake
Served with fresh cream and raspberry coulis

Chocolate fudge brownie
Topped with hot chocolate sauce and a scoop of ice cream

Apple pie
Served with fresh cream

Bread and butter pudding
Served with crème anglaise

Freshly brewed tea or coffee

€22.50

À LA CARTE MENU

Starters

Cream of vegetable soup €4.95
Served with homemade brown bread

Creamy seafood chowder €7.50
Served with homemade brown bread

Warm chicken salad €6.25
Cos leaves with bacon, sautéed potatoes, Parmesan shavings and mustard dressing

Seared scallops and black pudding €7.25
Served on a bed of mixed leaves and red onion marmalade

Garlic bread €5.50
Served with seasonal salad and basil pesto

Duck spring rolls €6.95
Served with seasonal salad and sweet chilli sauce

Golden fried garlic mushrooms €5.25
Served on a bed of mixed leaves with garlic aïoli

Main courses

8 oz fillet steak €27.50
Served with sautéed potatoes, battered onion rings and pepper sauce

Poached fillet of salmon €18.50
On a bed of colcannon with lemon beurre blanc and a selection of seasonal vegetables

Chicken and chorizo jambalaya €19.95
A Cajun-inspired rice dish with spicy Spanish sausage, sweet peppers and tomato

Vegetarian lasagne €14.95
Served with garlic bread and French fries

Thai pork and peanut curry €18.95
Served with rice, sweetcorn and coriander and soy sauce

Roast turkey and ham €15.25
Served with mashed and roast potatoes, seasonal vegetables and gravy

Confit of duck €22.95
Served with sautéed potatoes and seasonal vegetables

Don't Forget!
Fourteen allergens must be declared in pre-packed and loose food sold in shops or restaurants. So, menus and labels also need to include allergen advice **(see p. 80).**

Desserts

Apple, pear and walnut crumble €5.95
Served with custard or cream

Malteser cheesecake €6.75
Drizzled with chocolate sauce and served with fresh cream or ice cream

Hot chocolate fudge cake €7.25
Topped with hot chocolate sauce and honeycomb ice cream

Lemon meringue pie €5.75
Served with fresh cream or ice cream and raspberry coulis

Sticky toffee pudding €6.25
Served with butterscotch sauce and ice cream

Crème brûlée €6.50
A French classic with vanilla bean and caramelised sugar topping

Ice cream basket €5.75
Three scoops of ice cream served in a wafer basket, drizzled with chocolate sauce

Freshly brewed tea or coffee €2.50

Revision Toolkit

When planning a menu for school assignments and assessments, follow the menu planning and writing guidelines. Make an attractive menu from stiff card or folded paper. Write the menu neatly by hand or type and print off from a computer. Decorate attractively if you wish.

Classroom-Based Assessment

This section is linked to CBA2 and the Practical Food Skills exam.

Rules for writing menus

When writing menus:

- Present the menu in a neat box.
- Write it down the centre of the page.
- Courses should be written in the order in which they will be eaten.
- Leave a space between courses.
- Decide on suitable foods, taking into account things like nutrition, special requirements, occasion and cost.
- Include at least three out of the four main food groups.
- Do not offer choices, e.g. chips or mashed potato.
- Include different cooking methods if possible.
- Name the vegetables and accompaniments.

Sample menus

BREAKFAST

Orange juice

****

Weetabix and milk

****

Poached egg on toast
with grilled tomato
Brown bread, butter and
marmalade

****

Tea or coffee

LUNCH

Tuna salad on a
wholemeal roll

****

Strawberry yoghurt

****

Apple

****

Water

DINNER

Potato and leek soup
with a roll

****

Chicken curry with
boiled rice

****

Apple and berry
crumble with custard

****

Tea or coffee

Setting the table

Tables should be set with convenience in mind and with all the necessary utensils for the meal. Consider the menu and arrange the settings to suit.

- Tablecloths, mats, napkins, delph, glass and cutlery should be spotless and complement each other.

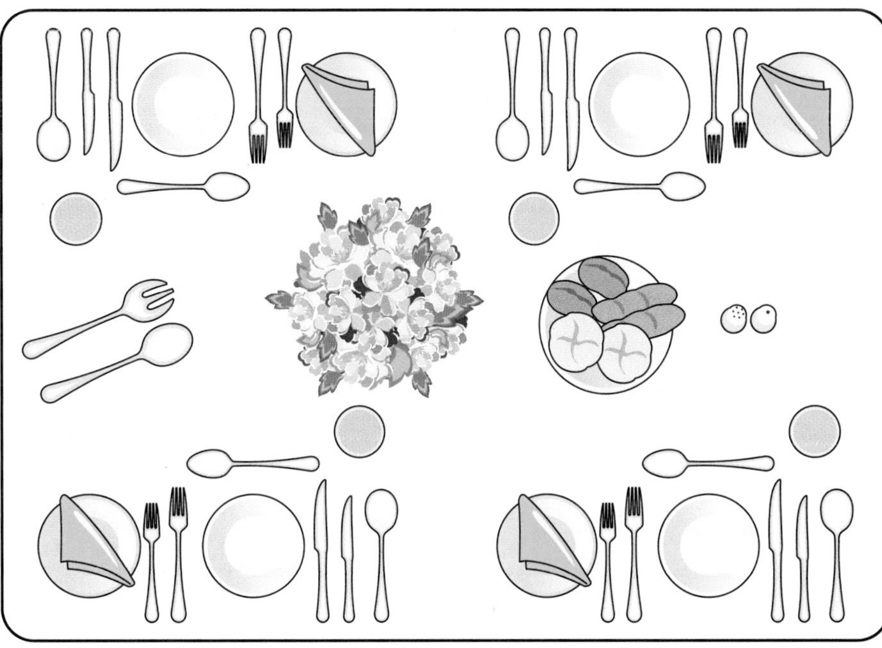
An example of a well set table

- Cutlery should be organised in order of use. The cutlery used first, i.e. for a starter, should be on the outside, then set moving inwards.
- Allow at least 60 cm per place setting.
- Place knives to the right with blades facing in, and forks to the left with prongs upwards (3 cm in from the edge of the table).
- Place drinking glasses upright above the dinner knife.
- Condiments (e.g. salt, pepper and mustard), butter and water should be placed in the centre of the table.
- A jug of cold water should be put on the table just before serving.
- Place heat-resistant mats and serving spoons in the centre of the table.
- Fold or roll napkins and leave on side plates.
- Table decorations, i.e. flowers or candles, should not be too tall as they could block the diners' views of each other.
- Serve food to the left and clear plates from the right.

Don't Forget!
If asked to set a table or tray, especially in a Practical Food Skills examination, make sure everything you need is clean and ready and beside your table.

Buffets

A buffet is the easiest way to entertain a big group of people. Food should be easy to eat by hand or with a fork. The food should be arranged so that guests can help themselves. The cutlery should be wrapped and placed beside the plates so guests can pick up both and work their way around the table, helping themselves to food. Drinks should be served at another table.

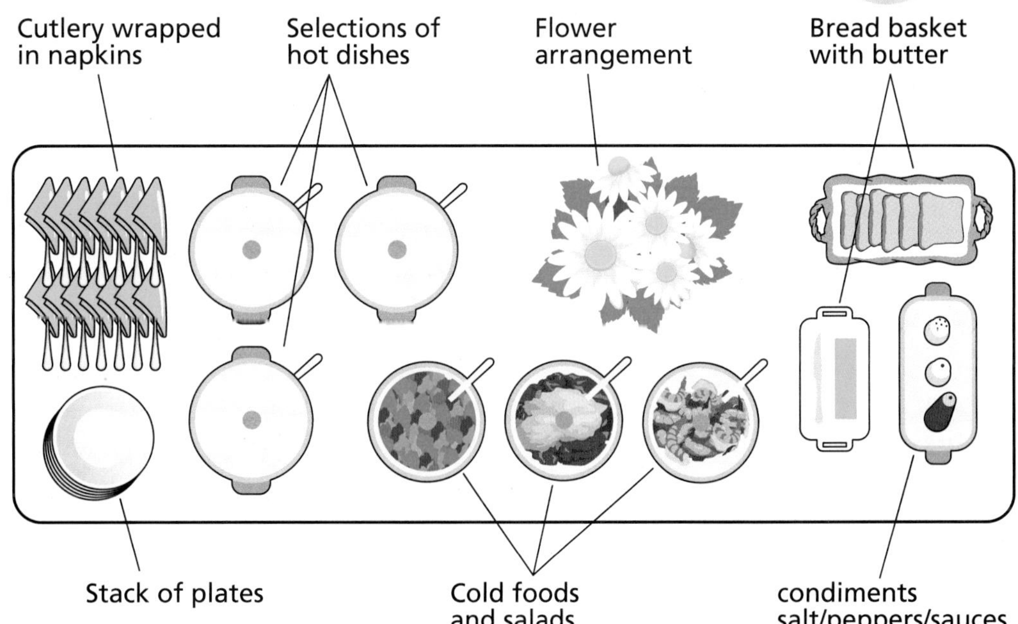

Planning a meal

Once you have decided what you are going to cook, the next step is to shop for the ingredients. Store them correctly before use, then prepare the meal efficiently by preparing a work time plan.

Tips to follow when shopping for food

As a large part of most household budgets is spent on food, it makes sense to shop around to get good service and quality. This requires advance planning.

- Try to plan your week's menu in advance before making out the **shopping list**. **Check** your store cupboards and list foods that are needed, then add the fresh foods you need.
- Try to shop once a week to **stay within your budget**. Avoid shopping when you are hungry, tired or in a hurry, as people tend to overspend in these situations.
- Buy food in a **clean**, **hygienic premises** with staff who are neat, clean and handle food hygienically. Choose a shop with a wide variety and quick turnover of goods. Ensure that foods that are stored correctly, e.g. frozen food cabinets at the correct temperature.
- Examine products – read the nutritional information on packages so you can choose the more nutritious options. Compare weights and prices, because a smaller pack can sometimes contain more (**how is this possible?**). Check expiry dates. Packaging should be intact. Tins should not be dented, 'blown' or rusted. Buy loose fruit and vegetables rather than pre-packed.
- Avoid convenience foods, which are usually more expensive and tend to be higher in additives, sugar, salt and starch, and lacking in fibre.
- It is important to shop in an environmentally friendly way. Avoid foods that have a lot of packaging. Use recyclable bags and look for organic produce and the Fairtrade mark.

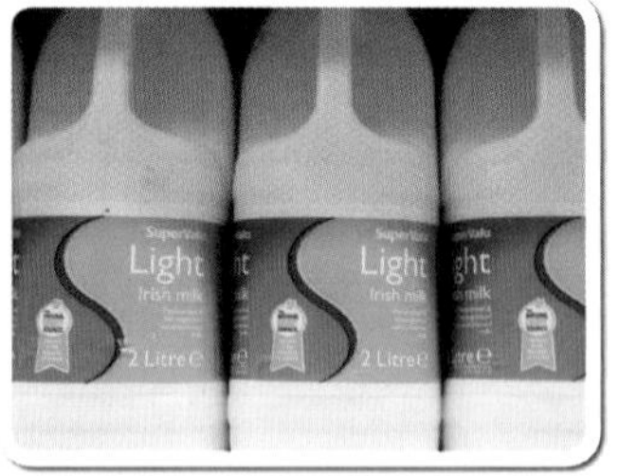

Being an ethical shopper

Don't waste: Prevent food waste by carefully planning and cooking the correct amounts for you and your family. Use food in rotation and keep an eye on expiry dates. Buy from shops that support **FoodCloud**, e.g. Aldi, Lidl and Tesco. Many supermarkets have a lot of food waste. FoodCloud matches businesses that have surplus (extra) food to charities in their communities.

Cut down on packaging: Use refillable jars with eco-refills, e.g. Kenco coffee.

Use Fairtrade products: This is a powerful way to reduce poverty through shopping. The Fairtrade mark on products such as tea, coffee and cocoa means that the people who produce these goods have received a fair price for them and that the goods have been produced with concern for the environment. When farmers and workers can sell and work on Fairtrade terms, it gives them a better deal and a chance to improve their lives and plan for their future.

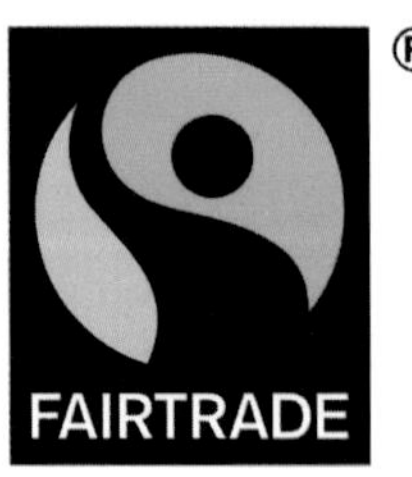

Look for this mark when shopping

Food miles

Food miles are a way of measuring the distance food has travelled from the farm to your plate. All methods of transport produce some carbon dioxide, which contributes to global warming. Therefore, the greater the distance the food has travelled, the more carbon dioxide will have been produced. It is a good way of looking at the environmental impact of foods and their ingredients. Food miles include getting foods to you, but also getting waste foods away from you and to landfills.

Did You Know?
Ireland has 48 officially recognised Fairtrade cities, towns and islands. Find out where they are and see if you live near one.

Food storage

It is essential to store food properly to ensure that it remains in prime condition for as long as possible.

Don't Forget!
Carry chilled and frozen food home from the shops in a cooler bag.

Proper storage:
- protects food from flies and dust
- prolongs its shelf life
- makes locating food in the kitchen easier
- ensures that the kitchen is clean and well organised

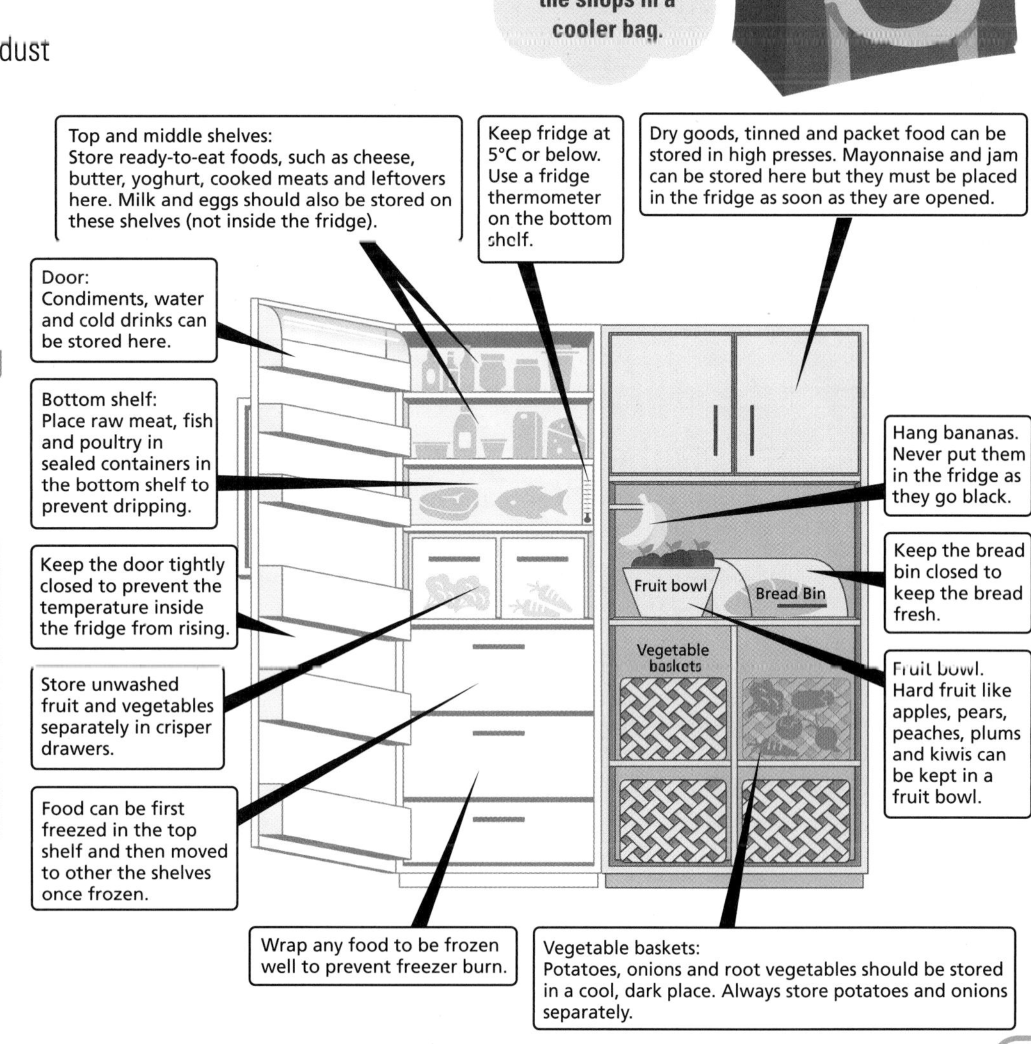

Guidelines for storing food correctly

The **shelf life** of a food is the length of time a food remains safe and fit to be eaten. Shelf life depends on the type of food and the conditions in which it is stored.

Storing foods correctly according to their type

- **Non-perishables**, e.g. dry, bottled and tinned foods. Store in a cupboard on their own or in airtight containers. Use **wall units** instead of floor units for food storage (**why?**).
- **Semi-perishables**, e.g. bread, cakes, fresh fruit and vegetables. Store breads and cakes in a bread bin or tin. Fruit and vegetables may be stored in a rack or basket. Some semi-perishables, e.g. salad vegetables, may be stored in the refrigerator.
- **Perishables**, e.g. eggs, milk, cream, fresh meat, frozen or fresh 'ready to cook' meals, etc. These have the shortest shelf life and must be used within three or four days. Store in the refrigerator at 4°C.
- **Frozen**: Store in the freezer at –18°C.

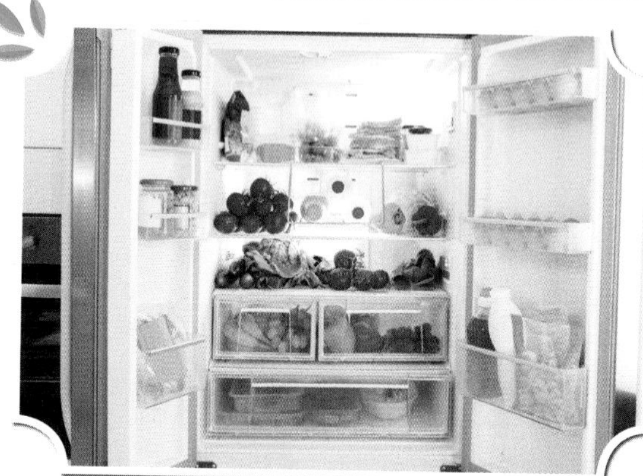

- Note **expiry dates**, e.g. 'sell by', 'use by' and 'best before' dates on foods. Use up older foods before opening new ones.
- Never store leftover **canned food** in the tin.
- Store foods away from cleaning agents.
- Keep cupboards and storage containers clean to prevent contamination by bacteria.
- Once packages are opened, store dry foods like rice and pasta in airtight containers to prevent them from becoming stale or infested by insects.
- Never refreeze thawed frozen food.

Each refrigerator has a star rating indicating the temperature in the icebox.

Star	Star rating	Temperature	Storage time
*	1 star	–6°C	1 week
**	2 stars	–12°C	1 month
***	3 stars	–18°C	3 months
****	4 stars	–18°C to –25°C	Up to 12 months. Fresh food can be frozen.

Packaging materials

Many disposable and reusable materials are available for storing foods.

Disposable packaging, such as greaseproof paper and cling film, should only be used once, as they cannot be cleaned thoroughly after use. Plastic, ceramic, glass and tin containers may be reusable. Some have sealable lids to prevent food from drying out.

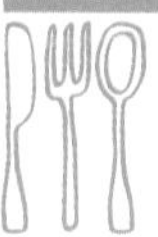

Costing

Costing means calculating the cost of a dish or a meal. Learning to be economical when cooking will help you stay within your budget. To be able to cost a dish you need to know the price of each ingredient (look at receipts or online shops, e.g. ***supervalu.ie***, ***tesco.ie***). You may have to use your calculator to calculate exact amounts. For example, if a 1 kg box of rice costs €1.29 and a recipe uses 200 g of rice, you must calculate how much you used. Do not put in the price of the total box.

Be Numerate

How do you work out the costings for a meal?

Revision Toolkit

Practise costing all the dishes you make. This will help you compare homemade and ready-made products for your CBA2 and Practical Food Skills examination.

Revision Questions

Use your workbook to revise this chapter

1. State the advantages of meal planning.
2. List the factors that affect meal planning.
3. Explain the differences between a table d'hôte menu and an à la carte menu.
4. Explain how to write a menu.
5. Plan a three-course meal for a family, including the following steps:
   (a) Design a menu card for the meal.
   (b) Draw a place setting for this meal.
   (c) Cost the main course of this meal.
6. Compile a set of guidelines for shopping wisely.
7. Explain why it is important to store food correctly.
8. Describe how to store (i) dried, (ii) frozen and (iii) perishable foods correctly.

Summary

- When **planning meals**, it is important to consider the following: good nutrition; individual dietary requirements or restrictions; time; money; equipment and ingredients available; the skill of the cook; the number of people; and the occasion.
- In Ireland, we usually eat three **meals** a day: breakfast, lunch and dinner or tea, depending on when the main meal is eaten. The main meal is usually made up of three courses: a starter, a main course and a dessert or cheeseboard. When eating out in a restaurant, there is a choice of the table d'hôte menu (set price/ fewer choices/cheaper) or the à la carte menu (individually priced dishes/more variety/more expensive).
- **When writing a menu**, follow these rules: present it neatly in a box in the centre of the page; list the courses in order; leave space between courses; choose suitable foods; put the main dish first, then accompaniments; and, finally, do not offer choices.
- **When setting a table**, everything should be clean and positioned correctly. Ensure there are condiments in the centre of the table; table decorations should be low; and place a jug of iced water on the table. Serve to the left and clear from the right.
- When **shopping** for food, choose shops that are clean with a wide range of good-quality and well-priced products. Write a shopping list; shop once a week; stay within budget; examine products; buy fresh; and avoid convenience foods as much as possible. Always think of the environment.
- **Correct food storage** is necessary to prevent waste and reduce the risk of food poisoning.

09 FOOD PREPARATION

Learning Outcomes 1.2, 1.3, 1.4, 1.5, 1.6, 1.7, 1.15, 1.16, 1.17, 2.7, 2.8, 2.9

What I Will Learn

- to prepare for a practical class
- to use a recipe
- to compile an equipment list
- to prepare a work station in a safe and hygienic manner
- to weigh and measure solid and liquid ingredients
- to follow a recipe and modify if necessary
- to present a work plan
- to discuss the use, care and cleaning of electrical appliances in the kitchen

Key Words

✓ Recipe
✓ Ingredients
✓ Equipment
✓ Appliances
✓ Weigh
✓ Measure
✓ Method
✓ Grams
✓ Kilograms
✓ Millilitres
✓ Litres
✓ Preheat
✓ Garnish
✓ Decorate
✓ Modify

Food preparation involves reading and following recipes, weighing and measuring ingredients, using equipment and appliances correctly and mastering a lot of new skills and cookery terms.

A **recipe** includes the following:

- The name of the dish
- The list of ingredients (foods) and the amount you need of each to make a dish
- Step-by-step instructions of how to prepare, cook and serve the dish (method)
- Oven temperatures required, cooking times and serving suggestions

Before you cook

- Study the recipe before class so you know what ingredients and equipment you will need, and the basic steps you will follow.
- Tie back and/or cover your hair and put on a clean apron. Remove all jewellery.
- Roll up your sleeves and wash your hands.
- Collect all equipment and set the table.
- Weigh and measure all the ingredients accurately.
- Prepare all tins and preheat the oven if needed.
- **Equipment** required depends on the recipe.

Apple crumble recipe

Ingredients	Method
2 large cooking apples 1 lemon 2 tbsp of caster sugar 100 g plain flour 50 g muesli 75 g margarine 50 g brown sugar 1 tsp cinnamon	1. Grease the pie dish. 2. Wash the apples, then core, peel and slice them. 3. Layer slices into the dish and sprinkle with the caster sugar. 4. Cut lemon in half and squeeze over the apples. 5. Sieve the flour into the bowl. 6. Rub in the margarine with your fingertips until it resembles fine breadcrumbs. 7. Mix in the muesli, the brown sugar and the cinnamon. 8. Cover the sliced apples with crumble mixture. 9. Bake in the oven for 30–35 mins until top is crisp.
Oven temperature	**Serve**
Preheat to 190°C/ fan 180°C/Gas Mark 5	With custard, cream or ice cream

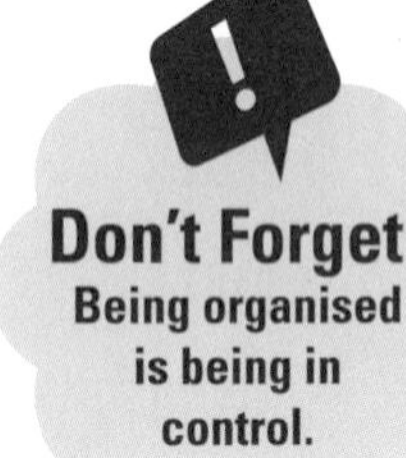

Don't Forget!
Being organised is being in control.

Equipment for recipe

Weighing scales	Vegetable peeler	Plates
Measuring spoons	Bowls	Oven gloves
Cutlery	Sieve	Dishcloth
Pie dish	Wooden spoon	Tea towel
Apple corer	Sharp knife	Pot stand
Chopping board	Cup or jug	Bin/compost bowl

Setting a table for a practical class

In every practical class:

- Wipe down the table surface with a disinfectant spray.
- Use a two-plate system (one for clean cutlery and one for dirty cutlery).
- Have a compost bowl (for egg shells, vegetable peelings, etc.).
- Place equipment being used on top of the table.
- Place cloths, serving dishes and tins on a shelf below the table until needed.
- Clear up as you go along, using the bin and the compost bowl.

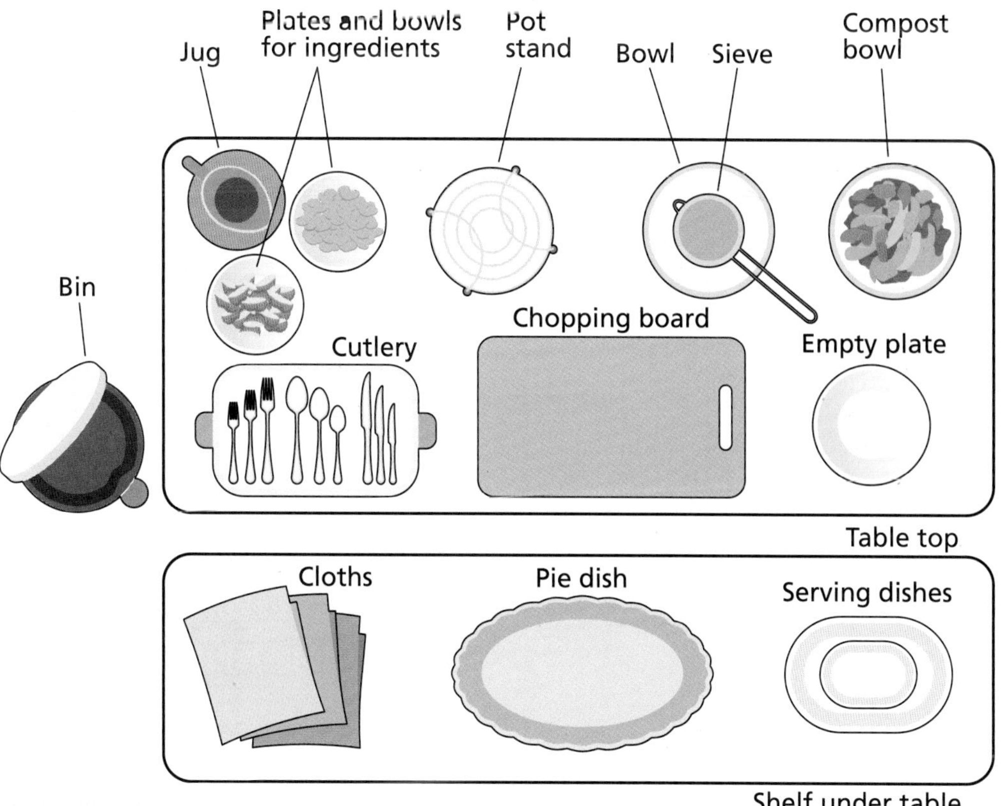

Work plans

A **work plan** is a detailed account of the order of work, from the beginning of the preparation of the dish/dishes to the serving, in an efficient manner. Work plans are important to help keep you on track and on time during a practical class.

Sample work plan for apple crumble

1. Prepare yourself – tie back or cover your hair, put on an apron, remove jewellery, roll up your sleeves and wash your hands.
2. Disinfect the table, collect all the equipment and set up the table.
3. Weigh and measure all the ingredients.
4. Preheat the oven to 190°C/fan 180°C Gas Mark 5.
5. Grease the pie dish.
6. Wash the apples and dry with kitchen roll, then core, peel and slice.
7. Layer slices into the pie dish and sprinkle with the caster sugar.
8. Cut lemon in half and squeeze over the apples.
9. Sieve the flour into the bowl.
10. Rub in the margarine with your fingertips until it resembles fine breadcrumbs.
11. Mix in the muesli, the brown sugar and the cinnamon.
12. Cover the sliced apples with crumble mixture.
13. Wipe the edges of the pie dish before putting in the oven.
14. Bake in the oven for 30–35 mins until the top is crisp.
15. Stack all the equipment for washing up beside the sink and clean the table.
16. Empty the compost bowl and bin.
17. Wash, dry and put away all the equipment.
18. Remove the crumble from the oven using oven gloves.
19. Serve with pouring cream.

Classroom-Based Assessment

This section is linked to CBA2 and the Practical Food Skills examination. Practise writing out work plans and evaluating them after the practical class. How could you change them to become more efficient in the kitchen?

Weighing and measuring

Solid foods, e.g. flour and sugar, are weighed in **grams** and **kilograms** using weighing scales. These can either be digital or spring scales.

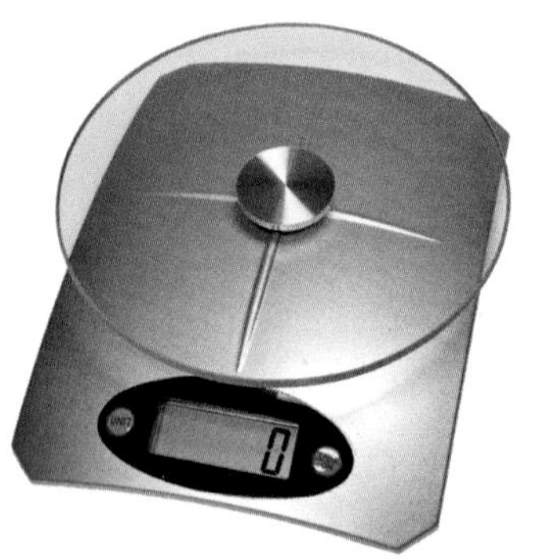

Digital weighing scales

Spring weighing scales

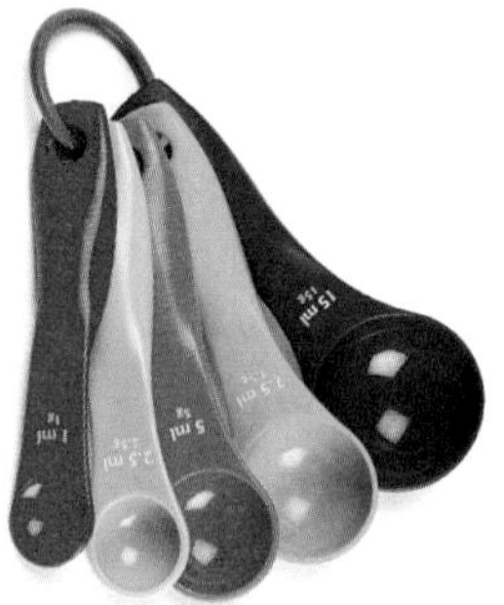

Measuring spoons

To weigh very small amounts of dry foods, e.g. spices and baking powder (under 25 g), use measuring spoons (level, unless heaped is specified).

Spoons	ml
1 teaspoon (1 tsp)	5 ml
1 dessertspoon (1 dsp)	10 ml
1 tablespoon (1 tbsp)	15 ml

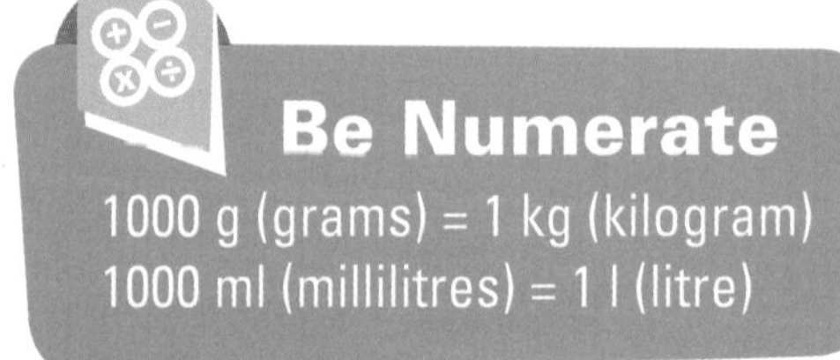

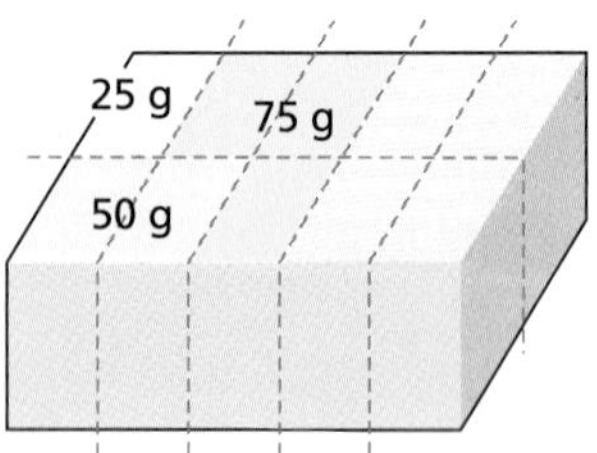

Margarine and butter can be measured by dividing the block.

Liquids are usually measured in a measuring jug made of plastic or Pyrex with measures marked on it.

Modifying recipes

Many basic recipes can be altered or modified to:

- Make a dish more nutritious and in keeping with the healthy eating guidelines (see p. 56), e.g. higher in fibre or lower in sugar or fat
- Cater for the needs of people with special dietary requirements, e.g. coeliacs (see p. 80)
- Cater for people with allergies, e.g. lactose intolerance (see p. 81)
- Increase or decrease the quantity of a recipe, i.e. most recipes provide four servings
- Economise by substituting inexpensive ingredients for more expensive ones, e.g. margarine for butter
- Add variety and choice to menus

How to modify a recipe

Modification	How
Reduce fat content	• Use low-fat or polyunsaturated spreads. • Use spray oil for cooking. • Remove any visible fat from meat. • Use low-fat milk, cream, yoghurt and cheese or non-dairy alternatives, e.g. soya. • Use low-fat meat like chicken or turkey. • Change your cooking methods, e.g. grilling for frying.
Reduce sugar content	• Reduce quantity of sugar in recipe. • Use artificial sweeteners like Canderel or Splenda. • Substitute sourer fruits for sweeter ones, e.g. put raspberries with apples in a tart. • Use fruit juice to sweeten food, e.g. fruit salads and desserts. • Use dried fruits to sweeten baked goods, e.g. crumbles and tarts.
Reduce salt content	• Omit salt. • Use low-sodium alternatives, e.g. LoSalt. • Avoid convenience foods and stock cubes. • Use herbs and spices to add flavour.
Increase fibre content	• Use wholemeal products, e.g. pasta, flour and bread. • Use wholegrain cereals, e.g. rice, Weetabix. • Add pulse vegetables to stews and casseroles. • Avoid removing the skins of fruits and vegetables.

Here is an example of recipe modification to lower fat and salt content:

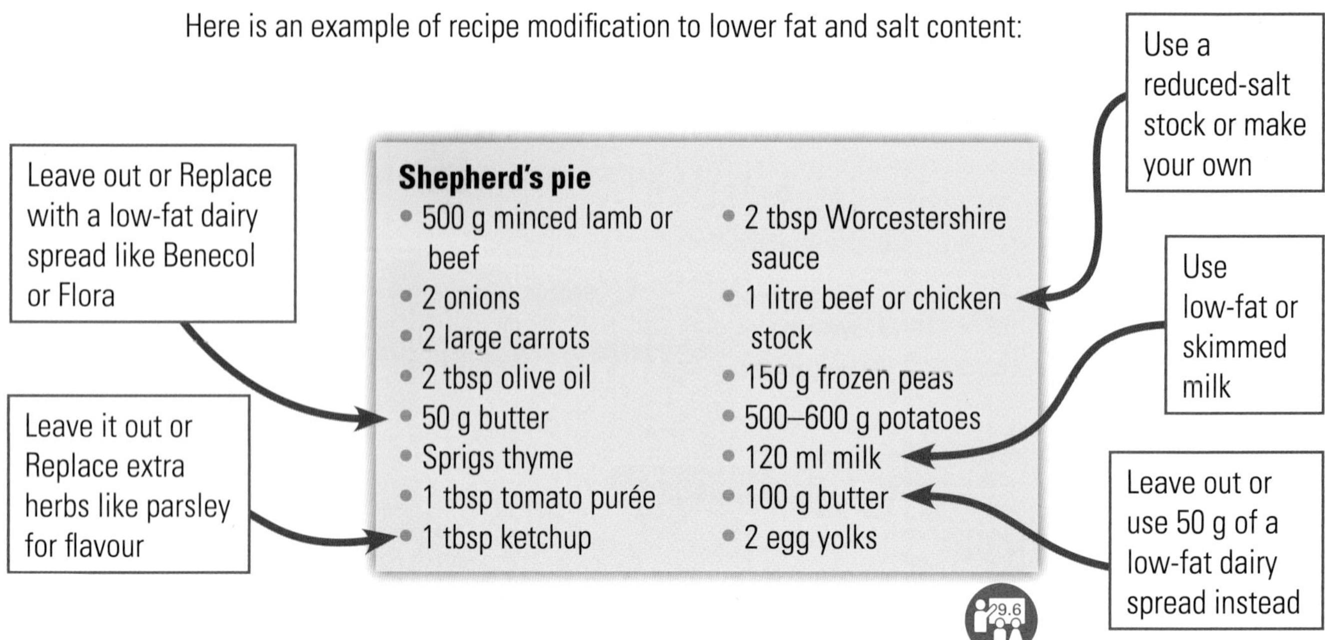

Oven management

All recipes should include the **cooking times** and the correct **temperatures** to use. Cookers are heated by gas, electricity or solid fuel, so it is important to learn how to use them correctly. Consider the following:

A **thermostat** is a device that keeps an oven or other heating appliances at the correct temperature.

1. **Shelf position:** Place the shelves in the correct position before you turn on the oven (**why?**).
2. **Starting the oven:** Become familiar with the cooker you are using.
3. **Electric ovens:** Turn the oven switch to the temperature required. A light usually comes on and goes out when the temperature is reached. It will turn on and off during the cooking as the thermostat cuts the fuel supply.
4. **Gas ovens:** Modern ovens have a push button ignition, but older cookers may need to be lit with a match or gas lighter. Turn on the oven, light the flame and then set the correct temperature.
5. **Preheating:** This means that the oven is heated to the correct temperature before the food is put in. Set the oven to the correct temperature – allow 15 minutes for an electric oven and 10 minutes for the gas oven for preheating.
6. **Temperature differences:** When a temperature is set in an oven, that is the temperature it will be on the centre shelf only. This is because hot air rises, so the temperature at the top will be hotter than on the bottom shelf, except in a fan oven (**why would this be different in a fan oven?**). A recipe may suggest a position. If not, use the centre shelf. Never place anything on the oven floor (**why?**).

7. **Temperatures in recipes:** These are given in descriptive terms for solid fuel cookers (e.g. hot, moderate), in Celsius (°C) or Fahrenheit (°F) for electric ovens, or Gas Mark for gas ovens. Use the table below to convert temperatures to suit your oven (**cooking methods, see p. 119**).

Further Investigation

To find out how a thermostat works, visit **www.explainthatstuff.com/thermostats**.

Description	°C	°F	Gas	Uses
Very hot	240	475	9	Sealing roast meats
Hot	230	450	8	Pastry
	220	425	7	Fast roasting and bread
Moderately or fairly hot	200	400	6	Sponges, cakes, scones and pastry
Moderate	190	375	5	Small cakes
	180	350	4	Fruit cakes, biscuits and crumbles
Very moderate	160	325	3	Slow roasting and casseroles
Cool	150	300	2	Milk puddings and custards
	140	275	1	Casseroles
Very cool	120	250	½	Slow stewing
	110	225	¼	Meringues and bottling

Food presentation

We see our food before we taste it, so how it is presented is very important. All tableware must be spotlessly clean. Wipe spills from dishes or plates before bringing them to the table. Savoury dishes are garnished and sweet dishes are decorated to make them more appetising.

Garnishes

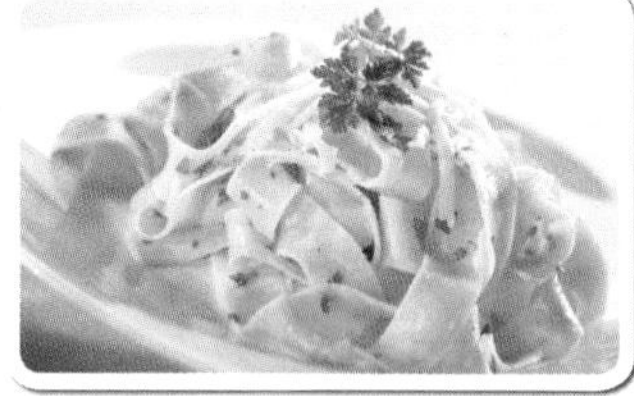

- **Herbs** such as parsley, dill, chives, coriander, basil, mint and oregano are used to garnish dishes. They can be chopped or used in sprigs.

- **Citrus fruits**, e.g. lime, lemon and orange, can be sliced, wedged, looped or twisted.

- **Tomatoes** can be sliced, cut into wedges, made into roses or used as a decorative collar for other vegetables, e.g. green beans or asparagus.

- **Vegetables** like cucumber, carrots and beetroot can be cut into spirals, wheels and roses. Spring onion tassels and small, attractive salads are also popular.

Decorations

- **Cream** can be piped onto dishes or plates or poured into soup and swirled.

- **Pastry** decorations like leaves can be used on the top of apple tarts.

- **Fruit** can be puréed, made into a sauce or coulis, frosted or fresh, or arranged attractively on the dish or plate.

- **Sugar** can be sieved directly onto the dish or onto a cake through a doily to create an interesting pattern on a cake. Sugar can also be spun or made into icing (fondant, glacé or royal).

- **Chocolate** can be used in many ways to decorate sweet dishes – it can be melted, curled, grated and piped into decorative shapes.

Don't Forget!
Be creative with your presentation. Always remember that we eat with our eyes first.

Food preparation appliances

There is a wide range of food preparation appliances available to speed up preparation time, including:

- kettles
- blenders
- liquidisers
- food mixers
- food processors
- juicers
- juice extractors
- carving knives
- smoothie makers

Did You Know?

Many small appliances like food processors and blenders have a pulse action that saves energy and reduces motor damage.

Discovery Learning

Look after our environment by choosing energy-efficient appliances. To learn more about these, visit ***www.europa.eu***, click on 'English' on the home page, then click on 'Life and Business in the EU', and then on 'Energy labels'.

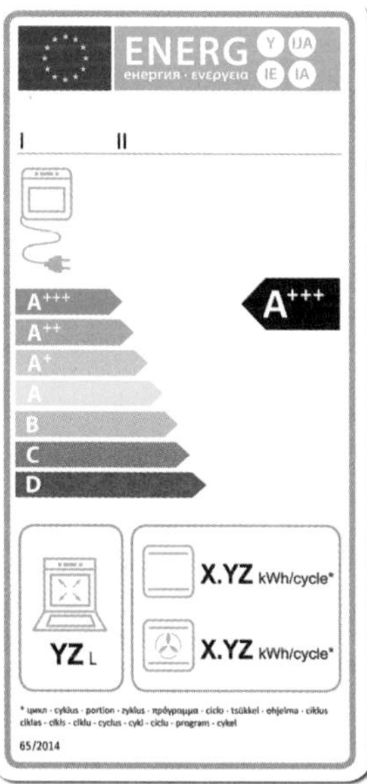

An energy label

Guidelines for using appliances

- Always follow the manufacturer's instructions.
- Assemble the appliance correctly.
- Do not overfill or run for long periods of time as it will damage the motor.

Safe use	Care and cleaning
• Do not handle with wet hands. • Unplug the appliance when you are cleaning it or it is not in use. • Be careful handling and cleaning sharp blades. • Only use the appliance if it is in good working order.	• Unplug and remove attachments. • Wash parts in warm, soapy water and dry well. • Wipe the body of the appliance with a damp cloth. • Store, unassembled, in dry area.

Discovery Learning

Find out more about food preparation, storage and cooking appliances by visiting ***home.howstuffworks.com***, clicking on 'Appliances' on the home page, and then by clicking on 'Kitchen Appliances'.

Revision Questions

1. Explain what you need to do to prepare for a practical class.
2. What is a recipe? Why is it important to read through a recipe prior to a practical class?
3. List six resources that you might need for every practical class.
4. Look up a recipe for scones and prepare for a practical class by doing the following:
   (a) Draw the equipment set-up for making scones.
   (b) Write a work plan.
5. Why is it important to preheat an oven?
6. Discuss three modifications to the scone recipe: (i) to make the scones healthier, (ii) to change the flavour and (iii) to suit a coeliac.
7. Choose a food preparation appliance with a motor. Discuss its use, care and cleaning.
8. Choose a food preparation appliance with a heating element. Discuss its use, care and cleaning.
9. Explain the following cookery terms: (i) baking blind, (ii) blanch, (iii) infuse, (iv) roux, (v) al dente, (vi) beat, (vii) fold and (viii) blend.

Summary

A **recipe** includes:
- the name of the dish
- the list of ingredients (foods)
- the amount you need of each to make a dish
- step-by-step instructions of how to prepare, cook and serve the dish (method)
- oven temperatures, cooking times and serving suggestions

When preparing for a practical class:
- Study the recipe before class so you will know what ingredients and equipment you need, and the basic steps you will follow.
- Prepare yourself: Tie back and/or cover hair, put an apron on, remove all jewellery, roll up sleeves and wash hands.
- Collect all equipment and set the table.
- Prepare all tins and preheat the oven if needed.
- Weigh and measure all the ingredients accurately.
- Follow a work plan to complete tasks in an efficient manner.

Recipes can be **modified** to make them healthier, to suit a special diet or to change quantities.

Use and **assemble electrical equipment safely** and follow all the manufacturer's instructions when using, caring for and cleaning the product.

10 COOKING FOOD

Learning Outcomes 1.1, 1.2, 1.3, 1.4, 1.5, 1.6, 1.7, 1.10, 1.12, 1.13, 1.14, 1.15, 1.16, 1.17, 1.18, 1.19, 2.7, 2.8, 2.9

What I Will Learn

- to explain why food is cooked
- to identify the changes that occur when food is cooked
- to examine three methods of heat transfer
- to describe moist cooking methods, dry cooking methods and methods that use fat
- to state the factors that affect the choice of cooking method
- to define each cooking method
- to suggest suitable foods for each cooking method
- to compile a set of guidelines for each cooking method
- to explain why food is coated before cooking

Key Words

✓ Coagulate
✓ Conduction
✓ Convection
✓ Radiation
✓ Boiling
✓ Simmering
✓ Stewing
✓ Mirepoix
✓ Casserole
✓ Poaching
✓ Steaming
✓ Pressure cooking
✓ Grilling
✓ Baking
✓ Frying
✓ Standing time
✓ Roasting
✓ Smoke point
✓ Flash point
✓ Coating
✓ Basting

Reasons for cooking food

Some foods, like fruits and vegetables, can be eaten raw. However, we usually cook food for the following reasons:

- To kill bacteria, making food safer to eat
- To preserve food so it lasts longer, e.g. cooked chicken lasts longer than raw chicken
- To make food easier to eat and digest, e.g. starchy foods like potatoes and rice soften
- To improve the appearance and flavour of food
- To stimulate digestive juices through the sight and smells of cooked food
- To add variety to our diets by combining ingredients and create new flavours, e.g. curries

Changes that occur when food is cooked

All cooking requires heat, which has the following effects on food:

- Bacteria are destroyed.
- Protein coagulates (hardens), e.g. the white of an egg.
- Colour changes, e.g. meat changes from red to brown or from pink to white.
- Foods soften, making them easier to digest, e.g. potatoes and apples.
- Water evaporates and food shrinks in size, e.g. meat and fish.
- Flavours and aromas are developed, e.g. meat extractives released from meat fibres, improving the tastes and smells.
- Fat melts.
- Starch grains swell, burst and absorb liquid, e.g. rice, pasta and sauces.
- Some vitamins and minerals are lost.

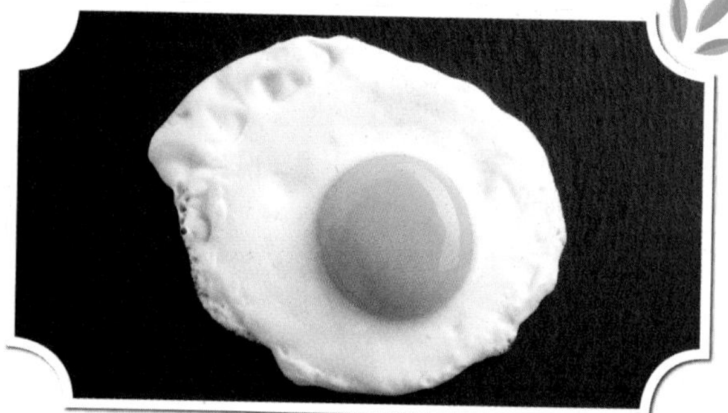

Overcooking

Be careful not to overcook food, as it causes the following:

- Loss of colour, flavour and texture
- Some foods become tough and indigestible
- More loss of vitamins and minerals
- Fuel wastage

Discovery Learning

To find out more about the science behind cooking and fascinating facts, visit ***www.scienceofcooking.com*** or ***www.exploratorium.edu/cooking***

Heat transfer

All cooking methods involve heat. The heat must be transferred from the heat source to the food. This can be done by conduction, convection and radiation.

Method	How it happens	Examples
Conduction	• Transfer of heat from one molecule to another by vibration. • The food being heated must be in direct contact with the heat source, e.g. heat passing from the cooker hob through the base of the saucepan into the food.	• Frying • Boiling • Simmering • Stewing • Barbecuing
Convection	• Molecules near heat source become hotter and less dense, and rise up. • This allows cold molecules to take their place. • This sets up convection currents and heat is spread through liquids and gases. • This movement of hot and cold gas/liquid creates an even temperature in the oven or saucepan.	• Simmering stews • Baking • Roasting
Radiation	• Heat passes in straight rays from the source to the first solid object they reach, without heating air in between. • The food needs to be as close as possible to the heat rays.	• Grilling burgers • Making toast • Microwaving

Did You Know?

Most cooking methods involve more than one method of heat transfer, e.g. boiling involves conduction (heating of the saucepan) and convection (heating the water and food), and grilling involves radiation (heating the surface molecules) and conduction (heating the food molecules).

Cooking methods

Cooking methods can be divided into groups.

Moist methods	Dry methods	Frying	Other
Boiling	Baking	Dry	Microwaving
Simmering	Grilling	Shallow	
Poaching	Roasting	Deep	
Steaming	Barbecuing	Stir	
Stewing			
Braising			
Pressure cooking			

Choosing cooking methods

When choosing cooking methods, consider:

- The ingredients available, e.g. stewing beef or sirloin steak. Stewing would be a better cooking method for cheaper cuts than frying (**why?**)
- The experience of the cook, e.g. boiling might be easier than using a pressure cooker
- The cost of fuel, e.g. it is uneconomical to cook small amounts in a large oven
- The time available to prepare and cook the meal
- The equipment available
- The result you want, e.g. soft, crisp, brown, moist, dry or low-fat
- Retention of nutrients
- Personal tastes, e.g. raw, rare, medium or well done

Moist methods of cooking

Boiling/simmering		
Definition	**Guidelines**	**Suitable foods**
• Boiling is cooking by convection and conduction in liquid at 100°C in covered saucepan on the hob. • Simmering is at 90°C.	• Keep at 100°C or 90°C (bubbling) at all times. • Use a small amount of liquid for vegetables. • Use cooking liquid as base for soups and sauces. • Cook food for the shortest possible time.	• Meat, e.g. bacon, mutton • Eggs • Pasta and rice • Vegetables, e.g. potatoes, carrots, turnips and cabbage

Advantages	Disadvantages
• Needs little attention • Clean • Food stays moist and juicy • Digestible • Less greasy • Little preparation • Nourishing method	• Little flavour added • Loss of nutrients • Lacks texture • Risk of overcooking

Don't Forget!
Use a heavy saucepan with a tight lid.

Poaching

Definition	Guidelines	Suitable foods
Cooking by convection and conduction in liquid at 85°C in covered container on the hob or in the oven.	• Keep at 85°C at all times. • Water barely moving, not bubbling. • Used for delicate foods that need gentle cooking.	• Fish • De-shelled eggs • Fruit, e.g. pears

Advantages	Disadvantages
• Clean • Food stays moist and juicy • Digestible • Not greasy	• Needs attention • Little flavour added • Loss of nutrients • Lacks texture • Slow

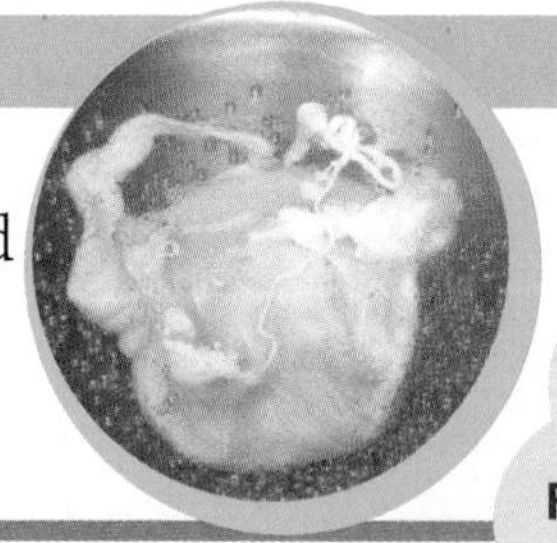

Don't Forget!
Do not let the water boil rapidly or the food will break up and be spoiled

Don't Forget!
Flavour foods with herbs and spices, as steamed foods can taste a little bland.

Steaming

Definition	Guidelines	Suitable foods
Cooking food slowly in steam rising from boiling water. Food can be steamed: (a) Between two plates (b) In a covered bowl in a saucepan of boiling water (c) In a steamer over boiling water (d) On a trivet or separator basket in a pressure cooker	• A tightly fitting lid prevents evaporation. • Water boiling before and during cooking. • Food must not touch liquid.	• Thin pieces of chicken and fish • Steamed puddings, e.g. jam roly poly, Christmas or chocolate pudding • Vegetables, e.g. potatoes, spinach

Advantages	Disadvantages
• Clean • Food stays moist and juicy • Digestible • Not greasy • No loss of nutrients	• Little flavour added • Lacks texture • Slow • Not suitable for large pieces of food

Did You Know?
Electric steamers are relatively inexpensive and are very economical as they allow you to cook more than one food at once. Place foods that take the longest to cook on the bottom tier and then add other tiers as needed.

Methods of steaming

Over a pan of boiling water

In a bowl placed into a pan of boiling water

Steam cannot escape. Pressure builds up, raising the temperature in the pressure cooker so that food cooks more quickly.
In a pressure cooker

In an electric steamer

Stewing/casseroling		
Definition	**Guidelines**	**Suitable foods**
Slowly cooking food in a little liquid by conduction and convection, using gentle heat (80°C–90°C) in a covered container, on the hob or in the oven.	• Bring to boil and then reduce heat to a constant temperature of 80°C–90°C to prevent meat becoming tough and fish or vegetables falling apart. • Keep covered to prevent evaporation of the liquid. • Use pressure cooker to reduce time.	• Tough cuts of meat/fish • Vegetables, e.g. potatoes, carrots, turnips • Fruit, e.g. apples and rhubarb
Advantages		**Disadvantages**
• Little attention needed • Food stays moist • Complete meal in one pot – saves fuel and washing up • Little nutrient loss • Digestible • Clean • Not very greasy • Suitable for large numbers		• A lot of preparation • Slow • Lacks texture • A lot of flavour needs to be added

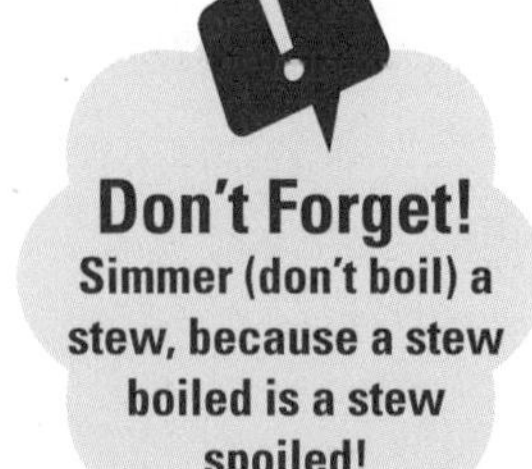

Braising		
Definition	**Guidelines**	**Suitable foods**
• Cooking meat in a small amount of stock on a layer of vegetables (mirepoix). • Meat is in a covered saucepan on the hob. • Combination of steaming and stewing.	• Use for delicate foods that need gentle cooking. • Use only enough stock to cover vegetables. • Food can be browned under grill before serving.	• Root vegetables • Chicken • Offal • Tougher cuts of meat
Advantages		**Disadvantages**
• Little attention needed • Food stays moist • Complete meal in one pot – saves fuel and washing up • Little nutrient loss • Digestible		• A lot of preparation • Slow • Lacks texture

Pressure cooking		
Definition	**Guidelines**	**Suitable foods**
• Fast, moist method of cooking food at high temperatures in a pressure cooker. • Used for boiling, stewing and steaming.	• Follow manufacturer's instructions. • Never overfill. • Build up steady stream of steam before applying weight. • Time the cooking very accurately. • Reduce pressure before opening by either standing for 15 minutes at room temperature or putting it under cold running water. • Remove lid carefully to avoid a burst of steam.	• Jam-making • Bottling • Soups, stocks and stews • Cooking vegetables and puddings

Don't Forget!
Time the cooking carefully following the manufacturer's instructions because overcooking is common.

Advantages	Disadvantages
• Saves time and energy • Little loss of nutrients • Little change in colour and flavour • Whole meal can be cooked in one pot	• Danger of overcooking the food • Needs constant attention • Danger of scalding from steam • Needs a storage space

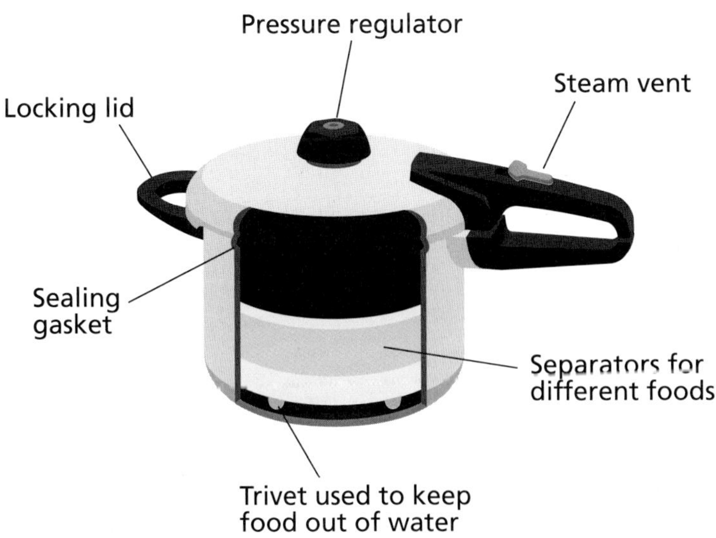

Pressure cooker components

Did You Know?

The sealed pressure cooker causes a controlled build-up of pressure. Steam under pressure reaches a higher temperature and cooks food faster.

Dry methods of cooking

Baking		
Definition	**Guidelines**	**Suitable foods**
Dry method of cooking food by convection currents in the oven.	• Preheat oven. • Steam made in the oven stops food drying. • Tin foil and greaseproof paper should also be used. • Avoid opening the oven door.	• Bread • Cakes • Biscuits • Pastries • Vegetables, e.g. potatoes, peppers, tomatoes • Fruit, e.g. apples, in puddings and apple crumble
Advantages	**Disadvantages**	
• Attractive appearance • Doesn't add fat • Little loss of nutrients • Adds lots of flavour • A number of items can be cooked at the same time, saving time and energy.	• A lot of preparation • Dries food • Slow	

Tips for baking

- Always preheat the oven fully.
- Bake in large batches to make full use of the oven and to save on fuel.
- Adjust the shelves before the oven heats up.
- Do not open the oven door, especially at the start of cooking, as the buns or cakes will collapse.

Discovery Learning
Do not forget about hygiene and safety when barbecuing. For more information, go to ***www.safefood.eu***, click on 'Food Safety' at the top of the home page, click on 'Seasonal Features' on the left-hand side of the page, and then on 'Top food safety tips for BBQs'.

Grilling/barbecuing		
Definition	**Guidelines**	**Suitable foods**
• Grilling is a method of cooking food by radiant heat under a grill. • Barbecuing is cooking food by radiant heat on a grid over glowing charcoal.	• Preheat grill or barbecue. • Seal surface of the food with high heat, preventing nutrient loss. • Use tongs to turn food. • Cook thin pieces of food only. • Don't salt food before grilling. • Oil grill grid to prevent sticking.	• Meat, e.g. chops, steaks, burgers, rashers • Vegetables, e.g. tomatoes, peppers • Fish fillets
Advantages	**Disadvantages**	
• Fast • Little loss of nutrients • Reduces fat content • Attractive appearance and taste	• Constant attention needed • Dries food • Spatters grease • Unsuitable for tough or thick cuts of meat	

Cooking methods using fat

Roasting/pot roasting		
Definition	**Guidelines**	**Suitable foods**
Cooking food in a little fat: (a) in a roasting tin in the oven (b) in a saucepan on the hob (pot roasting) (c) on a spit (spit-roasting), under a grill or in an oven	• Pre-arrange the shelves and preheat the oven. • Cooking time depends on weight. • **Baste** every 30 minutes. • Use cooking juices for gravy. • Time carefully. • Quick roasting (for tender cuts) – 220°C/gas 7 for 20 minutes then 190°C/gas 5 for remainder. • Slow roasting (for less tender cuts) – 180°C/gas 4 for all the cooking time.	• Meat, e.g. beef, lamb, pork • Poultry • Vegetables, e.g. potatoes, carrots, beetroot and parsnip

Basting means spooning hot fat over roasting meat to keep it moist.

Don't Forget!
Covering meat helps prevent it drying out, but uncover 30 mins before the end of cooking time to allow it to brown.

Don't Forget!
Allow food to reach room temperature before roasting. Prepare food and calculate cooking time.

Advantages	**Disadvantages**
• Vegetables and meat can be cooked together • Cooking liquid can be used as gravy • Attractive appearance and taste • Not much preparation required	• Spatters grease • Unsuitable for tough or thick cuts of meat • Greasy • Shrinkage occurs • Adds fat

Don't Forget!
Remove roasting dish from the oven using oven gloves.

Be Numerate

Cooking times for different types of meat.

Quick roasting	Slow roasting
Beef: 20 mins per 500 g + 20 mins	Beef: 35 mins per 500 g
Lamb: 25 mins per 500 g + 20 mins	Lamb: 35 mins per 500 g
Pork: 30 mins per 500 g + 30 mins	Pork: 50 mins per 500 g

A meat thermometer is an instrument with a sharp spike, which is stuck into the thickest part of the joint before cooking and left there for easy monitoring. It records the internal temperature of the meat. When the meat is cooked, the temperature should be between 60–80°C.

Frying

Definitions

Dry frying is cooking fatty foods by conduction in the frying pan or on the hob.	**Stir-frying** is tossing food in hot fat in a wok, e.g. strips of chicken and vegetables.	**Shallow frying** is cooking food in hot fat, e.g. pancakes.	**Deep frying** is cooking food immersed in hot fat, which is often coated, e.g. fish.

Guidelines	• Preheat oil or wok before oil is added • Use tongs for turning regularly • Drain before serving
Suitable foods	• Meats – thin pieces, e.g. rashers, chops, burgers, sausages • Fish – thin pieces, e.g. steaks, cutlets, fillets • Eggs • Vegetables and fruits, e.g. chips and onions, pineapples and bananas
Advantages	• Quick • Attractive taste and appearance
Disadvantages	• Constant attention needed • Spatters grease • Unsuitable for tough or thick cuts of meat • Not suitable when cooking for large numbers • Greasy • Not easily digested

Why do we coat foods for frying?

- It protects the surface of the food while the inside is cooking.
- It prevents foods from becoming soggy or greasy by absorbing too much fat.
- It prevents foods from breaking up during cooking.
- It improves the appearance and texture of food, e.g. golden colour and crispy coating.
- It improves the nutritive value and flavour, e.g. egg and breadcrumbs.
- It prevents strong flavours of some foods getting into the fat.

Coatings

Egg and breadcrumbs
Batter
Seasoned flour
Egg and oatmeal

Frying pan safety

- Never overheat the oil. If overheated, oil will reach:
  - **Smoke point:** A blue haze rises from the fat
  - **Flash point:** The fat ignites (burst into flames)
- Never leave the frying pan unattended.
- Never move the frying pan while the oil is hot.
- If the pan catches fire, place a damp cloth or ideally a fire blanket over the flames (**why?**).
- Do not unplug an electric deep fat fryer – place the lid or a fire blanket over the flames.
- Do not try to move the pan off the heat or throw water onto the fat (**why?**).
- If a burn occurs, treat it quickly (**see p. 334**).

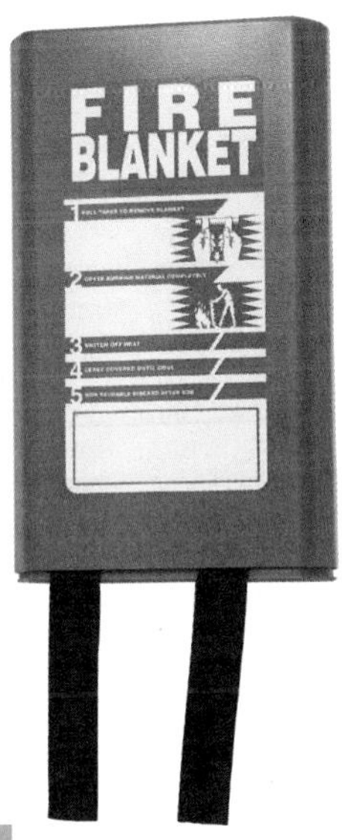

Microwave cooking

- Microwave cooking is a very fast method of cooking by conduction in a microwave oven.
- Electro-magnetic waves penetrate the food to a certain depth and cause the molecules to vibrate very rapidly, causing intense heat.
- The remainder of the food cooks by conduction.

Guidelines for microwaving	
	• Time food accurately and follow the manufacturer's instructions carefully. Timing is affected by: - **Composition of food**, e.g. foods containing fat or sugar cook very quickly - **Thickness**, e.g. small, thin pieces of food cook quicker than larger, thick pieces - **Density**, e.g. light, open foods like bread and cakes cook faster than dense foods like potatoes - **Temperature at the beginning**, e.g. the cooler the food the longer it takes to cook - **Amount of food**, e.g. the larger the quantity of food the longer it takes to cook • Cover food to prevent splatters and to retain steam, which keeps it moist and cooks it faster. • Turn or stir regularly to ensure even cooking. • Arrange food in a circle with the thickest piece facing outwards. • Pierce skins, e.g. potatoes, tomatoes and sausages, to prevent bursting. • Only use suitable containers – do not use metal or foil as it can damage the magnetron (the device that produces the microwaves). • Allow standing time as the food continues to cook until it begins to cool.

Suitable foods

Defrosting, e.g. meat, bread, cakes
Reheating, e.g. curry, lasagne
Cooking food, e.g. scrambled eggs
Melting chocolate
Heating liquids

Unsuitable foods

Pastry
Meringue
Food with **high fat and sugar** content

Microwave cooking	
Cleaning	• Unplug the microwave • Remove loose parts, e.g. turntable, and wash separately • Wash interior with hot, soapy water, then rinse and dry • Repeat on the outside • Avoid using abrasives
Advantages	**Disadvantages**
• Reduces cooking time and saves energy • Relatively inexpensive to buy • Reduces wash up • Good retention of colour, flavour and texture • Easy to clean and maintain • Good for defrosting food quickly	• Unsuitable for cooking some foods • Food overcooks easily • Requires suitable cookware 

Discovery Learning

To find out how to use a microwave oven to cook full meals, visit ***www.bbcgoodfood.com*** and search '10 dishes you can cook in a microwave in minutes'. For technique videos, recipes and lots of other information, visit ***www.chefs.com***.

Revision Questions

1. Give three reasons for cooking food.
2. Describe five effects of cooking on food.
3. Name two foods that are suitable for each of the following cooking methods:
   (a) Stir-frying
   (b) Poaching
   (c) Boiling
   (d) Roasting
4. Write a set of safety rules to follow when frying foods.
5. Give two advantages and two disadvantages of frying as a method of cooking.
6. Name the vitamins that are most likely to be destroyed in cooking.
7. List the effects of overcooking.

Further Investigation

Visit **gillexplore.ie** to find a full list of cookery terms and their definitions.

Summary

- Food is **cooked** to kill bacteria, to improve appearance and flavour, and to make it easier to digest.
- When **food is cooked** the protein coagulates, starch grains swell and burst, fat melts, vitamins and minerals are destroyed, water evaporates, the colour changes, the flavour develops and the bacteria are destroyed.
- Heat is **transferred** during cooking by conduction, convection and radiation.
- The **choice of cooking method** depends on available ingredients, the experience of the cook, costs, time available, the result you want and personal tastes.
- **Moist methods** include boiling, simmering, poaching, steaming, stewing and pressure cooking.
- **Dry methods** include baking, grilling and barbecuing.
- **Methods using fat** include frying (dry, stir, shallow and deep) and roasting.
- Sometimes **fried food is coated** to prevent it from breaking up and keep it moist, and to improve its appearance, texture and flavour.

Section 4: Focus on Food

11 BREAKFAST AND PACKED MEALS

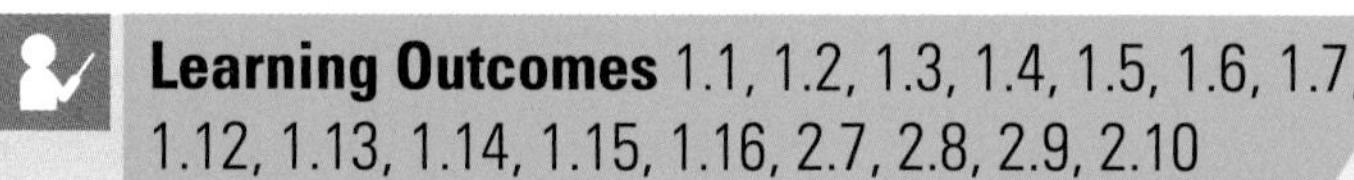

Learning Outcomes 1.1, 1.2, 1.3, 1.4, 1.5, 1.6, 1.7, 1.12, 1.13, 1.14, 1.15, 1.16, 2.7, 2.8, 2.9, 2.10

Family meals are an important part of family life, so in this section we will focus on food. First, we will look at breakfast and packed meals. Then we will look at the main foods, guided by the food pyramid, that are used in main course meals. Choosing healthy options is important, as is adapting recipes to meet individual needs.

Breakfast and packed meals

What I Will Learn

- to explain why a healthy breakfast is important
- to compile a set of breakfast planning guidelines
- to identify foods suitable for breakfast from the main food groups
- to create a nourishing breakfast
- to explain how to set a breakfast tray
- to identify the points to consider when planning packed meals
- to identify and make a variety of sandwiches
- to create a variety of healthy packed lunches

Key Words

- ✓ Breakfast
- ✓ Cereals
- ✓ Lunch
- ✓ Muesli
- ✓ Granola
- ✓ Croissants
- ✓ Bagels
- ✓ Breads
- ✓ Fruit juices
- ✓ Smoothies
- ✓ Salads
- ✓ Packaging

Breakfast

Breakfast is one of the most important meals of the day. The word breakfast comes from the 15th-century expression 'breaking the fast', because it's the first meal you have after fasting (not eating) overnight. As we sleep at night, our blood sugar levels drop. This can make a person tired and irritable in the morning.

It is important to never skip breakfast because it:

- Gives you energy and raises blood sugar levels
- May prevent you from snacking on high-calorie foods later in the day
- Will aid your concentration at school or work, and help you work more efficiently
- Prevents headaches and tiredness
- Prevents workplace accidents caused by fatigue

How to plan a healthy breakfast

- Get up early and leave time to sit down and enjoy your breakfast.
- Include at least three of the four main food groups (see below).
- Include fruit or fruit juices to rehydrate and provide vitamin C.
- Use high-fibre cereals to provide fibre, vitamin B and iron and avoid those high in sugar.
- Wholemeal bread can be included to increase fibre, e.g. wholemeal toast, brown breakfast scones or oatmeal blueberry muffins.
- Spreads like butter, Flora, LowLow, honey or marmalade can be used in small amounts.
- Milk or yoghurt provides calcium, vitamins A and D.
- Main course dishes should have a protein food, e.g. eggs, beans, grilled bacon or kippers.
- Drinks like milk, tea, coffee or hot chocolate can also be included.

Did You Know?

9 out of 10 (87%) Irish people have breakfast every day, with this rising slightly (to 89%) at the week-ends. Half of us will never miss breakfast, while those that never or rarely eat breakfast are likely to be single and aged 21–29. Source: An Bord Bia.

Did You Know?

Almost 1 in 4 (23%) people have recently changed their breakfast choices for health reasons. Some 44% of these claim to be cutting back on sugar, while 13% of them are trying to reduce their carbohydrate intake.

Don't Forget!

Be literate: Look up any words you do not understand in your dictionary or online.

Foods suitable for breakfast

Food groups	Foods
Vegetables, salad and fruit	**Fruit**: Juices, smoothies, segments of grapefruit or mandarins, mixed fresh fruit, stewed fruits like apple and prunes, in cereals or whole, e.g. bananas **Vegetables**: Juices, grilled tomatoes, grilled mushrooms
Wholemeal cereals and breads, potatoes, pasta and rice	**Breakfast cereals**: Porridge, muesli, granola, All-Bran, Bran Flakes, Weetabix, Shredded Wheat. **Breads**: Brown or white bread, soda bread, scones, muffins, bagels, croissants, baguettes, French toast, pancakes, waffles and crackers **Potatoes**: Potato farls, potato cakes **Rice**: Kedgeree
Milk, yoghurt and cheese	**Milk**: On cereals (hot or cold), milkshakes, in tea, coffee (latte) or hot chocolate **Yoghurt**: In smoothies, on cereals and in muffins **Cheese**: In slices, chunks, or cream cheese
Meat, poultry, fish, eggs, beans and nuts	**Meat**: Grilled rashers, sausages, black and white pudding, ham, salami and chorizo **Fish**: Kippers and kedgeree and smoked salmon or mackerel **Eggs**: Boiled, poached, scrambled, fried or in an omelette **Beans**: Baked beans and hummus **Nuts and seeds**: Can be sprinkled into cereals, smoothies or muffins, peanut butter
Fats, spreads and oils	Flora, low-fat butters and spreads, e.g. Benecol and LowLow
Foods and drinks high in fat, sugar and salt	Use honey, syrups, jam or marmalade sparingly

Discovery Learning

Design a healthy breakfast for each of the following people

(i) an active, school-going teenager
(ii) a woman in her thirties working in an office (sedentary)
(iii) a man in his fifties recovering from a heart attack.

Use the guidelines for planning a healthy breakfast above.

How to set a breakfast tray

- Collect everything you need – tray, cutlery, delph and glassware. Make sure everything is clean.
- The tray should be attractive and colour-coordinated, with a small flower to decorate.
- Use a tray cloth to decorate a plain tray.
- Choose small dishes, jugs and teapots to suit the tray.
- Place items in a logical order, e.g. teapot, milk and sugar near each other (see diagram below).
- Make sure to include cutlery for each dish, as well as condiments and a napkin.
- The hot main course should be covered.

Discovery Learning

Find out the differences between a Continental breakfast and a Full Irish breakfast. Suggest a menu for each type of breakfast.

Revision Questions

1. Explain why a healthy breakfast is important.
2. List the guidelines that should be followed when planning a breakfast menu.
3. Design a breakfast menu suitable for an active, school-going child and give reasons for your choices.
4. Plan a breakfast to be served on a tray. Draw the tray setting.

Packed meals

Many people, particularly school-going children and teenagers, eat a packed lunch each weekday. This meal should be nutritionally balanced and follow the healthy eating guidelines as it is one of the main meals of the day. Foods are also packed for picnics and for travelling.

How to plan packed meals

- The meal should be nutritious and tasty.
- Include at least three of the four main food groups (see below).
- Try to vary the menu as much as possible and include enough food to meet the needs of the individual.
- Consider the age of the individual, their likes and dislikes, and the length of time until the next meal.

Discovery Learning

Suggest a picnic menu suitable for a family of five going to spend a day at the beach. Suggest suitable packaging for this picnic.

- Include unprocessed carbohydrates, fruit and salads for fibre and vitamin C.
- Avoid too many sweet or fatty foods.
- Choose foods that keep well and that are easy to pack and carry.
- Wrap different foods separately in secure packaging. Pack the heaviest items on the bottom.
- Include drinks like fruit juices, milk, smoothies, milkshakes or water for hydration.

Foods suitable for packed lunches

Food groups	Foods
Vegetables, salad and fruit	**Fruit**: Juices, smoothies, segments of grapefruit or mandarins, mixed fresh fruit salad, guacamole, dried fruit or whole, e.g. bananas, apples **Vegetables**: Salads like coleslaw, green, Waldorf, crudités; juices, soups, quiches, vegetable sticks and dips
Wholemeal cereals and breads, potatoes, pasta and rice	**Breads**: Brown or white bread, soda bread, scones, muffins, bagels, baguettes, baps, wraps, pitta, crackers or naan **Potatoes**: Potato salad, baked potatoes **Rice**: Tabbouleh and rice salads **Pasta**: Salads Quinoa and couscous salad
Milk, yoghurt and cheese	**Milk**: On its own, in milkshakes, in tea, coffee or hot chocolate **Yoghurt**: In smoothies, muffins, dips and on its own **Cheese**: In slices or chunks, cream cheese, quiches and tarts
Meat, poultry, fish, eggs, beans and nuts	**Meat**: Cooked meats, e.g. ham, chicken or beef, sausage rolls, quiche, savoury tarts **Fish**: Salmon and tuna in salads or sandwiches **Eggs**: Hard boiled in salads or sandwiches **Beans, nuts and seeds**: Hummus, pesto, olives on their own or in salads
Fats, spreads and oils	Flora, low-fat butters and spreads, mayonnaise, mustard and dressings
Foods and drinks high in fat, sugar and salt	Use honey, syrups, jam or marmalade sparingly

Discovery Learning

Design a packed lunch menu suitable for two of the following people:

(i) an active teenager who is a vegetarian
(ii) an office worker who is a coeliac
(iii) a man working on a building site
(iv) an elderly man living alone

Don't forget to use the guidelines for planning a healthy packed meal and consider the specific needs of the individual.

Classroom-Based Assessment

This section can be linked to CBA1. Can you come up with a design for a bag that could be used to carry your lunch to school each day? Use the Design Brief Process (**see p. 223**), be creative and use recycled materials. Don't forget to annotate your design!

Packaging for packed meals

Packaging for packed meals should be strong and can include plastic lunch boxes, aluminium foil, polythene bags, empty margarine tubs, foil cartons, plastic bottles, insulated cool bags, greaseproof paper, paper bags and a vacuum flask.

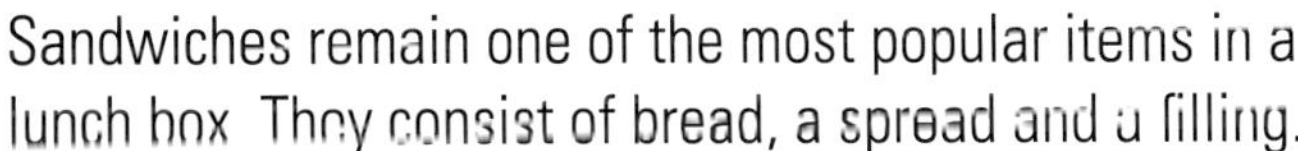

Sandwiches remain one of the most popular items in a lunch box. They consist of bread, a spread and a filling.

Breads vary in size, shape and texture	Sliced wholemeal or white sliced pan, soda bread, rolls, wraps, baps, bagels, pittas, crispbreads, crackers, baguettes or paninis	
Spreads provide a waterproof layer that prevents moist foods making the bread soggy. They also add flavour.	Butter, soft margarine, low-fat spreads that can be seasoned with herbs or mustard	
Fillings vary in colour, texture and flavour. Combine textures and moisten with sauces and dressings.	Sliced or torn cooked meats, flaked fish, pâté, sliced or grated hard cheese or spreadable soft cheese, apples, bananas, avocados, sweetcorn, salad vegetables, e.g. cucumber, lettuce and tomato, peanut butter, mustard, mayonnaise and sweet chilli dressing	

Did You Know?

The largest sandwich ever made was a corned beef sandwich made by the staff of Wild Woody's Chill and Grill in Michigan, USA, in 2005. It weighed 5,440 pounds (388 stone, or 2,464 kg).

Types of sandwiches

- **Single sandwich**: Two slices of bread with spread and filling.
- **Double/club sandwich**: Three slices of bread and at least two fillings.
- **Toasted sandwich**: A single sandwich toasted under the grill or in a sandwich toaster.
- **Open sandwich**: Contains only one layer of bread, covered with filling and garnished attractively.
- Filled **pitta pockets, baps or wraps**.
- Filled **rolls, baguettes, ciabatta and paninis**.
- Thinly sliced crustless bread filled and rolled for parties.

Club sandwich

Wraps and single sandwiches

An open sandwich

Guidelines for making sandwiches

- Decide on bread type: white, brown, wholemeal, rolls, bagels, baguette, pitta, panini or ciabatta.
- Spreads (butter, low-fat, mayonnaise) provide a waterproof layer.
- Select fillings: combine two or more – be creative.
- Season well or add flavour with a dressing.
- Cut and wrap.
- Store in fridge if made night before.

Discovery Learning

Afternoon tea has become very popular for celebrations. Investigate what is offered for afternoon tea in two Irish hotels, then plan an afternoon tea menu for six people, containing a variety of sandwiches and sweet treats for a friend's birthday. Present your menu in a creative manner.

Revision Questions

1. List four guidelines for making successful packed meals.
2. Name five types of packing that can be used for packed meals.
3. Design a selection of sandwiches suitable for a buffet.

Summary

- A nourishing **breakfast** 'breaks the fast', gives you energy, helps with concentration and prevents accidents.
- In order to be balanced, breakfast should contain three out of the four major food groups.
- When serving breakfast on a **tray**, ensure everything is clean and positioned correctly for ease of use.
- **Packed meals** should be balanced, but use foods that are easy to pack and carry. Pack carefully and separate foods, placing heavy items at the bottom.
- **Sandwiches** are a popular option for packed meals and they come in a variety of types, including filled rolls, wraps, toasted and open sandwiches. Salads, soups and pasta dishes are also an option.

12 VEGETABLE, SALAD AND FRUIT GROUP

Learning Outcomes 1.1, 1.2, 1.3, 1.4, 1.5, 1.6, 1.7, 1.9, 1.12, 1.13, 1.14, 1.15, 1.16, 1.17, 1.18, 1.19 , 2.7

Vegetable, salad and fruit group

What I Will Learn

- to classify vegetables and fruit
- to discuss the nutritive and dietetic value of vegetables and fruit
- to explain how vegetables and fruit are graded within the EU
- to compile a set of guidelines to follow when buying, storing, preparing and cooking vegetables and fruit, in order to retain maximum nourishment
- to discuss the effects of cooking and processing on vegetables and fruit
- to explain how fruits and vegetables can be preserved to add variety to the diet
- to suggest ways to increase a person's fruit and vegetable intake
- to discuss the value of salads in the diet
- to compile a set of guidelines for making salads
- to explain how soups and sauces can add variety to the diet
- to classify soups and sauces
- to compose a set of guidelines for making soups and sauces
- to compare homemade soups/sauces with convenience soups/sauces

Key Words

✓ Pulses
✓ Legumes
✓ Grading
✓ Produce
✓ Organic
✓ Salads
✓ Purée
✓ Broth
✓ Consommé
✓ Liaison
✓ Preserves

Vegetables and fruit provide fibre. They are also low in calories and provide many important vitamins and minerals. It is important to eat five or more servings each day.

Don't Forget!
More is better from this food group!

Vegetables

Vegetables are versatile, nutritious foods that add a wide variety of colours, textures and flavours to the diet. They can be eaten raw or cooked and bought fresh or processed.

Classification of vegetables

Roots grow below ground 	Divided into: • **Roots:** Beetroot, carrot, parsnip, turnip • **Tubers:** Potatoes, sweet potato • **Bulbs:** Garlic, leek, onion, shallot, spring onion
Greens grow above the ground 	Divided into • **Leafy greens:** Cabbage, kale, lettuce, spinach • **Flowers:** Broccoli, Brussel sprouts, cauliflower • **Stems:** Celery, asparagus
Fruits are the fruits of a vegetable plant 	**Fruit:** Aubergine, courgette, cucumber, marrow, pepper, pumpkin and tomato
Pulses/legumes grow in pods and are often dried 	• **Beans:** Green, French, broad and runner • Lentils • Peas

Don't Forget!

Buy vegetables and fruits when they are in season (see p. 16) as they are at their best nutritionally and are cheaper to buy.

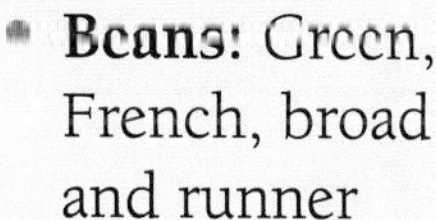

Did You Know?

Although often referred to as vegetables, mushrooms are fungi.

Legumes are the edible seeds which grow within the pods of leguminous plants, e.g. beans, peas and lentils. Usually only the seeds are eaten but sometimes the pod is too, e.g. green beans, mangetout and sugar snaps. They are among the most versatile and nutritious foods available and are invaluable in a vegetarian diet.

Don't Forget!

Dried seeds from pumpkins are healthy too.

Nutritive value of vegetables

- **Proteins:** Vegetables are generally not a good source of protein, except for pulses, which can be a good protein alternative for vegetarians.
- **Lipids:** Most vegetables lack fat, but it can be added during cooking, e.g. in stir-frying.
- **Carbohydrates:** Vegetables are an excellent source of fibre, especially if eaten raw and unpeeled, so they are great for a healthy digestive system. Some also supply a little starch and sugar for energy.
- **Vitamins:** Vegetables contain vitamin A for skin, membranes, eyes and growth, and vitamin C for general health.
- **Minerals:** Vegetables contain small amounts of calcium, iron and potassium.
- **Water:** The water content in greens and fruits is very high; there is less in roots and pulses, especially when dried.

Al dente means serving vegetables with a slightly crunchy texture.

Dietetic value of vegetables

- Vegetables are very versatile. They can be prepared and cooked in a variety of ways, adding colour, flavour and texture to the diet (**how?**). They are also available frozen, canned or dried.
- Cellulose in vegetables is an important source of dietary fibre, which adds bulk to the diet, preventing bowel disorders and filling you up for longer.
- Pulses are a good alternative to meat for vegetarians (**see p. 68**) as they are an important source of protein, especially in vegan diets (**why?**).
- Vegetables lack fat and are low in kilocalories, so they are useful in slimming and low-cholesterol diets.
- Fresh vegetables are cheap and plentiful when in season.
- Vegetables are a good source of vitamins and minerals and more nutritious when eaten raw or al dente.
- Vegetables high in starch, like potatoes, are a good source of energy.

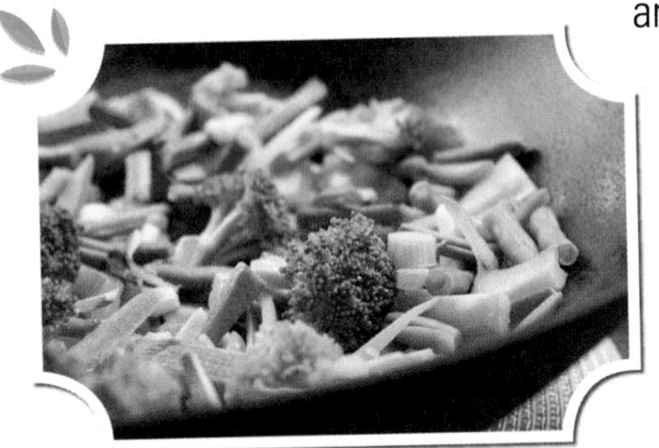

Culinary uses of vegetables

Vegetables can be used:

- as garnishes and decorations, e.g. tomato roses, spring onion sprigs, lemon slices
- for starters, e.g. stuffed mushrooms, Caesar salad
- as a snack, e.g. crudités and dips, salads, hummus (chickpea paste)
- in beverages such as veggie shakes, smoothies and juices, e.g. green smoothie, tomato or carrot juice
- in main courses, e.g. ratatouille, vegetable curry or stir-fry
- as an accompaniment, e.g. mashed potatoes, chips, roasted root vegetables, green salad
- in sauces, stocks and gravies, e.g. red wine jus, potato and leek soup
- in soups, e.g. potato and leek, carrot and orange, tomato
- in desserts and baking, e.g. carrot cake and chocolate beet cake
- for preserves (relishes, jellies, chutneys and pickles)

Fruit

Fruit is very nutritious – it contains many vitamins and minerals, as well as antioxidants, fibre and water. It also adds colour, flavour and texture to the diet.

Classification of fruit

Classification of fruit					
Berries	**Citrus**	**Dried**	**Hard**	**Stone**	**Others**
Blackcurrant	Grapefruit	Currant	Apple	Avocado	Banana
Blueberry	Lemon	Date	Pear	Apricot	Kumquat
Gooseberry	Lime	Fig		Cherry	Mango
Raspberry	Orange	Prune		Nectarine	Melon
Strawberry	Satsuma	Raisin		Peach	Passion fruit
	Tangerine	Sultana		Plum	Pineapple
					Rhubarb
					Star fruit

Nutritive value of fresh fruit

- **Proteins**: Only traces of protein are present; dried fruit is the best source.
- **Lipids**: Found in most fruits except avocados and olives.
- **Carbohydrates**: Not fruit contain sugar, starch, cellulose and pectin in varying amounts. Sugar is in all fruit in the form of sucrose, glucose and fructose. Starch is found in under-ripe fruit. Pectin is found in ripe fruit cell walls. Cellulose (fibre) is found in the cell walls, especially in pears, apples, oranges and melons.
- **Vitamins**: All fruit has vitamin C, especially blackcurrants, strawberries, citrus and kiwis. Yellow/orange/red fruit has beta-carotene (pro-vitamin A).
- **Minerals**: Small amounts of iron, calcium and trace elements. Bananas are good for potassium.
- **Water**: Very high in all fresh fruit; lower amount in dried fruit.

Dietetic value of fresh fruit

- A wide variety of fresh fruit is available throughout the year, adding a variety of colours, flavours and textures to the diet.
- Useful in low-calorie, low-cholesterol and high-fibre diets as it is high in water and fibre and low in fat.
- Can be eaten raw or cooked in a wide variety of sweet and savoury dishes.
- Fruit is a cheap and healthy snack that needs no preparation except washing and perhaps peeling.
- Vitamins and minerals protect against disease and help to maintain good health. Antioxidants vitamin C and beta-carotene help prevent disease, e.g. heart disease, cancer.
- High water content makes fruit a very refreshing food.

Culinary uses of fruits

Fruit can be used:

- As garnishes and decorations, e.g. strawberry fans, lemon butterflies
- For starters, e.g. fan of melon, stuffed avocado
- As a snack, e.g. apples and grapes
- In milkshakes and smoothies, e.g. strawberry milkshakes and banana smoothies
- In main courses, e.g. sweet and sour chicken
- In sauces, e.g. orange, plum sauce
- In desserts, e.g. apple crumble
- With a cheeseboard, e.g. grapes
- For preserves (jams, jellies, chutneys and pickles)

EU grading

All vegetables and fruit sold in Ireland must be correctly labelled and graded according to European Union regulations.

The **produce** must be sound (in good condition and blemish-free), relatively clean, chemical-free and graded according to size.

Labels must show:

- Quality or class
- Country of origin
- Variety

Classes

- Extra Class – best quality
- Class I – good quality
- Class II – marketable, but could have small defects

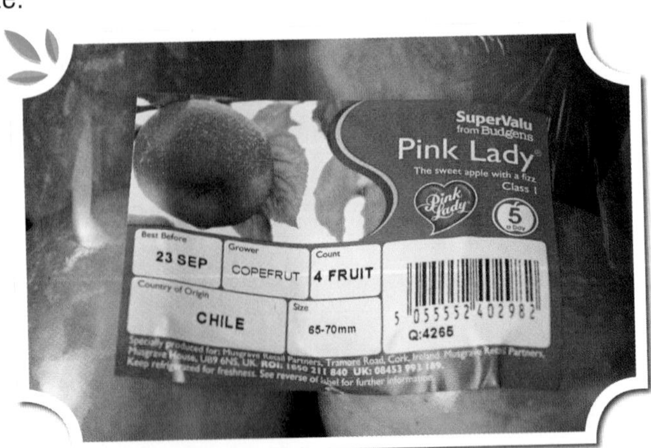

EU labelling on food packaging

Prices of fruit and vegetables depend on availability, demand, quality, production costs and the weather. Unusual fruit and vegetables are usually more expensive.

Produce is a general term for a group of farm-produced crops and goods, including fruits and vegetables, meats, grains and oats.

Organic fruit and vegetables are produced in a safe and sustainable way, producing healthy crops, while minimising damage to the environment. They avoid the use of artificial pesticides and chemical fertilisers but are often more expensive.

Further Investigation

To find out more about Irish food producers and their commitment to sustainability, visit **www.origingreen.ie**, or watch the video 'The World is Hungry for Food Sustainability - Saoirse Ronan (Origin Green)' (4:02) on YouTube.

Further Investigation

To find out more about organic farming, go to the website of the Department of Agriculture, Food & the Marine **www.agriculture.gov.ie**, click on 'Farming Sectors' under 'What We Do' on the home page, and then scroll down and click on 'Organic Farming'.

Discovery Learning

Find out what fruit and vegetables are **not** grown in Ireland. Then find out where they are grown and calculate the air miles they travel to get to Ireland.

If a food is **perishable**, it is likely to decay, rot or go off quickly.

Guidelines for retaining maximum nourishment

Vitamins and minerals are lost if fruit and vegetables are handled carelessly when buying, storing, preparing and cooking. To minimise nutrient loss, follow the guidelines below.

Buying fresh fruit and vegetables

- Buy usable amounts of good-quality fruit and vegetables when they are in season.
- Buy loose fruit and vegetables rather than pre-packed in plastic (**why?**).
- Root vegetables should be firm and heavy for their size, with no excess soil on them.
- Greens should be crisp and firm with tightly packed heads. They should be free of slugs.
- Pods should be green and firm, but not bulging.
- Medium-sized fruit and vegetables have the best flavour and texture.
- Look out for bruising, discolouration or mould growth.

Storing fresh fruit and vegetables

- Remove any plastic packaging.
- Root vegetables and some fruits like apples can be stored openly in a rack or basket, in a cool, dry place.
- Store green, pulse and fruit vegetables in the vegetable drawer of the fridge. Fruit like berries also need to be stored in a fridge.
- Fresh peas, beans and lettuce should be stored in a sealed bag or container in the fridge.

Preparing fruit and vegetables

- Use fresh fruit and vegetables – eat raw when possible.
- Remove any damaged or discoloured parts or wilted leaves.
- Wash well in cold water, but do not soak in water.
- Prepare shortly before use to prevent loss of vitamin C and discolouration.
- Avoid peeling fruit because the skin is a good source of fibre.
- If peeling, use a sharp knife or peeler and peel thinly.
- Slice, dice or chop with a sharp knife.

Did You Know?

Lemon juice will help prevent discolouration of prepared fruit. Can you find out why?

Cooking fruit and vegetables

- Eat raw when possible.
- Cover and cook quickly.
- Use a small amount of cooking liquid and use it to make a sauce or gravy.
- Cook for the shortest time possible.
- Avoid overcooking or keeping warm.

The effects of cooking fruit and vegetables

(**For recipes, see p. 238**)

- Eat raw if possible to avoid loss of vitamin C.
- Starch grains swell and burst and absorb liquid and become digestible.
- Cellulose softens, which in turn softens the texture.
- Some vegetables absorb water and swell.

Classroom-Based Assessment

This section can be linked to CBA1. Can you come up with a design for a storage bag for potatoes or onions that could be used in your kitchen? Use the Design Brief Process (**see p. 233**), be creative and use recycled materials. Don't forget to annotate your design!

- Minerals dissolve in cooking water.
- Vegetables lose colour, flavour and texture, so only cook for a short time.
- Micro-organisms are destroyed, so decay is delayed.

Did You Know?

Sweetcorn is a cereal, not a vegetable, although it is treated as one.

Preserving vegetables and fruit

Vegetables and fruit can be preserved in the following ways:

Process	Suitable vegetables	Suitable fruit	Advantages	Disadvantages
Freezing	Broccoli Carrots Peas Peppers Runner beans Sweetcorn	Berries Kiwi Melon	• Can be used for a wide variety of fruits and vegetables • Nutrients are unaffected • The foods retain good colour, texture and flavour • Frozen foods cook relatively quickly • Little preparation required • Little waste produced	• Must be stored in a deep freeze or freezer food compartment • Can be expensive
Canning and bottling	Beans Kidney beans Peas Runner beans Tomatoes	Grapefruit Mixed fruit Peaches Pears	• Can be used for a wide variety of fruits and vegetables • Relatively cheap • The food is already cooked, so it only needs reheating • Little preparation required • Little waste produced	• Loss of vitamin C • Minerals dissolve into the canning or bottling liquid • May contain artificial colours • There can be changes in flavour and texture
Dehydration (drying)	Chickpeas Lentils Peas Soya beans	Apricots Currants Prunes Raisins	• Can be used for a wide variety of fruits and vegetables • Relatively cheap • Has a long shelf life	• Vitamins are lost during the drying process • Must be soaked before cooking • Needs a longer cooking time • There can be changes in colour, flavour and texture

Don't Forget!

When buying tinned fruit, choose it in fruit juice rather than syrup.

Fruit and vegetables are also in preserves, e.g. in pickles, chutneys, relishes and jams (**recipes, see p. 238**).

Did You Know?

Making preserves is a great way of using up garden produce and ensuring that they are available out of season, e.g. jam and chutney. They also add a variety of flavours, colour and texture to the diet.

Discovery Learning

Some people need to increase their intake of fruit and vegetables every day. Suggest ways that they can do this. Design a poster, or a radio, TV or magazine advertisement to encourage people to eat more fruit and vegetables.

Salads

The best way to eat fruit and vegetables is raw, so salads are a really popular option as an accompaniment, snack, starter or light lunch. The nutritive value of a salad depends on the type and amount of ingredients used, e.g. green salad with raw ingredients will be rich in fibre, vitamins and minerals and low in fat, while a potato salad with mayonnaise would be higher in fat and lower in minerals.

Pasta salad

Quinoa salad

Suitable ingredients
Most **vegetables** used in salads are raw, e.g. carrots, celery, cucumber, spring onions, lettuce, radishes, tomatoes, rocket, spinach and cress. Cooked vegetables, like beetroot, peas, sweetcorn and potatoes, can also be used.
Fruits like apples, grapes, raisins, berries and bananas are used.
Other ingredients that can be used include: cheese, rice, pasta, couscous, quinoa, seeds, nuts, eggs, fish and meats.
Dressings: Mayonnaise, vinegars, vinaigrette dressings, yoghurt, crème fraiche, citrus juices.

Nutritive value of salads

(For recipes, see p. 238)

- Salads are a very good source of vitamins, minerals and fibre.
- Salads are refreshing, cool and tasty, especially in hot weather.
- Salads are low in calories, so they are useful in a low-fat diet. Don't forget to use low-fat dressings.
- Salads add variety, colour and texture to the diet.
- Protein foods can be added to make them more nourishing and filling, e.g. chicken, tuna or eggs. Carbohydrate-rich foods like rice, cous cous, potato and pastas make them more filling too.
- Salads are easy to prepare, require little cooking – which will save on fuel – and are useful in emergencies.
- Salads are useful in vegetarian and high-fibre diets.
- Salads can use up leftovers and prevent waste.

Discovery Learning

Design a salad suitable for a packed lunch for (a) an active teenager who is a vegetarian, and (b) a woman working in an office.

Guidelines for preparing salads

- Use really fresh ingredients and prepare just before serving.
- Cover and refrigerate until required.
- Wash salad vegetables gently under cold running water, then trim and spin in a salad spinner.
- Vegetables should be firm before cooking.
- Use herbs, seeds, nuts and seasonings to add contrasts in flavour and texture.
- Arrange ingredients attractively in a bowl or dish – do not over garnish.
- Serve salads with a dressing separately on the side or added just before serving.

Revision Questions

1. Give three reasons why vegetables and fruit are important in the diet.
2. Outline the nutritive and dietetic value of vegetables and fruit.
3. Explain how vegetables and fruit are graded within the EU.
4. Compile a set of guidelines to follow when buying, storing, preparing and cooking vegetables and fruit to retain maximum nourishment.
5. State the effects of cooking and processing on vegetables and fruit.
6. Outline the value of salads in the diet.
7. Compile a set of guidelines for making salads.

Soups and sauces

Soups are one of the most versatile, nourishing and widely available foods in our diet. Soup is a liquid food made from stock with vegetables and possibly meat or fish. Soups are used as a starter or snack, for lunch or as part of a dinner menu. They can be served hot or cold. Homemade soups should be made with good stock.

Stock is a well-flavoured liquid used as a base for soups and sauces.

Stock

Stock is made by gently simmering a combination of fresh ingredients (bones, meat, fish, herbs and vegetables) in a liquid until soft. When the liquid is drained off, it is used as a base for soups and sauces. It can be stored in the refrigerator for two to four days, or frozen in ice-cube trays for up to three months.

Guidelines for making stock

- Use fresh – preferably raw – vegetables rather than preserved or processed vegetables.
- Use a heavy-based saucepan or a pressure cooker to cook your stock.
- Simmer the stock gently; do not boil as it will make the stock cloudy and unattractive.
- Skim the top of the stock frequently to remove scum and fat, which affect the clarity of the stock.
- Do not use starchy or fatty foods, milk or green vegetables as they cause the stock to sour more readily.

Convenience stocks

A range of stocks in cube, gel or granular form are available in the shops. Flavours include beef, chicken, fish, vegetables and herbs, e.g. garlic and parsley. Convenience stocks are usually high in salt. Dried organic stocks and gluten-free varieties are also available.

Reasons for including soup in the diet

- To stimulate the appetite and aid digestion when used as a starter.
- To provide warmth on a cold day.
- To add nutritive value, as soups made from fresh ingredients are a source of protein, vitamins, minerals and fibre, and are free from artificial flavours, colours and preservatives.
- To add variety to the diet, as soups vary in consistency, flavour and texture.
- They can be served hot in winter, e.g. mixed vegetable, or chilled in summer, e.g. gazpacho.
- Useful as a snack, a starter or for lunch.
- Vegetable soups made without the addition of fat or thickening agents are useful to add bulk to low-cholesterol or slimming diets.

Nutritive value

The nutritive value of a soup depends on the ingredients used. A thick soup with meat or fish and plenty of vegetables will provide more protein and fibre than a thinner soup with more water and less vegetables. Do not overcook because it destroys the vitamins and minerals.

Characteristics of a good soup

- ✓ Free of grease
- ✓ Has a good colour and texture
- ✓ Tastes of the main ingredient, e.g. carrot and orange, tomato, mushroom
- ✓ Has the right consistency
- ✓ Well seasoned
- ✓ Served piping hot or chilled

Classification of soups

Thin soups

Clear soup: based on a concentrated clear stock, e.g. consommé
Broth: a clear soup with finely chopped meat and vegetable, e.g. chicken broth

Thick soups

Purée: Blended or sieved soups with a smooth consistency and texture, e.g. potato and leek
Thickened: contains a thickening agent (liaison), e.g. mushroom

Guidelines for preparation and cooking of soups

- Use a heavy saucepan with a well-fitting lid
- Use fresh good-quality ingredients
- Dice and finely chop ingredients to release maximum flavour
- Sauté ingredients to improve the flavour
- Use fresh stock if possible
- Blend thickening agents well and whisk into soup
- Simmer soup gently to develop flavour
- Season well and taste before serving
- Serve either piping hot or chilled

Discovery Learning

A bouquet garni is sometimes used to flavour a soup. Can you find out what it is?

Thickening soups

Liaisons are used to thicken soups and to hold ingredients in suspension so they do not sink to the bottom, e.g. starch such as cornflour, flour or arrowroot, cereals like pasta or pearl barley, eggs and cream or a **roux**, which is made of equal amounts of fat and flour (25 g to one litre of liquid in soup).

Don't Forget!

Soup-making can be sped up considerably by using a food processor in the preparation and a pressure cooker to cook.

Convenience soups

A wide variety of dried, canned, cook-chill and frozen soups are available in most supermarkets.

Advantages of convenience soups	Disadvantages of convenience soups
1. Good variety available	1. Expensive
2. Quick to make, saves fuel and time	2. May contain artificial colours, flavours and preservatives
3. Useful in emergencies	3. May be high in salt
4. Cans and packets have a long shelf life	4. Lower nutritional value
5. Can be used to thicken and flavour casseroles and stews	

12.7

Did You Know?

Recipes should always state how the garnish is presented, e.g. chopped, finely chopped, julienne, swirled, grated, etc.

Garnishes and accompaniments for soups

Garnishes	Accompaniments
Fresh herbs: chives, parsley **Julienne of vegetables:** carrot, cucumber **Cream:** a small spoonful of sour cream, yoghurt or crème fraiche **Croutons:** fried cubes of bread **Chopped bacon:** scattered over soup **Orange or lemon rind:** Finely grated **Grated cheese**, e.g. Parmesan, Gruyère	**Bread:** Garlic bread, sage and onion bread, slices of wholemeal or soda bread, French baguette **Rolls or dinner buns:** yeast buns, tomato rolls **Melba toast:** very thin slices of toasted bread

Sauces

A sauce is a well-flavoured liquid that is used to enhance the appearance, colour or flavour of food. It should not overpower the main ingredient of the dish. Sauces can be served hot or cold, be sweet or savoury and add variety to the diet.

Sauces are used to:

1. Aid digestion
2. Enhance the flavour of bland foods
3. Introduce new flavours, colour and textures
4. Counteract the richness of some dishes, e.g. apple sauce with pork
5. Moisten dishes

6. Improve the nutritional value of a dish but this depends on the ingredients used
7. Add variety and interest to the diet:
   - as accompaniments, e.g. cranberry sauce with turkey
   - as a main part of the dish, e.g. stews, lasagne
   - to coat fish, meat or vegetables, e.g. cheese sauce on cauliflower (au gratin)
   - to bind ingredients together, e.g. panards

Classification of sauces

(Food groups, see p. 54)

Class	Principles	Example
Simple	Fruits or vegetables are stewed or puréed to give a smooth texture	• Apple sauce • Cranberry sauce
Roux-based	Equal quantities of flour and fat, and varying amounts of liquid; brown or white in colour	• Parsley sauce • Cheese sauce • Béchamel sauce
Egg-based	Eggs thicken sauce by emulsification or coagulation	• Mayonnaise • Hollandaise • Custards
Cold sauces and dressings	Combining cold ingredients; no cooking involved	• French dressing • Mint sauce
Sweet sauces	Served hot or cold with desserts/puddings	• Chocolate sauce • Toffee sauce • Raspberry coulis
Others	Variety of methods and ingredients	• Curry sauce • Tomato sauce • Bread sauce

Roux-based sauces

(For recipes, see p. 238)

A roux-based sauce consists of equal amounts of flour and fat with **varying amounts** of liquids.

Type	Flour	Fat	Liquid
Pouring	25 g	25 g	500 ml
Stewing	25 g	25 g	375 ml
Coating	25 g	25 g	250 ml
Binding	25 g	25 g	125 ml

Further Investigation

To see a demonstration of how to make a béchamel sauce (a roux-based sauce, also known as white sauce), go to **www.bbcgoodfood.com**, search for 'Make béchamel', and watch the video 'How to make béchamel (white sauce)' (3:58).

Method of making a roux-based sauce

1. Melt the fat in a heavy-based saucepan. Add the flour and cook gently for one minute.
2. Remove from the heat and allow to cool slightly.
3. Gradually add the liquid a little bit at a time, stirring well between each addition.
4. Return the pot to the heat and stir until the roux comes to a boil. Turn down the heat and simmer gently for around five minutes until glossy.
5. Taste and adjust the seasoning as required.

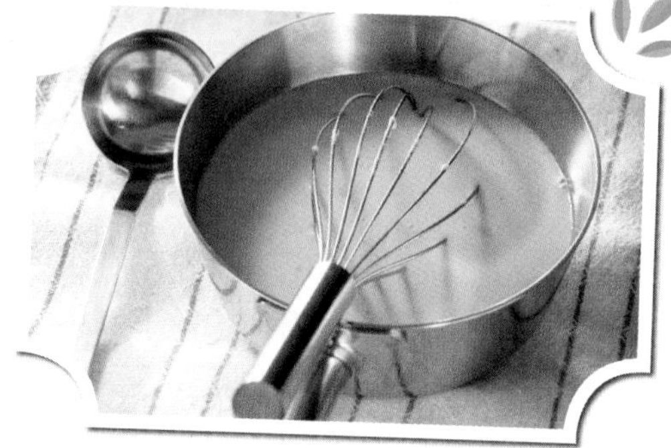

Guidelines for preparation and cooking of sauces

- Use a heavy-based saucepan
- Use fresh ingredients in the correct proportions, especially for roux-based sauces
- Use milk or stock as the liquid for additional flavour
- Ensure the sauce is the correct consistency
- Season well and taste before serving
- Serve hot sauces piping hot and serve cold sauces chilled
- A sauce can be thickened using a roux base, an egg yolk or by reduction during the cooking process

Discovery Learning

You can take a basic white sauce and use it in many ways by adding different ingredients. Find as many variations as you can, then find a recipe using each one.

Characteristics of a good sauce

- ✓ Has the right consistency and texture for the sauce type
- ✓ Free of lumps
- ✓ Free of grease
- ✓ Has a good colour
- ✓ Well-cooked
- ✓ Well-flavoured

Presentation and serving sauces

- Sauces may be served piping hot or chilled.
- They can be part of the dish or served separately on the side, in a sauceboat or ramekin.
- Sauce can be served over or under foods like chicken or fish.
- It's important not to cover food entirely with sauce.
- Sweet sauces (e.g. fruit coulis, chocolate, crème anglais) served with desserts can be used to make the dish aesthetically pleasing, adding variety and texture to a meal.

A **coulis** is a thick sauce made from puréed and strained vegetables or fruit, used to garnish a savoury dish or decorate a sweet dish.

Revision Toolkit

Presentation of dishes is very important, and will be a factor considered in the Practical Food Skills examination. Choose your garnish or decoration carefully and practise presenting your dishes beforehand. Remember to clean the edges of your dishes before serving.

Did You Know?

A sauce can be prepared in advance. To store, dampen a piece of greaseproof paper and place directly on the surface of the sauce to prevent a skin from forming. The sauce can then be reheated when needed.

Further Investigation

Visit **www.dressings-sauces.org** for lots of recipes and ideas for using sauces and dressings.

Convenience sauces

A wide variety of dried, bottled and chilled sauces are available in most supermarkets.

Advantages of convenience soups	Disadvantages of convenience soups
• Good variety available • Quick to make; saves fuel and time • Useful in emergencies • Cans, jars and packets have a long shelf life • Useful if part of a complicated dish, e.g. lasagne	• Expensive • May contain artificial colours, flavours and preservatives • May be high in sugar and salt • Lower nutritional value

Classroom-Based Assessment

Practise cooking dishes using fruit and vegetables and modifying them to meet the needs of individuals with special diets (CBA 2).

Revision Questions

1. Explain why we use soups and sauces in the diet.
2. Compare a homemade soup with a convenience soup.

Summary

- **Vegetables** are classified as roots, greens, fruit and legumes/pulses.
- **Nutritive value**: Vegetables are high in water, fibre, vitamins C and A, calcium and iron, but low in protein and fat. In the diet they add colour, flavour and texture. The pulses provide protein in vegan diets and are useful in low-fat diets. The fibre and vitamins keep the body healthy.
- **Fruits** are classified as berries, citrus, hard, dried, stone and others.
- **Nutritive value**: Fruits are high in water, fibre, vitamins C and A, calcium and iron, but low in protein and fat. In the diet they add colour, flavour and texture. They are cool and refreshing and useful in vegan and low-fat diets.
- Vegetables and fruits are **graded** and **labelled** according to class, origin and variety.
- **Price** depends on availability, demand, quality, production costs and the weather. Unusual fruit and vegetables are usually more expensive, as is organic produce.
- To **prevent nutrient loss**, buy fresh, good quality, medium sized and in usable quantities. Avoid prepacked produce. Store in a basket in a cool place or in a salad box in the fridge. When preparing, wash well to remove chemicals and dirt, remove damaged parts, avoid peeling or use a peeler to peel off in a thin layer and don't soak. Prepare shortly before cooking. When cooking, cook quickly, cover and use the cooking liquid, if possible.
- **Effects** of cooking on vegetables and fruit: cellulose softens, starch grains burst, liquid is absorbed and vitamins and minerals are lost.
- Both can be **preserved** by freezing, canning, bottling and drying. Preserves like jam, chutney, relishes and pickles add flavour, colour and texture to the diet. They also avoid waste by using vegetables or fruits out of season.
- **Increase your intake** of fruit and vegetables by including them in all meals, adding them to cereals, yoghurt, juices and smoothies, and into soups, salads and sauces.

- **Salads** are a good source of fibre, vitamins and minerals and are useful in vegetarian, diabetic and low-fat diets. Wash all vegetables well, slice and arrange attractively, prepare just before serving and use a dressing to add flavour.
- **Stock** is a well-flavoured liquid used in soups and sauces. It is made by gently simmering a combination of fresh ingredients (bones, meat, fish, herbs and vegetables) in a liquid until soft. When the liquid is drained off, it is used as a base for soups and sauces. It is valued for its flavour rather than its food value.
- **Soups** are one of the most versatile, nourishing and widely available foods in our diet. They are a liquid food made from stock with vegetables and possibly meat or fish. Soups are used as a starter or snack, for lunch or as part of a dinner menu. They can be served hot or cold.
- Soups are classified into **thin**, e.g. consommé and broth, and **thick**, e.g. purée and thickened.
- **Liaisons** are used to thicken soups and to hold ingredients in suspension so they do not sink to the bottom, e.g. starch such as cornflour, cereals like pasta or pearl barley, eggs and cream, or a **roux**, which is made of equal amounts of fat and flour.
- **Sauces** add variety, nourishment, moisture, flavour, colour and texture to the diet. They can form part of the dish or can be served separately.
- **Convenience** soups and sauces come cook-chilled, dried and frozen. There is a good variety available, they are quick to make so save fuel and time and can be useful in emergencies. However, they can also be high in sugar and salt, and lack fibre. They often contain additives and preservatives and are usually more expensive.

13 WHOLEMEAL CEREALS AND BREADS, POTATOES, PASTA AND RICE GROUP

Learning Outcomes 1.2, 1.3, 1.4, 1.5, 1.6, 1.7, 1.9, 1.12, 1.13, 1.14, 1.15, 1.16, 1.17, 1.18, 1.19, 2.10, 3.4

What I Will Learn

- to classify cereals and give examples of each type
- to discuss the nutritive and dietetic value of cereals
- to explain how cooking affects cereals
- to describe the structure of a cereal grain
- to examine wheat and wheat products
- to examine potatoes and potato products
- to examine rice and rice products
- to describe products made from a variety of cereals
- to state the advantages of home baking
- to propose a set of guidelines for home baking
- to identify the basic ingredients used in home baking
- to make cakes and breads using a variety of methods
- to devise a set of guidelines for making pastry
- to compare home baking with commercial products

Key Words

- ✓ Staple
- ✓ Wheat
- ✓ Rice
- ✓ Maize
- ✓ Oats
- ✓ Barley
- ✓ Rye
- ✓ Germ
- ✓ Endosperm
- ✓ Bran
- ✓ Husk
- ✓ Gluten
- ✓ Milling
- ✓ Refined
- ✓ Fortification

Wholemeal cereals and breads, potatoes, pasta and rice group

Foods on this shelf are the best energy providers for your body, so the more active you are, the more you need.

Choose any six or more servings each day for all ages, and up to 12 servings if you are active. Body size will also affect the number of servings a person should have per day.

Discovery Learning

Look after our environment: Find out what groups of people should increase their servings from this group and explain why this is the case.

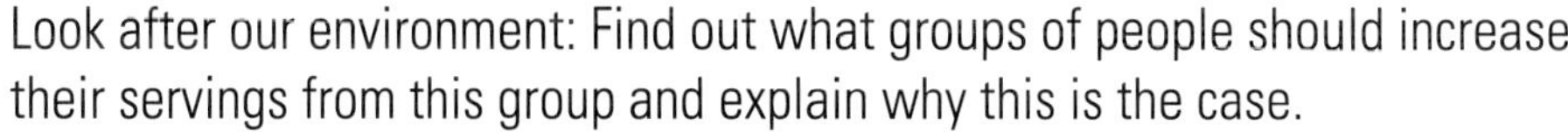

Cereals

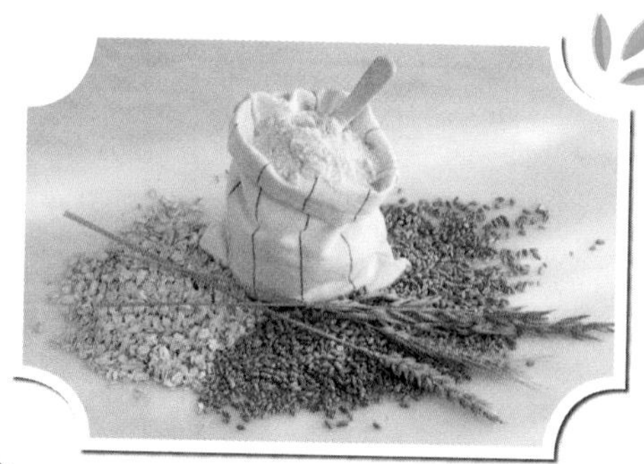

Cereals are the **staple** food of many countries, because they form the major part of carbohydrate intake in the diet, about 33% of our energy intake. They are the grains of cultivated grasses, which are cheap and easy to grow whatever the climate.

The main cereals we use are:

- wheat
- rice
- maize (corn)
- oats
- barley
- rye

A **staple food** is plentiful and the main part of the diet in a country, e.g. rice in Asia, bread and pasta in Europe.

Discovery Learning

Many food products are made from the six cereals named. List as many products as you can that are made from each of them.

Nutritive value

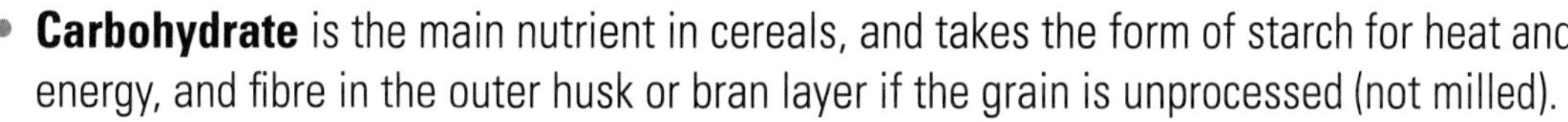

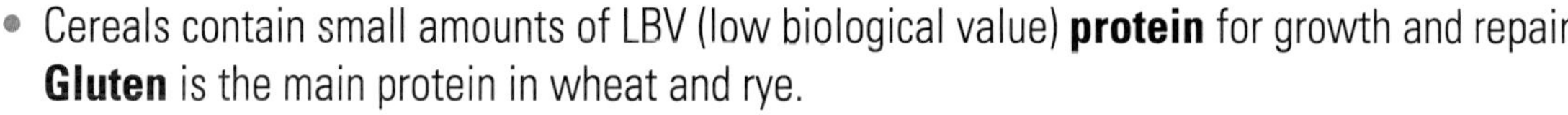

- **Carbohydrate** is the main nutrient in cereals, and takes the form of starch for heat and energy, and fibre in the outer husk or bran layer if the grain is unprocessed (not milled).
- Cereals contain small amounts of LBV (low biological value) **protein** for growth and repair. **Gluten** is the main protein in wheat and rye.
- There is a small amount of polyunsaturated **fat** present in cereals, mainly in the germ.
- Cereals are an important source of B-group **vitamins**, but processing removes these. Vitamin E is present in the germ of the grain.
- **Minerals** in cereal grains include calcium, iron and some phosphorus.
- Low **water** content means cereals have good keeping qualities and a long shelf life.

Dietetic Value

- Cereals are readily available, versatile and cheap to produce and buy.
- They are rich in starch so are an important energy food for all age groups.
- When unprocessed (wholegrain), they are rich in fibre which aids digestion (**how?**).
- They provide unsaturated fat which helps prevent cholesterol build up.
- Wholegrains are a good source of vitamin B (energy release), calcium (healthy bones and teeth) and iron (blood) so are good for vegetarians.
- **Coeliacs** have an intolerance to gluten, so must avoid wheat, oats, barley and rye.
- Cereals are easy to store, prepare and cook with no waste.

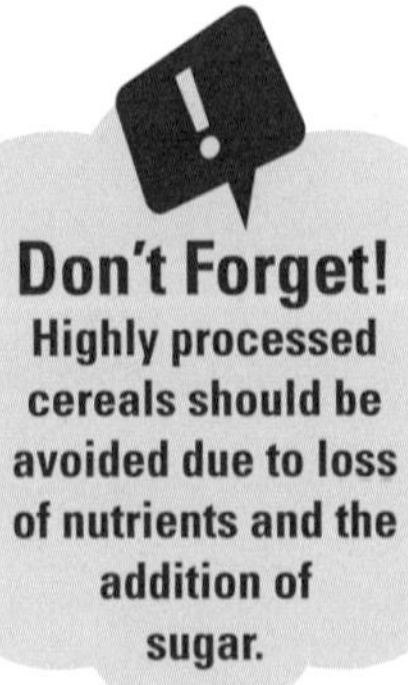

Don't Forget!
Highly processed cereals should be avoided due to loss of nutrients and the addition of sugar.

Did You Know?

The healthiest starchy foods are those that are high in fibre. For most starchy foods, there is a high-fibre version you can choose. So try out brown rice, wholemeal pasta and wholegrain bread instead of white rice, white pasta and white bread. Wholegrain breakfast cereals (including porridge) and baked potatoes eaten with their skins are great for fibre, too.

Effects of cooking on cereals

- The cellulose softens and starch becomes **more digestible**, e.g. cooked rice or pasta becomes soft and easier to digest.
- Moist heat causes starch grains to **burst**, **absorb** moisture and **thicken** liquids, e.g. roux sauces (**see p. 152**).
- Dry heat causes starch grains to **swell**, **burst** and **absorb** fats, e.g. pastry, popcorn.

Structure of cereal grain

All cereal grains have a similar structure. Wheat is the most widely grown cereal in the world.

- The **bran** or **husk** (14%) is the outer layer, and provides fibre, B-group vitamins and iron. It is usually removed during the processing of cereals. This process is known as 'refining'.
- The **endosperm** (84%) contains the energy store of the grain (mainly starch) and a protein called gluten. Coeliacs cannot absorb gluten.
- The **germ** (2%) contains protein, fat and Vitamin B and is the most nutritious part of the grain.

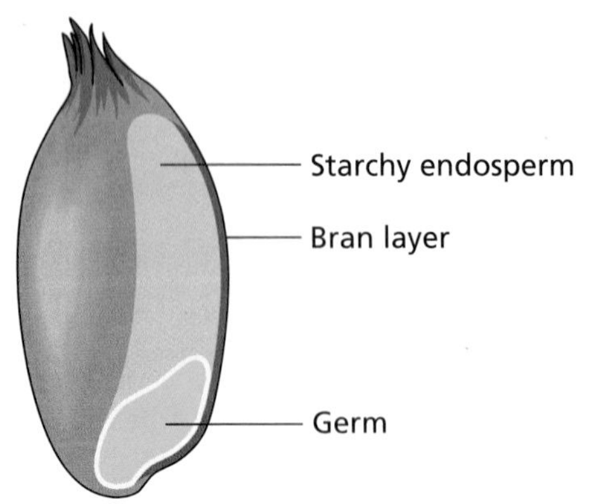

A wheat grain is composed of three main parts

Did You Know?

Gluten is the protein found in wheat and rye. It becomes stretchy when wet, which allows the dough to stretch when it is rising. Dough rises in the oven, as the gases (CO_2) expand, sets and forms a crust.

Flour

Flour can be made from rice, maize, oats and rye, but the most common type of flour is made from wheat.

To produce flour, the cereal grains are 'milled', or ground down. The production of white flour involves more refining than wholemeal flour (wholegrain), as the bran and germ are removed.

How flour is made

1–3. Grain is washed, dried and broken open between metal rollers. If the process stops here you have wholemeal flour.
4–5. Grain is sieved and rolled again and again, until the germ and bran are separated from the endosperm.
6–7. Air is blown through the flour to lighten it, and then extra ingredients are added to fortify it, e.g. calcium, B-vitamins. It may be bleached, too.
8. Finally, it is weighed and packed for sale.

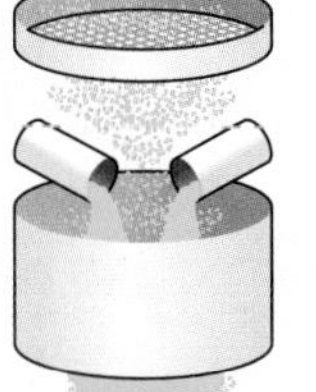

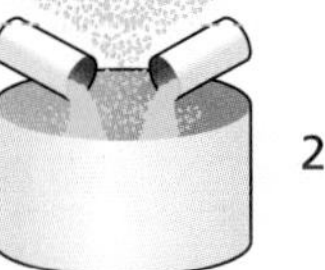

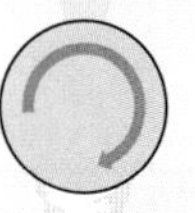

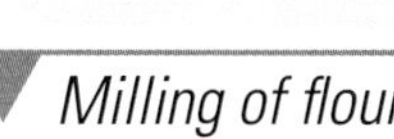
Milling of flour

A **refined** cereal product is processed by removing the bran and germ, e.g. white flour or white rice.
A product is **fortified** by adding back vitamins and minerals that were lost during processing to improve the nutritive value, e.g. breakfast cereals and milk.

Types of flour

Gluten-free flour	Starch is washed out, leaving behind the protein – gluten. This flour is used to make products for coeliacs.
Self-raising flour	Raising agents – sodium bicarbonate and cream of tartar – are added to flour to make it rise when cooked. These react to heat and moisture, producing carbon dioxide. It keeps for about two or three months.
Strong flour	High-gluten flour from spring wheat is used for yeast cookery and some pastries.
Wheatmeal/ brown flour (85% extraction)	Some bran removed, light in texture, brown in colour, less fibre and B-group vitamins, keeps for up to two months.
Wholemeal flour (100% extraction)	When none of the grain is removed, wholemeal flour is produced. It is light brown in colour, and an excellent source of B-group vitamins, protein and dietary fibre.
White flour (70-75% extraction) plain or cream	White flour is created when the bran and germ are removed, but the starchy endosperm and gluten remain. It contains B-group vitamins, may be fortified with calcium and iron and keeps for up to six months.

Don't Forget!
Coeliacs need to buy gluten-free products, which are labelled with this symbol (special diets, see p. 65).

Discovery Learning
Germ and bran are sold as separate products. Can you suggest ways of including them in the diet?

Further Investigation
To find out more about flour and home baking, visit **www.odlums.ie**. To learn the science behind how gluten in flour contributes to baking, watch 'Fun Kitchen investigates different flours for bread making for AQA' (6:47) on YouTube.

Bread

Bread is one of our staple foods. There is a wide variety of breads available from all over the world; a lot of larger supermarkets have in-store bakeries. Recently, there has also been a big increase in the popularity of bread-making at home.

Discovery Learning
Name as many different types of breads as you can – think about different countries, different grains and different flavours.

Further Investigation
To find out more about bread, watch 'How It's Made: Bread' (6:21) on YouTube.

Potatoes

Potatoes are another staple food rich in starch, so they are included in this food group even though potatoes are technically root vegetables. They are a very versatile ingredient and are used in many ways in the diet (recipes, see p. 238).

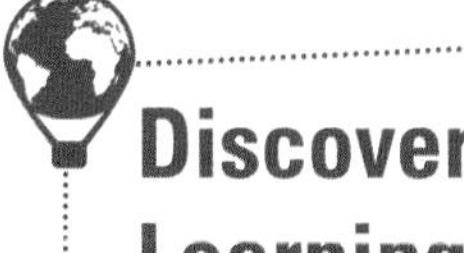

Discovery Learning
Name as many different potato dishes as you can.

Further Investigation
To learn more about the potato, visit **www.potato.ie**.

Pasta

Pasta is made from the endosperm (**semolina**) of durum wheat, which is mixed with water or egg to form a paste. The paste is pressed into different shapes and dried. Fresh pasta is partially dried and must be used within days. Dried pasta is fully dried and keeps for up to a year.

Brown pasta is made with wholegrain semolina.

Sometimes other ingredients are used to flavour and colour the pasta. Spinach is added to make green pasta (pasta verde), tomatoes are added to make it red, while squid ink makes pasta black. Fresh herbs like basil are also used.

Further Investigation
To find out how pasta is made commercially, watch 'How It's Made: Pasta' (3:44) on YouTube.

Discovery Learning
Find out the names of as many different pasta shapes as you can.

Rice

Rice is one of the world's most popular cereals and is grown in Asia, the USA and Italy. It contains less protein, fat and minerals than other cereals. Many varieties are now available, which can be used for a range of sweet and savoury dishes.

Type	Description	Uses
Short grain	Short fat grain with a tender, sticky texture when cooked, sometimes called Carolina rice	Sweet dishes, milk puddings
Medium grain	Narrow, between short and long grain rice, grown in Italy	Risotto, rice salads, puddings
Long grain	Very long, thin grain with a light, fluffy texture	Savoury dishes, e.g. serve with curry, Chinese dishes, casseroles
Brown	Some of the outer bran layer removed, takes longer to cook, rich in dietary fibre, minerals and vitamins	Casseroles, curries, rice salads
White	Germ and bran removed	Savoury dishes
Arborio	Plump rice with a soft, moist texture when cooked	Risotto
Basmati	Long grain rice grown in India, good aroma, flavour and texture	Indian and Middle Eastern dishes
Jasmine	Long grain rice with nice aroma and flavour	Savoury dishes
Easy-cook	Long grain rice that is steam treated so that it cooks quickly	Savoury dishes
Sushi	Short grain rice that is sticky and slightly sweet	Sushi and other Japanese dishes
Wild	Has a chewy outer sheath covering a nutritious grain inside and a nutty flavour. This type of rice grows on short stalks in shallow marsh water	Savoury dishes, pilau

Did You Know?

Wild rice has many health benefits. It improves digestion and heart health, and stimulates growth and repair of body cells, slowing down the signs of ageing. It also protects against diseases like diabetes, cancer and osteoporosis, and boosts the immune system, strengthens bones and aids weight loss. If you want to find out more about wild rice, watch the following video on YouTube: 'Nutritional Benefits of Wild Rice, A "Wild" and Cultivated Grain Alternative' (20:02).

Discovery Learning

Sushi has become very popular in Ireland. Find out what you can about Japanese cuisine and share your findings with the class.

Further Investigation

To find out how rice is produced, watch 'How It's Made: Rice' (4:18) on YouTube.

Seeds

Seeds include sesame seeds, sunflower seeds, linseeds, pumpkin seeds and poppy seeds.

They are important in the diet because they are rich in omega, fatty acids, fibre and vitamin E. They also add colour, texture and variety (**fats, see p. 28**).

Discovery Learning

Can you suggest a variety of ways to include seeds in your diet?

Breakfast cereals

- There is a wide variety of breakfast cereals made from different grains.
- They come flaked (corn, bran), shredded (wheat) and puffed (rice).
- Other ingredients are added, such as dried fruit, honey, nuts, cocoa, sugar and salt.
- They are often fortified with vitamins and minerals.
- The nutritive value depends on ingredients and the milk used.
- Porridge, muesli and high-bran cereals are good cereals to choose, as they are rich in fibre. Others are high in sugar and salt, and those should be avoided.

Revision Questions

Use your workbook to revise this chapter

1. Explain what a cereal is and name six types of cereal.
2. Outline the nutritive and dietetic value of cereals in the diet.
3. Explain how cooking affects cereals.
4. Write an informative note on two of the following: (i) potato, (ii) pasta, (iii) rice and (iv) seeds.

Home baking

Home baking refers to baking bread and cakes at home rather than buying baked products from the shops.

Home baking involves a lot of time and some skill, but has many **advantages**.

- Home-baked goods tend to have a better, fresher flavour.
- They often have a more attractive appearance than bought goods.
- Baking your own bread and cakes is usually cheaper than buying them in.
- Home-baked goods have no added preservatives.
- When you make your own bread and cakes, you can control the ingredients used in them.
- Home-baked goods are more nutritious than bought goods.

Guidelines for home baking

- Prepare your tins and oven shelves in advance.
- Preheat the oven to the correct temperature.
- Use fresh ingredients – so check expiry dates before you start.
- Weigh the ingredients accurately and follow the recipe carefully, especially if you are new to baking. With more experience, you will be able to modify and adapt recipes.
- Sieve the flour to add air.
- Be careful when you are adding liquid.
- Handle the ingredients, dough and batter as little as possible, and knead lightly.
- Once the dough or batter is in the tin, put it in the oven as quickly as possible.
- Time the baking carefully, and avoid opening the oven door during cooking.
- Test the bread or cake to see if it is cooked properly; if not, return to the oven.
- Cool the bread or cake on a wire tray.

Don't Forget!
Wash and dry equipment and work surfaces thoroughly. If any food remains on them, what could happen?

Basic ingredients for baking

Flour: Wheat flour is most commonly used because it contains gluten, but other types of flour can be used too.
Fat: Fat keeps bread fresh. Butter has the best flavour for baking, while margarine is more economical.

Sugar: Granulated or caster sugar can be used for sweetness, brown sugar adds a spicy flavour and icing sugar is used for decorating.
Eggs: Eggs are used to bind the mixture and to trap air. They should be fresh and at room temperature when used.
Fruit: Fresh or dried fruit can be used to add flavour.
Liquid: Water, milk and eggs are used to make a dough or batter.
Raising agent: Makes product light and spongy, can be natural, chemical or biological.

Raising agents

Raising agents make bread and cakes rise in the oven so that they have a spongy texture.

Raising agents put a gas (air and/or carbon dioxide) in the mixture. In the oven, the heat makes the gas expand, which pushes up the mixture. The mixture is able to stretch because of the gluten in the flour. After a while, the heat in the oven sets the gluten, so that the mixture keeps the risen shape.

Further Investigation

To find out more about how raising agents work, watch 'Fun Kitchen investigates how raising agents work for AQA' (9:31) on YouTube.

Classification of raising agents

Natural	Chemical	Biological
Air	Baking powder Bread soda	Yeast

Natural raising agent

Air: Air is used alone in sponge cakes and pastry or with another raising agent in other baked goods. Air is put into mixtures by:

- Sieving the flour
- Rubbing fat into flour
- Creaming sugar and fat
- Whisking eggs with sugar

Chemical raising agents

These depend on a chemical reaction to make the gas in the dough. An alkali and an acid react to make a gas called carbon dioxide (CO_2).

Baking powder: Baking powder contains both an **acid** and an **alkali**, which, when mixed and moistened with a liquid, produce a gas (CO_2) in the mixture. When the CO_2 is heated, it expands and rises, causing bread and cake mixtures to rise.

Don't Forget!
If you don't have buttermilk, just add a little lemon juice or vinegar to fresh milk.

Bread soda: Bread soda is an alkali that must be combined with an acid and moistened to produce CO_2. Buttermilk is an acidic liquid, so it is used with bread soda to produce CO_2 in the mixture. This, when heated in the oven, expands and rises, causing bread and cake mixtures to rise.

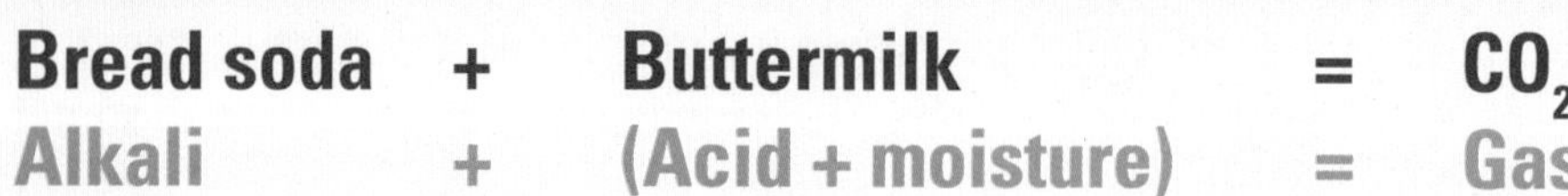

Biological raising agent

Yeast: Yeast is made of tiny living organisms that make CO_2 in the dough. In the oven, the bubbles of CO_2 expand and push up the dough, until the gluten sets the dough. The heat also kills the cells of the organism.

Oven temperature

Preheat the oven to the temperature indicated in the recipe before you put in the bread or cake. If the oven is too cool (under-heated), the gas escapes through the top of the mixture before it has time to set, so it does not rise. If the oven is too hot, the outside burns before the inside cooks fully.

How to prepare tins

Baking trays	• Sprinkle with flour for bread or plain scones • Brush with melted fat or oils, or line with greaseproof paper for biscuits or small cakes
Queen cake tins	• Brush with oil or use paper or tin foil cases
Cake tins	• Place a circle or square of greaseproof paper on base and grease the sides for a plain cake • Line the base and sides with greaseproof paper for a fruit cake
Sponge cakes	• Grease tin, then sprinkle with equal amounts of caster sugar and flour mixed together • Line bottom and sides of a swiss roll tin with greaseproof paper

Did You Know?

Silicone bakeware has become popular because it is lightweight, easy to clean, and does not rust or stain. You do not have to grease it, and it heats quickly and bakes evenly. Easy to remove, it is freezer, refrigerator, microwave, dishwasher and oven safe, so you can bake, store, freeze and reheat in the same container.

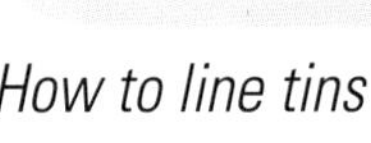

How to line tins

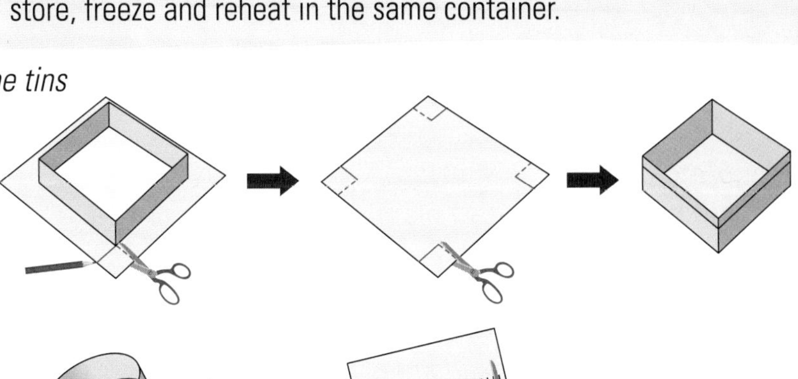

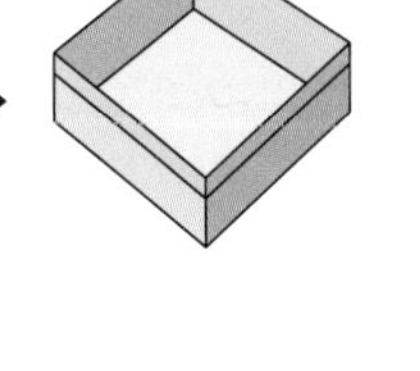

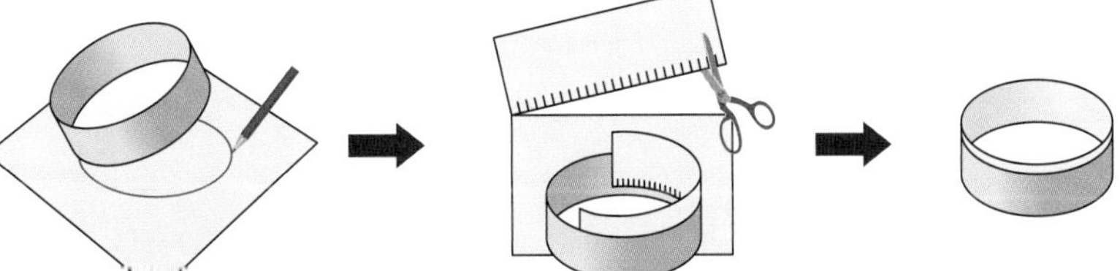

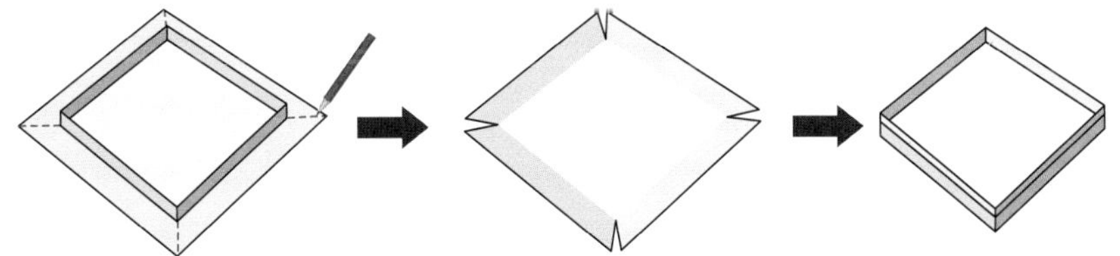

Methods for making breads and cakes

The ingredients may be combined in a variety of ways that influence the texture of the bread or cake.

Method	Explanation	Used for	
Rubbing in method	Fat and flour are lifted by the fingertips and rubbed high above the bowl until resembling breadcrumbs.	Scones, muffins, plain cakes and buns, shortcrust pastry, yeast bread, and shortbread biscuits	
Creaming method	Fat and sugar are beaten or creamed together until pale and there is no sugar at the bottom of the bowl. Then the liquid, eggs and flour are mixed in.	Queen cakes, muffins, cupcakes, madeira cakes, fruit cakes and biscuits	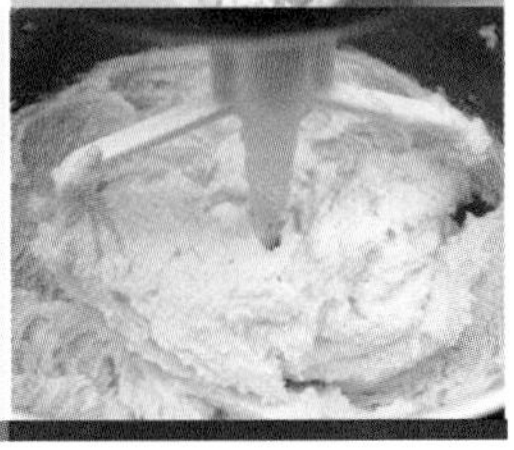

Method	Explanation	Used for
Whisking method	Eggs and sugar are whisked together until thick and foamy. Then flour is folded in.	Sponges, swiss rolls, flans, roulades and meringues
Melting method	All ingredients that can melt are melted together in a pot, then the mixture is added to the dry ingredients (add wet to dry and mix).	Gingerbread, boiled fruit cakes, choux pastry and some biscuits
All-in-one method	All the ingredients are placed in a bowl together and beaten.	Madeira, Victoria sandwich and plain cakes

How to check if it is cooked

Bread	Should have a hollow sound when tapped on the base.
Sponge	The surface springs back when pressed gently with a finger.
Cakes	A skewer inserted into the centre of the cake comes out clean.

Cake mixes

- Cake mixes are a mixture of flour, fat, sugar, raising agent, salt and additives that are sieved, blended and sealed in a packet.
- When buying a cake mix, check the expiry date and that it is sealed properly. Store in a cool place.
- When using a cake mix, follow the instructions when adding the liquid.

Advantages of cake mixes	Disadvantages of cake mixes
• Save time and labour • Simple to use • Quick in emergencies • Useful for beginners and children	• Expensive • Contain additives • Lack fibre and have too much salt and sugar

Pastry

- Pastry is a mixture of flour, fat and water, which is made into a dough, then kneaded, shaped and baked.
- It may be enriched by the addition of other ingredients, such as sugar, eggs or extra fat.
- Pastry may be used in sweet and savoury dishes.

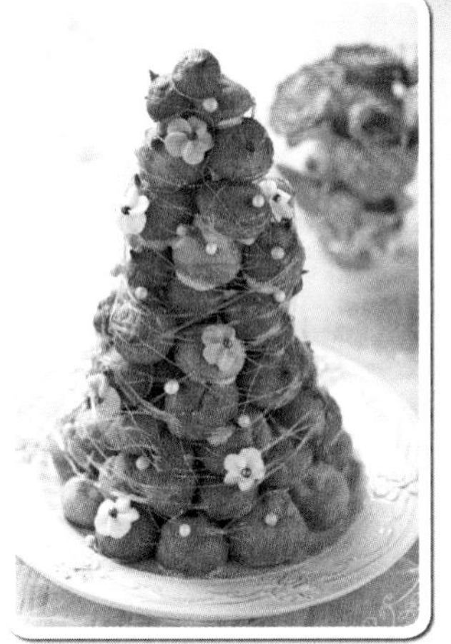

Types of Pastry	Uses
Shortcrust	Sweet and savoury tarts, pies, flans, sausage rolls
Rich shortcrust	Sweet tarts, flans, pies
Cheese	Cheese straws, biscuits, quiche, savoury flans
Wholemeal	Savoury flans, quiches, pies, tarts
Flaky/puff/rough puff	Pies, tarts, sausage rolls, millefeuille, vol au vents, mince pies
Choux	Profiteroles, éclairs
Filo	Spring rolls, savoury baskets, Baklava

Pastry ingredients

Flour: Plain flour should be used rather than self-raising flour, as it makes the pastry soft. Strong flour is suitable for richer pastries, e.g. flaky.

Fat: Butter gives good flavour, while margarine is economical and lard makes pastry light and crispy. A mixture of margarine and lard can be used. Suet is used in suet-crust pastry, while oil may be used in some shortcrust pastry recipes.

Water: Water should be cold and added a little at a time to make stiff pastry. Lemon juice can be added to the water to soften the gluten, making the pastry more elastic.

Raising agents: Air makes pastry rise, so the more air in the pastry, the better. Air is introduced by sieving, rubbing in, rolling and folding. Self-raising flour may be used for suet-crust pastry; alternatively baking powder can be added. Steam can also act as a raising agent in choux and in rich crust pastry.

Other ingredients: Eggs and ground almonds enrich pastry, while sugar sweetens it.

Did You Know?

If a recipe states 200 g of pastry, this refers to the amount of flour used. Shortcrust pastry is half fat to flour, so it would be 100 g fat to 200 g flour.

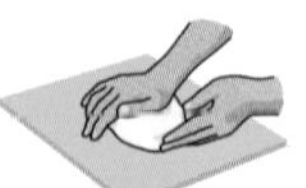
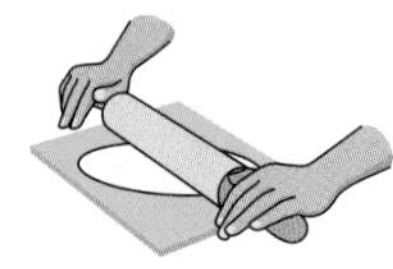

Rules for making pastry

- Weigh ingredients accurately and use the correct proportions.
- Keep the ingredients and utensils as cool as possible.
- Add the water carefully. Use just enough to bind the ingredients without becoming sticky.
- Mix with a knife and knead lightly on a floured board.
- Avoid over-handling.
- Roll pastry lightly and as little as possible.
- Avoid stretching pastry, as it will shrink during baking.
- Allow pastry to relax in a refrigerator before baking.
- Bake in a hot oven so that the starch grains in the flour burst and absorb the fat. Then reduce the heat to allow it to cook through so it has an even texture and is not shrunken or uneven.

Further Investigation

To find out more about pastry-making, techniques, tips, videos and recipes, visit **www.bbcgoodfood.com** and **www.deliaonline.com**.

Baking blind is baking a pastry case without a filling, e.g. for quiche or a fruit flan.

- The base of the case is pricked with a fork.
- Greaseproof paper is spread over the base and weighted down with dried beans or rice to prevent the pastry rising.
- The case is then baked for 15 minutes at 200°C.
- The paper and beans/rice are then removed and the case put back in the oven for a further five minutes to make the base crisp.

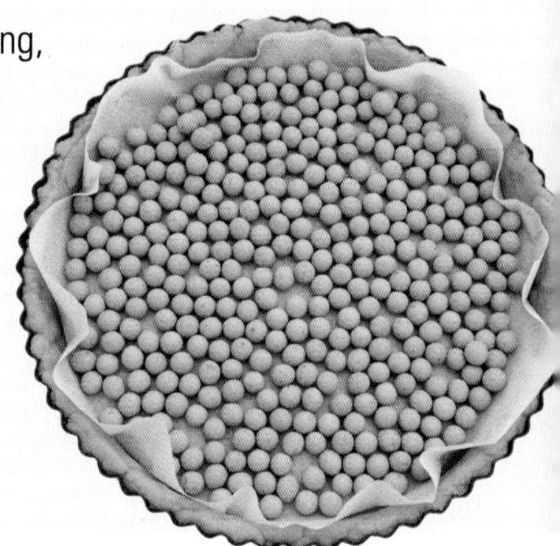

Revision Questions

1. List three guidelines to follow when baking at home.
2. State the advantages of home baking.
3. Name four raising agents, explain how one of them works and give examples of a use.
4. Identify the basic ingredients used in home baking.
5. Outline four methods of making cakes, giving an example of each one.
6. Classify pastry and give examples of dishes made with each type.

Summary

- **Wholemeal cereals and breads, potatoes, pasta and rice** are on the second shelf of the food pyramid and are the best **energy** providers for your body, so the more active you are the more you need. Choose between six and twelve servings each day – more if you are active – for all ages. They are a staple food in many countries.
- Cereals contain **starch, LBV protein, unsaturated fat, vitamin B, calcium and iron**. Wholegrain cereals also provide **fibre**. They are valuable in the diet because they are nourishing, cheap, filling, and easy to store and prepare. They can be high in calories.
- Cooking makes the cellulose in cereal soften, so starch becomes more **digestible**. Moist heat causes starch grains to burst, absorb moisture and thicken liquids, while dry heat causes starch grains to swell, burst and absorb fats.
- Cereal grains are composed of a **bran layer (husk), germ and endosperm**.
- **Gluten** is a **protein** in wheat. When wet it becomes elastic, allowing bread to rise and set in the oven. It cannot be digested by a coeliac.
- Wheat is **milled** to produce a variety of **flours**, including wholegrain, brown, strong, plain, self-raising and gluten-free. Other wheat products include pasta, couscous, bran, semolina and breakfast cereals.
- **Potatoes** and **rice** are popular in cooking.
- **Home baking** is usually cheaper, more appetising and has a better flavour than bought-in baking. Home-baked goods have **no artificial additives**.
- The **basic ingredients** used in baking are flour, fat, sugar, eggs, raising agents and flavourings.
- **Raising agents** make bread and cakes rise. They are air, baking powder, bread soda and yeast.
- The **guidelines for home baking** include: prepare tins and Preheat oven; use fresh ingredients; weigh accurately; follow recipe; sieve flour; add liquid carefully; handle as little as possible; place in oven quickly; time; test; and cool. Clean up all surfaces and equipment thoroughly.
- **Methods of making cakes** include **rubbing in** fat to flour (scones and bread), **creaming** sugar and fat (Madeira), **whisking** sugar and eggs (sponge), **melting** wet ingredients and mixing with dry (gingerbread), and just **mixing** all ingredients together.
- **Cake mixes** are a mixture of flour, fat, sugar, raising agent, salt and additives sieved blended and sealed in a packet. They are quick, useful for beginners and in emergencies, and produce little waste. However, they are expensive, contain additives, are high in sugar and salt, and are low in fibre.
- Types of **pastry** include shortcrust, filo, flaky, puff, suet and choux.
- The **guidelines for making pastry** include: weigh ingredients accurately and in proportion; keep everything cool; add water carefully; knead lightly; avoid over-handling; allow to relax; bake in a hot oven, then after 10 minutes reduce heat. Bake pastry case blind (without a filling) to keep it crisp.

14 MILK, YOGHURT AND CHEESE GROUP

 **Learning Outcomes** 1.1, 1.2, 1.3, 1.4, 1.5, 1.6, 1.7, 1.9, 1.12, 1.13, 1.14, 1.15, 1.16, 1.17, 1.18, 1.19, 2.7, 2.10

What I Will Learn

- to identify sources of milk
- to identify the nutritive value of milk and milk products
- to assess the importance of milk and milk products in the diet
- to discuss the effects of cooking and processing on milk
- to state how milk and milk products are used in cooking
- to describe how milk is processed
- to compile a set of guidelines for buying and storing milk and milk products
- to consider the role of milk alternatives in the diet
- to explain why some milk products, e.g. butter and cream, are not as healthy as others
- to describe how yoghurt and cheese are made
- to suggest ways of increasing our milk product consumption

Key Words

✓ Lactose
✓ Skimmed
✓ Pathogenic
✓ Homogenised
✓ Pasteurised
✓ Evaporated
✓ Condensed
✓ Rennet
✓ Ultra-high temperature
✓ Culture
✓ Coagulate
✓ Lactic acid
✓ Curds
✓ Whey

Milk, yoghurt and cheese provide calcium needed for healthy bones and teeth. Calcium is important for children, teenagers and older adults. Children aged nine to eighteen need five servings a day, while older and younger people require three servings each day.

When choosing foods from this shelf on the food pyramid, milk and yoghurt should be consumed more often than cheese as it can be high in saturated fat – especially full-fat cheese.

Discovery Learning

Skimmed milk is not suitable for children under five and low-fat milk is not suitable for children under two. Can you find out why?

Milk

Irish people drink more milk than most other people in the world. Milk is a refreshing drink that is full of nutrients. Cows are the most common source of milk, but milks from sheep, goats, buffalo and camels are also used in some cultures. Soya, coconut and almond milk are increasing in popularity, though they are not technically 'milk'. Infants can live on milk alone for the first six months of their lives. Milk is used to manufacture butter, cream, yoghurt and cheese.

Nutritive value

- Milk is a good source of HBV **protein**, which is needed for growth and repair of cells.
- **Fat** in milk is an easily digested saturated fat, so it is a suitable drink for children, invalids and the elderly. It also provides heat and energy. When milk is skimmed, most of the fat is removed.
- The **carbohydrate** in milk is in the form of a sugar called lactose, which provides heat and energy.
- **Calcium** is the main mineral in milk, which contributes to healthy bones and teeth. It also contains **phosphorus**.
- Milk contains **vitamin B** for a healthy nervous system. The fat-soluble **vitamin A** is needed for growth, and healthy eyes, skin and membranes and **vitamin D** is needed for healthy bones and teeth.
- Milk contains a large amount of **water**.

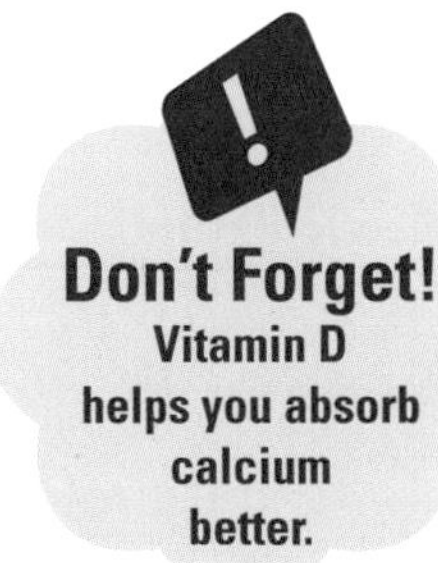

Don't Forget!
Vitamin D helps you absorb calcium better.

Dietetic value

- Milk is a nourishing food because it contains many nutrients. It is important in the diets of toddlers, children and adolescents, as well as pregnant and nursing mothers.
- It is relatively cheap and readily available in a variety of types.
- It is easily digested and necessary in the diet of invalids and older people.
- Skimmed milk is suitable for those on a low-kilocalorie diet, but it is not suitable for children as it **lacks** vitamins A, D and fat.
- Milk is available fortified with vitamins A and D, calcium, iron, folic acids and omega-3 fatty acids, e.g. Supermilk.
- As milk is lacking in iron, fibre, starch and vitamin C, it is best combined with cereals and fruit to provide a balanced meal.

Fortified milk

Uses of milk

Milk is a very versatile food with many culinary uses:

- **Drinks:** Milkshakes, coffee, hot chocolate
- **Sauces:** White roux and custards
- **Enriching dishes:** Soup, mashed potatoes
- **Milk-based desserts:** Milk puddings, custard dishes

- **In baking:** Bread, scones
- **Batters:** Pancakes, coating, Yorkshire pudding
- **Glazing:** Baked goods

Effects of heat on milk

- Loss of vitamins C and B group.
- Flavour is changed.
- Bacteria are destroyed.
- Protein coagulates and forms a skin on the surface of milk. Steam builds up under this skin and causes the milk to boil over.

Buying and storing milk

Milk is a perishable food that is easily infected by bacteria, which can lead to food poisoning. Store milk safely using the guidelines below.

- Check the expiry date before buying and do not mix milks of different dates, e.g. topping up a milk jug.
- Keep out of sunlight as vitamins will be lost and it will sour quickly.
- Keep milk and dairy products cool, clean and covered in a container or a clean jug. Store in a refrigerator.
- Keep away from strong-smelling food.

Milk processing

Milk is processed, i.e. homogenised, to improve its flavour and make it safe to drink by destroying **pathogenic** bacteria, e.g. during pasteurisation and other heat treatments. This all helps to increase the shelf life of milk.

Pathogenic means disease-causing bacteria.

Homogenisation

Milk is homogonised to distribute the fat. This makes the milk creamier before it is heat treated.

Heat treatments

All milk on sale in Ireland is heat treated in some way, usually by **pasteurisation** or **UHT sterilisation**

Pasteurisation	• Milk is heated to 72°C for 25 seconds, then cooled rapidly and packed in bottles and cartons. • It does not alter the flavour, but kills harmful bacteria. • Pasteurised milk lasts three to four days in the fridge.
Ultra-high temperature (UHT) sterilisation	• Milk is heated to a high temperature of 132°C for one to three seconds, then cooled rapidly and packed in sterile containers. • There is a change in flavour, all bacteria are killed and vitamins C and B are destroyed. • Sealed cartons don't need refrigeration and keep for months.

Type of milk		Uses
Whole milk	Nothing added or taken away, just homogenised and pasteurised. This is the most popular type of milk in this country.	Recommended for young children
Low-fat milk	Over half the fat is removed.	Adults, low-cholesterol and low-kilocalorie diets
Skimmed milk	Almost all fat removed.	As above
Fortified milk	(Super) with extra vitamins and minerals added.	Suitable for everyone, especially for those at risk of bone disease.
Long-life milk	UHT. If unopened, it keeps for months.	Good for camping, on planes and in warm countries
Buttermilk	The acidic liquid that is left over after butter is made.	Used for baking
Flavoured milk	Flavourings like vanilla, chocolate and strawberry are added.	Suitable for children but can be high in sugar
Dried	All moisture removed, keeps for a long time in a sealed container.	Useful for camping, baby milk and in emergencies
Evaporated	Some water removed, sterilised and sealed in a can. Keeps for over a year.	Desserts and baking
Condensed	Some water removed, sugar added, sterilised and sealed in a can. Keeps well.	Desserts and baking

Milk substitutes

- People who are **lactose intolerant** cannot convert lactose (milk sugar) to glucose. For this reason, **lactase** is added to milk to convert it before consumption.
- Milk is not consumed by **vegans**, so they need an alternative. **Soya** milk is used as a substitute, but it has to be fortified because it lacks calcium and some vitamins.
- Some people may be allergic to cow's milk and find goat's milk more suitable.
- Other alternatives available include **almond**, **coconut**, **hazelnut**, **cashew** and **rice milk**.

Milk substitutes

Revision Questions

1. Explain why milk is important in the diet.
2. Outline the effects of cooking and processing on milk.
3. Describe two ways that milk is processed.
4. Discuss the role of milk alternatives in the diet.

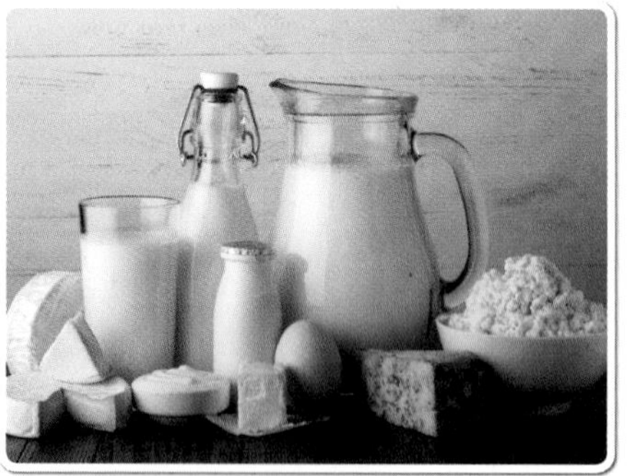
Milk products

Milk products

Milk p roducts include cream, butter, yoghurt and cheese. Cream and butter are high in fat and so they are on the top shelf of the food pyramid.

Cream

Cream is the fat of milk, which rises to the top and is separated from the milk in the dairy.

Fresh cream is heat treated using pasteurisation, sterilisation or UHT.

Type	Fat content	Use
Standard cream	30–40%	Desserts, fillings, decorating
Double cream	48%	Decoration and garnishes – it doubles in volume
Whipping cream	35%	Decorating desserts and cakes
Single/ pouring cream	18%	Pouring into coffee and desserts – cannot be whipped
Half cream	12%	Pouring into coffee and desserts – cannot be whipped
Long-life/ UHT cream	18–40%	Topping for desserts and pastries that have a longer shelf life, e.g. trifles and flans
Sour cream (lactic acid)	18%	As a dip, used in salad dressings, added to sweet and savoury dishes, e.g. beef stroganoff

Did You Know?

There are healthier low-fat options that can be used instead of cream. These include crème fraîche, fromage frais, Greek yoghurt, natural yoghurt and Quark.

Discovery Learning

Find out what crème fraîche, fromage frais and Quark are.

Cream is available frozen, flavoured (e.g. brandy), whipped or in aerosol foam.

Butter

- Butter is manufactured from the cream of milk.
- The cream is pasteurised, cooled, heated and then churned.
- The fat globules separate from the liquid (buttermilk) and are drained off.
- The butter is then washed, blended, salted, wrapped, weighed and packed for distribution.
- Low-fat (light) butter and dairy spreads are also available.

Did You Know?

It takes 10 litres of milk to produce a 450 g block of butter.

Further Investigation

To find out butter is made, go to YouTube and watch the video 'How It's Made – Butter' (5:06).

Yoghurt

Yoghurt is one of the oldest and most popular fermented foods. Its discovery is attributed to herdsmen using containers made from animals' stomachs to store their milk. The natural enzymes curdled the milk, making yoghurt. Yoghurt is a nutritious and economical natural food.

- Yoghurt is a form of thickened milk.
- A **culture** of harmless **lactic acid** bacteria is added to warm milk.
- These bacteria turn milk sugar to acid, which flavours and thickens the milk, forming natural yoghurt. It can be made from whole, low-fat or skimmed milk.
- It can be flavoured with sugar, fruit, chocolate, vanilla, seeds and nuts.
- It can be in the form of a drink, or it can be stirred, set or frozen.
- It provides nutrients, which benefit toddlers, children, adolescents, and pregnant and nursing mothers for growth and development.
- Low-fat varieties are useful for low-fat diets.
- It is easy to digest, making it suitable for invalids and older people.
- The addition of bacterial cultures can aid digestion and give additional health benefits like reducing cholesterol.
- It is a convenient food that can be used in packed lunches, on breakfast cereals, and as dips, salad dressings, marinades, snacks and desserts.
- It can be used as a substitute for cream in desserts, e.g. cheesecake.

Did You Know?

The word *yoğurt* comes from Turkey and refers to a tart, thick milk.

Further Investigation

For more information on yoghurt visit the following websites:
www.glenisk.com
www.yoplait.com
To watch a video on making yoghurt, go to YouTube and search for 'Cheese Making Process' (4:29).

Did You Know?

Most yoghurt sold in Ireland is 'live' or 'bio', which means that it still contains live bacteria. Such organisms are thought to stimulate the gut's friendly bacteria and suppress harmful bacteria. It is also a good moisturiser for skin, and it cools down sunburn and heals the skin.

Cheese

Cheese is another fermented dairy food. It is usually made from cow's milk, but can also be made from buffalo, sheep and goat's milk.

Rennet is a natural enzyme present in the lining of a cow's stomach.

How cheese is made

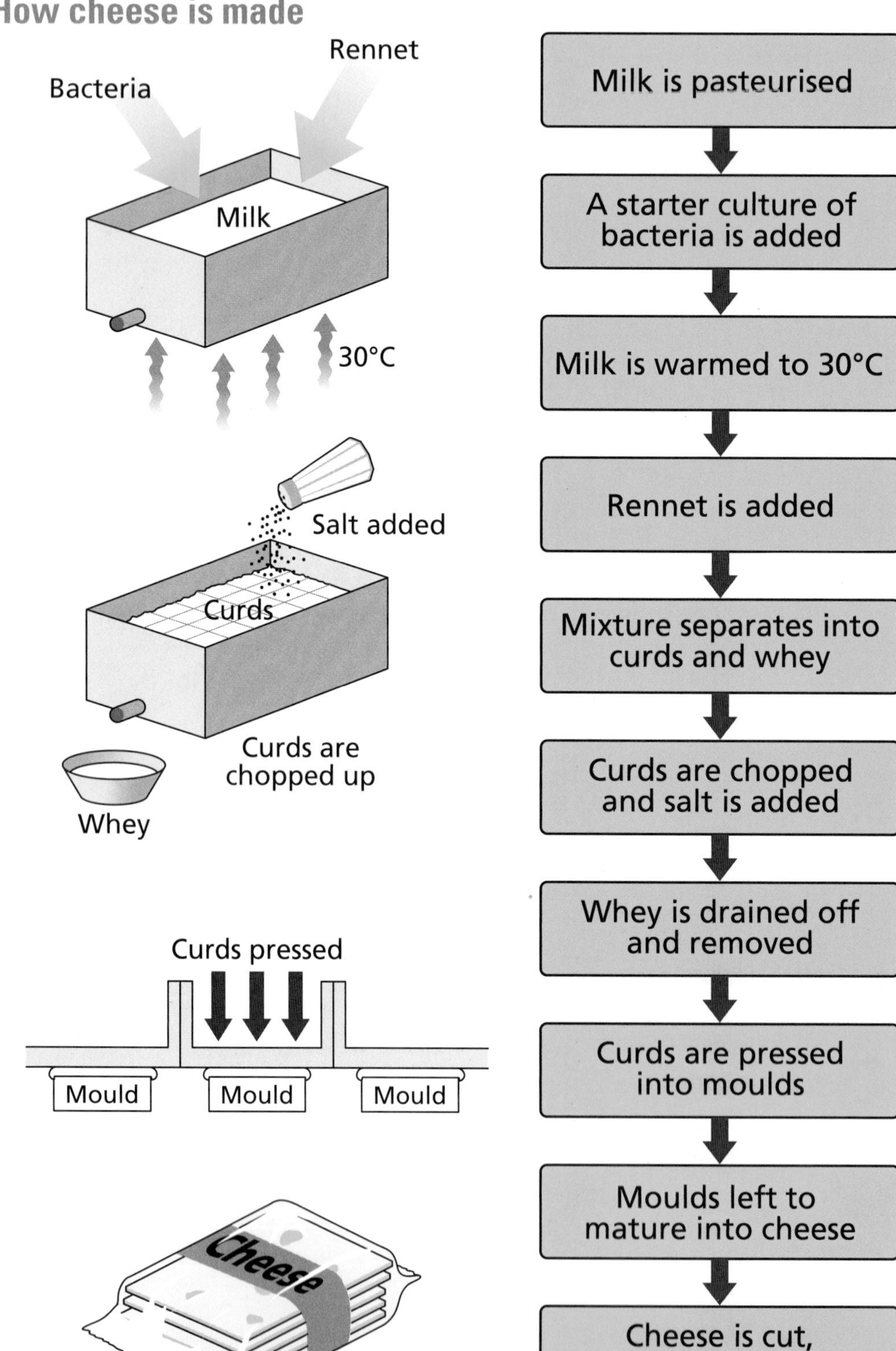

Cheese production

Further Investigation

Whey is removed during the cheese-making process. Can you find out what happens to it?

Nutritive value of cheese

- Cheese is a good source of HBV **protein**, which is needed for the growth and repair of cells.
- Most cheeses contain a high percentage of saturated **fat**, which provides heat and energy. Hard cheeses have more fat than soft cheeses. Cheeses made from low-fat milk, e.g. cottage cheese, have much less fat.
- Cheese lacks **carbohydrates** because all lactose changes to lactic acid, so it is often served with a carbohydrate food, e.g. crackers and cheese.
- **Calcium** is the main mineral in cheese, which contributes to healthy bones and teeth.
- Cheese is rich in vitamins A, B and D.
- Milk contains **vitamin B** for a healthy nervous system. Fat-soluble **vitamin A** is needed for growth, healthy eyes, skin and membranes, and **vitamin D** is needed for healthy bones and teeth.
- The water content of cheese varies depending on the type of cheese – the harder the cheese, the lower the water content.

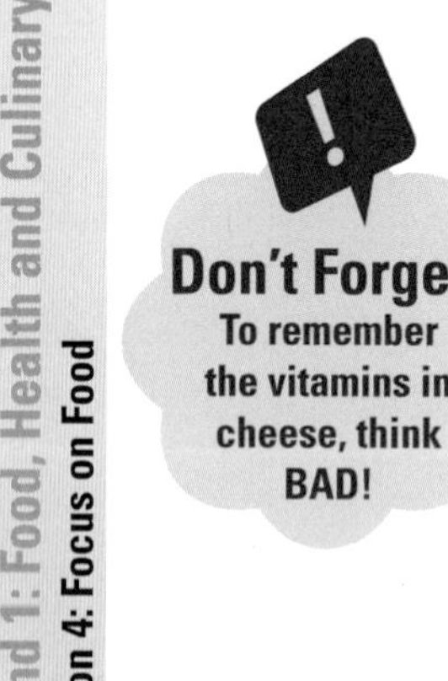

Don't Forget!
To remember the vitamins in cheese, think BAD!

Dietetic value of cheese

- Cheese is a versatile food that can be used in a variety of sweet and savoury dishes. It is suitable for snacks and lunches because it is easily packed.
- It is quick, convenient, and is good value for money as there is no waste.
- There is a large variety of cheeses available, so there is usually one to suit all tastes.
- Cheese is a concentrated source of HBV protein (for growth) and calcium (for strong bones and teeth), so is important in the diets of children, teenagers, pregnant and nursing mothers, and as an alternative to meat, fish and poultry in lacto-vegetarian diets.
- Cheese should be eaten in small quantities because it is high in kilocalories and cholesterol.
- Cheese can be difficult to digest due to the amount of fat present, so it should be given in small amounts to children, invalids and older people.
- Pregnant women should avoid soft cheese to reduce the risk of listeria food poisoning (**see p. 87**).

Discovery Learning

Cheese comes from all over Europe. Find out the names of two popular cheeses from each of the following countries: Ireland, Britain, France, Italy, Switzerland, Greece, the Netherlands and Spain.

Classification of cheese

Cheese can be classified into four groups.

Hard	Semi-hard or semi-soft	Soft	Processed
Cheddar Cheshire Emmenthal Gruyère Parmesan	Edam Feta Gouda Port Salut Roquefort Stilton	Brie Camembert Cottage Ricotta Mozzarella	Cheese slices Cheese strings Cheese spreads Flavoured cheese, e.g. smoked or herbed Foil-wrapped triangles

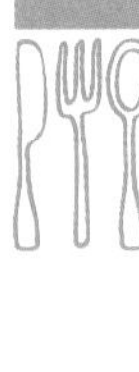

Discovery Learning

Some cheeses are blue-veined and others have an outer coating. Can you find out what causes this to happen in cheese?

Further Investigation

Learn more about making cheese by watching these informative videos on YouTube:
'Cheese Making Process' (cheddar) (4:49)
'How It's Made: Mozzarella Cheese' (4:47)

Uses of cheese

- On its own, as a snack with crackers or grapes
- In plain or toasted sandwiches
- As a filling, e.g. in baked potatoes or omelettes
- In baking, e.g. cheese pastry, scones and biscuits
- As a main ingredient, e.g. lasagne, cheese and potato pie
- Grated as toppings (au gratin), e.g. cauliflower cheese, potato gratin, pizza
- To improve the nutritive value of a dish, e.g. cheesy garlic bread, cheesy mash
- As a garnish in soups, baked potatoes or pasta
- Sliced, cubed or grated in salads
- In sauces, e.g. cheese sauces
- In dips, e.g. cream cheese and herb dip
- As a dessert, e.g. cheesecakes and soufflés
- To end a meal as a cheeseboard

Guidelines for buying and storing cheese

- Buy freshly cut cheese in small amounts and use when fresh (within 2–3 days).
- Check date stamps and use before the expiry date.
- Ensure that wrappers on pre-packed cheeses are not damaged.
- Store open cheese in a refrigerator, wrapped in greaseproof paper.
- Store soft, unripened cheese in a covered container in a refrigerator.
- Bring cheese to room temperature to develop flavours 30–60 minutes before use.
- Grate leftover hard cheese, store in a jar and use as a garnish.

Further Investigation

To find out more about the value of milk and milk products in the diet, go to the National Dairy Council website **www.ndc.ie**. It also contains great recipes, downloads and nutritional information.

Effects of heat on cheese

- Heat makes the protein coagulate and shrink.
- Fat melts.
- Overcooking:
  - Causes fat to separate and become stringy
  - Turns cheese brown
  - Causes cheese to become tough and harder to digest
- Bacteria is destroyed.
- Vitamin B is lost.

Don't Forget!

To make cheese easier to digest, grate or slice it. When cooking cheese in a dish, add mustard and cook as little as possible, towards the end of the cooking time.

How to increase dairy consumption

Include more dairy products in your diet by following the guidelines below:

- Drink milk-based drinks instead of high-sugar fizzy drinks.
- Add yoghurts to fruit smoothies.
- Use cheese, yoghurts and fromage frais for snacks.
- Serve dishes that include dairy, e.g. gratin dishes, lasagne.
- Add grated cheese to salads and serve with yoghurt-based dressings, and to soups and pasta dishes.

Revision Questions

1. Why are cream and butter not on the same level as milk on the food pyramid?
2. Describe how yoghurt is made.
3. Write an informative account on the nutritive and dietetic value of cheese in the diet.
4. Suggest some easy ways for a teenager to increase their intake of milk products.

Summary

- Serve **three portions** daily from the milk, yoghurt and cheese group. Teenagers should have up to **five portions** a day.
- **Milk** is a good source of HBV protein (growth and repair), calcium (healthy bones and teeth), vitamins A, B and D (essential for growth) and carbohydrate in the form of lactose (heat and energy). Milk lacks iron, vitamin C, starch and fibre.
- **Uses of milk:** Drinks, sauces, enriching dishes, desserts, baking, batters and glazing baked goods.
- **Effects of heat on milk:** Loss of vitamins C and B group; flavour is changed; bacteria are destroyed; protein coagulates and forms a skin on the surface of milk and steam causes the milk to boil over.
- Milk is **homogenised** to distribute the fat. This makes the milk creamier before being heat treated. Milk can be **pasteurised** – this is where it is heated to 72°C for 25 seconds, cooled rapidly and then packed. It can also be **ultra-high temperature (UHT) sterilised** – this is where it is heated to 132°C for one to three seconds. These treatments extend the shelf life of the milk and destroy pathogenic bacteria.
- Milk is available in the following types: whole, low fat, skimmed, fortified, long life, buttermilk, flavoured, dried, evaporated and condensed. It should be stored safely to prevent souring and contamination with bacteria.

- Milk products include butter and cream, which are high in fat, so they are not in the same food group as milk, yoghurt and cheese.
- **Yoghurt** is a form of thickened milk. A **culture** of harmless **lactic acid** bacteria is added to warm milk, turning milk sugar to acid, which in turn flavours and thickens the milk, making natural yoghurt. Yoghurt can be made from whole, low-fat or skimmed milk. It can also be flavoured and comes in liquid, stirred, set or frozen form.
- Yoghurt provides nutrients, is easy to digest, can aid digestion and provides additional health benefits like reducing cholesterol. It can be used in packed lunches, on breakfast cereals, as dips, salad dressings, marinades, and as snacks and desserts. It can also be used as a substitute for cream.
- To make **cheese**, a culture of bacteria is added to pasteurised milk. This changes the sugar (lactose) in the milk to lactic acid, providing the flavour. It is warmed and rennet is added to separate the milk into curds and whey. The curds are then drained, chopped and salted and pressed into moulds, and the whey is removed. The moulds are left to mature and ripen into cheese. They are then cut, packaged and labelled.
- Cheese is an excellent source of **protein, calcium, and vitamins A, B and D**. However, it is high in **saturated fat**.
- Cheese is **classified** as hard, semi-hard/semi-soft, soft or processed. It has **many uses** in snacks, salads, dips, sauces, sandwiches and in sweet and savoury dishes. Cooked cheese can be indigestible, so eat it raw, grate it or cook it lightly.

15 MEAT, POULTRY, FISH, EGGS, BEANS AND NUTS GROUP

Learning Outcomes 1.1, 1.2, 1.3, 1.4, 1.5, 1.6, 1.7, 1.9, 1.12, 1.13, 1.14, 1.15, 1.16, 1.17, 1.18, 1.19, 2.10

What I Will Learn

- to classify meats and give examples of each type
- to identify the nutritive and dietetic value of meat and meat products
- to describe the structure of meat
- to explain why meat becomes tough and how to tenderise it
- to compile a set of guidelines for buying, storing and cooking meat
- to describe the effects of cooking and processing on meat
- to classify fish and give examples of each type
- to identify the nutritive and dietetic value of fish and fish products
- to compile a set of guidelines for buying, storing and cooking fish
- to identify the effects of cooking and processing on fish
- to identify the nutritive value of eggs
- to assess the value of eggs and their uses in the diet
- to identify the culinary uses of eggs
- to explain how eggs are graded and labelled
- to compile guidelines for buying, storing and cooking eggs
- to state the effects of cooking on eggs
- to assess the value of protein alternatives like beans and nuts in the diet

Key Words

✓ Offal
✓ Game
✓ Fibres
✓ Extractive
✓ Tenderise
✓ Marinating
✓ Traceable
✓ Gelatine
✓ Poultry
✓ Brine
✓ Opaque
✓ Translucent
✓ Free range
✓ Custard
✓ Batter
✓ Reconstituted
✓ Mycoprotein

Much of the protein in our diet comes from foods on this shelf of the food pyramid. It is important to eat a wide variety of food from this group. Choose lean meat, trim excess fat from meat and remove skin from poultry. Limit processed meats such as bacon or ham, because these are usually high in fat and salt. Use red meats and eggs for iron. Try to eat fish at least twice a week and oily fish at least once a week. Other good sources of protein are beans and peas which are also fat free. They are better when eaten with wholegrain breads, rice or pasta. Choose any **two** servings from this group each day (meat, poultry, fish, eggs, beans and nuts).

Meat

Meat is the flesh of animals and birds and their edible internal organs (offal). Meat varies in flavour, composition and texture according to the following:

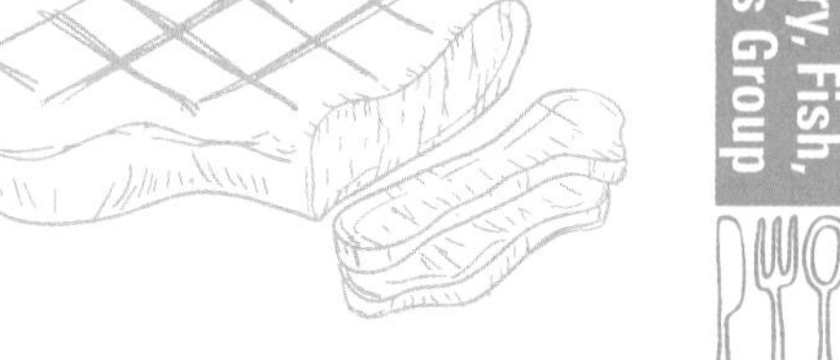

- Type of animal
- Age of the animal
- Breed of animal
- Feeding and rearing methods

In Ireland, we consume a wide variety of high-quality meat, including beef, lamb, pork, bacon and poultry, as meat production in Ireland adheres to very strict standards.

Classification of meat

Meat is divided in to the following categories:

Category	Examples
Carcass	Cattle – Beef and veal Sheep – Mutton and lamb Pig – Pork, bacon and ham
Poultry	Chicken, turkey, duck, goose, ostrich
Game (wild animals and birds)	Deer (venison), rabbit, grouse, pheasant
Offal (edible internal organs)	Liver, kidney, heart, tongue, tripe, brain, sweetbreads

Nutritive value of meat

- Meat is a good source of HBV **protein**. It is needed for the growth and repair of cells.
- **Fat** in meat is **saturated fat**, which provides heat and energy. The amount varies depending on the animal, the cut of meat and the cooking method.
- Meat lacks **carbohydrates**, so it should be served with high-carbohydrate foods like bread, rice and pasta.
- Meat is rich in **B-group vitamins** for release of energy and a healthy nervous system. Offal, e.g. heart and liver, is a good source of **vitamins A and D**.
- Red meat and offal are very good sources of easily absorbed **iron** for the blood and **phosphorus** for bones and teeth.
- The amount of water varies – the more fat the less water.

Dietetic value of meat

- Meat is popular. It can be expensive but some cuts like mince, lamb shanks or offal can be cheaper and just as nutritious.
- Meat is an excellent source of HBV protein for growth and repair so it is important in the diet of children, adolescents and pregnant women.

Don't Forget!
The three 'Cs' are missing from meat: carbohydrates, vitamin C and calcium. Can you suggest ways to include them by planning a day's menus for a family?

- Red meat is high in cholesterol and saturated fat so should be reduced in the diet of those with high cholesterol or heart disease. Obese people should choose chicken, turkey and lean meat to avoid fat.
- Meat is one of the best possible sources of iron, especially in the diet of teenage girls and pregnant women.
- It is a good source of B-group vitamins, especially B12 for red blood cells.
- Meat adds variety to the diet as there are many types and cuts suitable for a variety of dishes.
- Meat is not essential in the diet – it can be replaced by fish, eggs, cheese, lentils, beans and nuts.

Structure of meat

Meat is the muscle of the animal. It is made up of bundles of long, hollow fibres filled with meat juices that contain **extractives**, vitamins, minerals and proteins.

They are held together with an elastic substance called connective tissue. Fat cells, known as marbling, are found between the fibres (invisible). They also cover the outside of the meat (visible).

Extractives give each meat its distinct flavour and aid digestion.

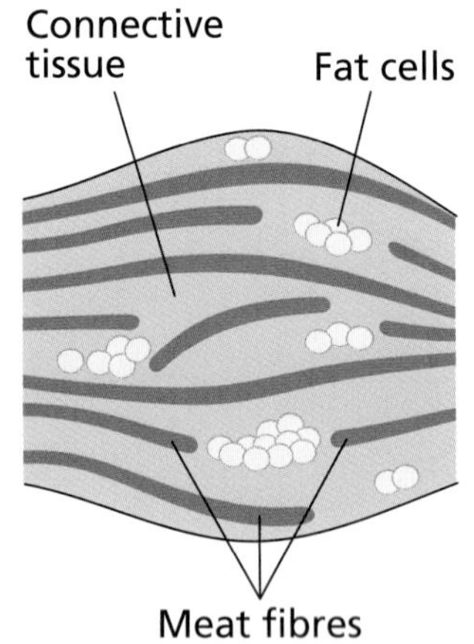

The structure of meat

Tough or tender?

- In tough meat the fibres are longer and coarser and there is more connective tissue. Tough meat needs moist, slow cooking to make it tender, e.g. stewing.
- In tender meat the fibres are shorter and finer and there is less connective tissue. Tender meat can be cooked by frying, grilling or roasting.

The toughness or tenderness of meat depends on the following factors:

Age	The older the animal, the tougher the meat.
Activity	Meat from a more active part of an animal is tougher than meat from a less active part.
Hanging	Meat must be hung for a certain length of time or it will go tough.
Cooking method	The method must suit the type of meat, e.g. a slow, moist method for tough meat.

How to tenderise meat

Meat can be tenderised in a number of ways. (**Cooking methods, see p. 119**)

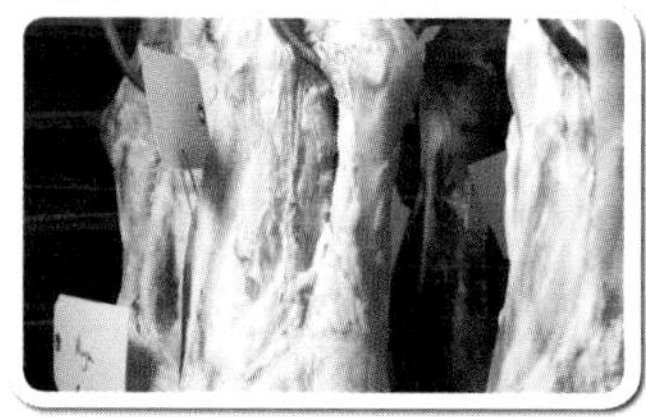

Resting animals before slaughter and **hanging** after slaughter allow enzymes to make the muscles tender.

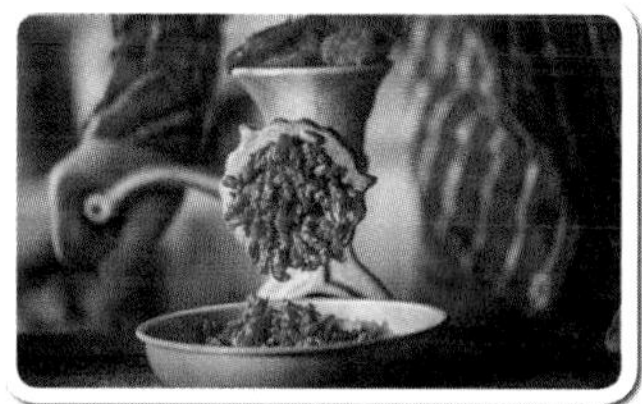

Mincing or chopping breaks up the fibres, making the meat more tender.

Beating meat with a steak hammer breaks up the fibres.

Marinating: Steeping raw meat in a mixture of wine, lemon juice/vinegar (acid) and oil, alcohol and flavourings prior to cooking has a tenderising effect on meat.

Meat tenderisers: Animals can be injected with tenderising agents like Papain (papaya) and bromelain (pineapple) prior to slaughter. These can also be sprinkled on meat before cooking.

Slow, moist methods such as stewing or casseroling may be used to tenderise meat.

Cuts of meat

Beef

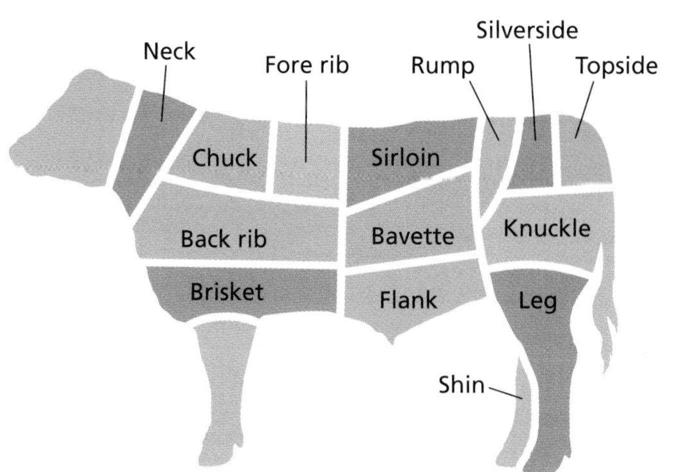

Did You Know?

A cow is more valuable for its milk, cheese, butter and yoghurt than its meat.

Lamb

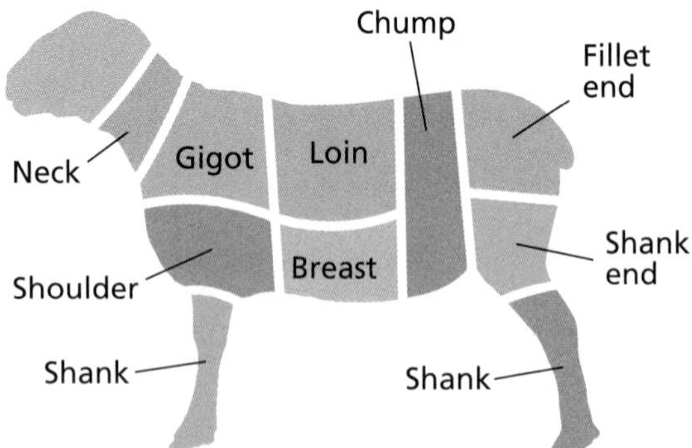

Pork

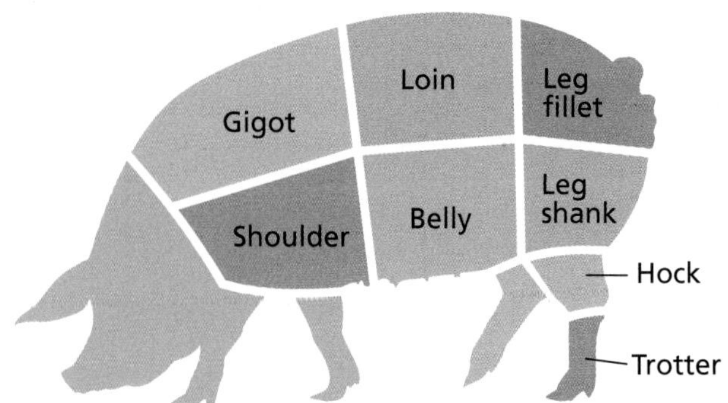

Further Investigation

To learn more about the different cuts of meat, go to **www.bordbia.ie**, click on 'Consumer' at the top of the home page, then on 'About Food', and then on 'Meat'. You can choose a type of meat, e.g. beef, and then click on each cut to find out more about how it is cooked, and how it can be used in recipes.

Guidelines for buying meat

- Buy meat from a clean, reliable shop, where assistants, surfaces and equipment are clean and hygienic.
- Ensure that raw and cooked meats are stored and handled separately to prevent cross-contamination.
- Ensure that the meat supplied is traceable and, if pre-packed, has the Quality Assurance label.
- Buy fresh meat in small quantities.
- Unless freezing, cuts should be firm and moist.
- Choose the correct cut of meat for the dish being cooked and method of cooking.
- Avoid cuts that have a lot of bone, gristle and fat.
- Cheaper cuts of meat are just as nutritious as leaner, more expensive cuts.
- Organically produced meat tends to be more expensive.
- Always check date stamp on packaged meat.

Did You Know?

Bacon is one of the oldest meats consumed by humans – the Chinese were preserving pork bellies from 1500 BC.

Discovery Learning

Find out how long meat carcasses should be hung before use. Why are there different times for different types of animal?

The Bord Bia Quality Assurance Scheme

- This scheme ensures that meat meets the highest standards at each step of the production chain (from farm to table).
- All farms and food premises are inspected and passed before the quality mark can be used.
- This ensures traceability, quality and safety standards for the meat, animals and the environment.
- The mark can also be found on eggs, fruit, vegetables, potatoes and plants.
- To find out more visit www.bordbia.ie, click on 'Consumer' on the home page, and then on 'Quality Assurance'.

Guidelines for storing meat

- Remove packaging, put on a clean plate and cover loosely in greaseproof paper or cling film.
- Refrigerate as soon as possible.
- Use within two to three days.
- Store raw meat below cooked meat to prevent cross-contamination (**see p. 90**).
- Follow instructions on pre-packed and vacuum-packed meat labels.
- If freezing meat, place in the freezer on the day of purchase.

(**Food storage and kitchen hygiene and safety, see p. 84**)

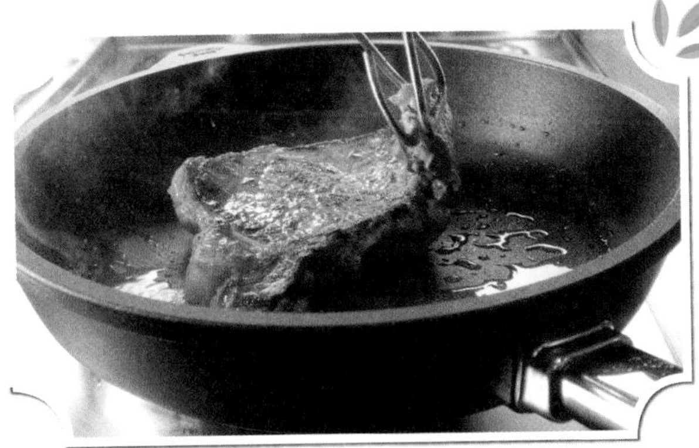

Guidelines for cooking meat

Meat is cooked:

- To kill bacteria, making it safe to eat.
- To improve its flavour and make it more appetising.
- To make it more tender and digestible.

Preparing and cooking meat:

- If frozen, defrost slowly in the fridge or in a microwave.
- Remove excess fat and gristle and wipe with damp kitchen paper.
- Weigh meat and calculate the cooking time.
- Cook all meat, particularly minced meat, thoroughly at the correct temperature to make sure it is safe to eat.

Effects of cooking on meat:

- Colour changes from red to brown or from pink to white.
- Bacteria are destroyed.
- Protein coagulates, causing meat fibres to shrink due to loss of water, which causes meat to shrink in size.
- Meat fat melts, moistening leaner meat and adding flavour.
- Collagen changes to gelatin in moist heat – this causes the fibres to fall apart, causing meat to become more tender and digestible.
- Some B-group vitamins are destroyed or can be lost to the cooking liquid.
- Texture is improved as the meat becomes firmer.
- Extractives are released and flavour develops.
- Overcooking causes the meat to become tough and indigestible and causes further shrinkage.

Using leftover cooked meat

To safely use leftover meat, follow the guidelines below:

- Store in a refrigerator, covered and on a clean plate.
- Use within two days of first cooking.

- Prepare just before using.
- Reheat thoroughly.
- Only ever reheat cooked meat **once**.
- Add herbs and seasoning as recooking meat makes it lose its own flavour.
- Reheating in a sauce adds moisture.

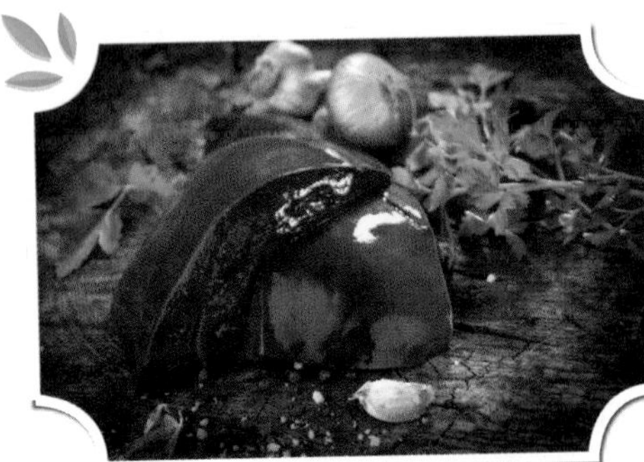

Offal

- These are the edible internal organs of an animal, e.g. kidney, liver and heart.
- Offal is cheap and very nourishing as it is high in protein, vitamins A, B and iron.
- Offal from younger animals is better as the flavour is not too strong.
- It must be eaten on the day it is bought.
- Rinse in warm water before use and cook gently.

Discovery Learning

Offal is cheap but nourishing. Can you suggest some tasty offal recipes that could be used to provide protein in the diet?

Meat processing

Fresh meat has a short shelf life, so it undergoes processing to extend it. It can be frozen, canned, cured, salted, smoked, dried or vacuum packed (**see p. 214**).

Meat products

There is a wide variety of meat-based products on the market, including:

- Sausages, which come fresh (beef or pork), cooked (frankfurters, black or white pudding) or dried (chorizo, pepperoni, salami)
- Burgers
- Processed cooked meats, including corned beef, Billy roll and luncheon meat
- Pies, pastries and stews
- Pâté
- Stock cubes, pastes, concentrated gel, powder or cubes
- Fats such as suet, dripping and lard
- Gelatin, which is used to set desserts

Don't Forget!
By law, the percentage of meat in a product must be stated on the label.

Poultry

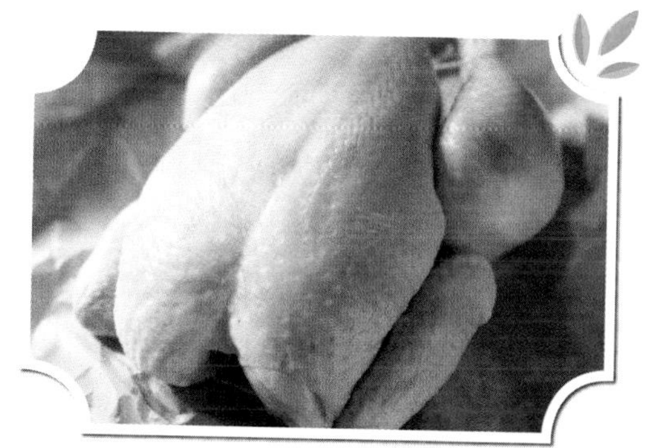

- Poultry includes birds such as chicken, duck, turkeys and geese. Edible wild birds, e.g. pheasant and grouse, are called game.
- Chicken is the most common poultry. It is available fresh or frozen, whole, jointed or filleted.

Nutritive value of poultry

- Poultry is a good source of high biological value **protein** that is easily digested.
- The amount of **fat** varies depending on the type and age of bird. Chicken fillets are low in fat while duck breast has a higher fat content.
- There are **no carbohydrates** present so serve with starchy foods.
- Contains **B-group vitamins** but fewer than in red meat.
- Contains **less iron** than red meat, and has traces of **calcium** and **phosphorus**.
- Contains a large amount of **water**. The amount varies depending on the fat content.

Dietetic value of poultry

- Poultry is a relatively inexpensive but tasty meat.
- The protein is easy to digest so it is useful in the diets of children, older people and convalescents.
- Poultry has a lower fat content than red meat, so it is a good alternative for those following low-calorie and low-cholesterol diets.
- Poultry adds variety to the diet. It can be combined with a variety of ingredients to produce a range of dishes.
- It is important to consider the cooking method and the recipe used, as the fat content could be significantly increased.

Guidelines for buying poultry

- Buy from a reliable source.
- If pre-packed, always check the 'use by' or 'best before' label.
- Check for signs of freshness, i.e. avoid poultry with a bad smell, poor colour and blemishes on the skin.
- Chicken breasts should be firm and plump.
- Frozen poultry should be frozen solid, with undamaged packaging.

Guidelines for storing poultry

- Frozen poultry should be stored in a freezer as soon as possible after purchase.
- Fresh poultry should be stored on a clean plate, covered, put on a lower shelf in the refrigerator and used as soon as possible.
- Do not leave poultry in the car or lying on a kitchen work surface (**why?**).
- Defrost thoroughly before cooking to avoid food poisoning.
- Remove giblets when thawed. Never refreeze a thawed chicken (**why?**).

Guidelines for cooking poultry

- Wash hands thoroughly before and after handling raw poultry.
- Wash chopping board and knives to prevent cross-contamination.
- Remove wrapper and giblets, and thaw frozen poultry thoroughly in a refrigerator.
- Cook stuffing separately.
- Cook poultry thoroughly to destroy bacteria.
- Cool leftover poultry quickly.
- Cover and store in the refrigerator.
- Use leftovers quickly. Never reheat poultry remaining on the bone.

Processed poultry products include chicken nuggets, coated and breaded chicken, burgers, sausages, kievs, rissoles, and frozen ready meals and cook-chill meals like chicken curry and sweet and sour chicken.

Revision Questions

Use your workbook to revise this chapter

1. Classify meats and give examples of each type.
2. Outline the nutritive and dietetic value of meat and meat products.
3. Explain (a) why meat becomes tough, and (b) how to tenderise it.
4. Compile a set of guidelines for buying, storing and cooking meat.
5. Describe the effects of cooking and processing on meat.

Fish

Fish is a very nutritious and healthy substitute for meat. There are many different types of fish and it can be cooked in a variety of ways. As it cooks quickly it saves fuel. In Ireland we have fresh water, sea water and farmed fish.

Did You Know?

Fish farming is popular as a method for producing oysters, mussels, salmon and trout. It is known as **aquaculture**.

Classification of fish

Fish can be classified according to its nutritive value. The fish in each group are similar in structure and food value.

Type	Description	Examples
White	• Flesh contains little or no fat • Fat stored in liver	Cod, haddock, plaice, sole, hake and whiting
Oily	Unsaturated fat is found throughout, so the flesh is a darker colour	Herring, mackerel, salmon, trout, tuna and sardines
Shellfish	• Flesh inside a tough outer shell • Lower in fat than oily fish	**Crustaceans:** Have claws, e.g. prawns, lobsters and crabs **Molluscs:** Outer shell with fish inside, e.g. mussels, oysters and cockles

Fish also differ in terms of shape:

Round: e.g. mackerel

Flat: e.g. plaice

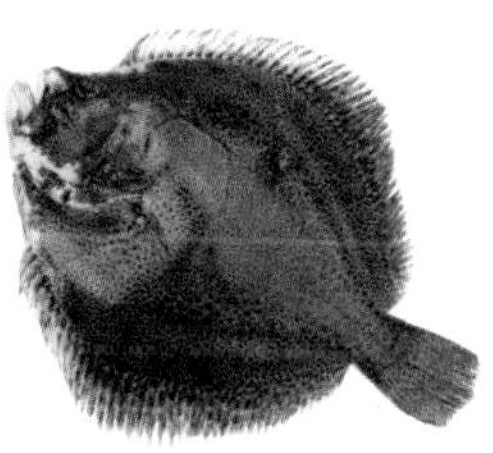

Nutritive value of fish

- Fish is a good source of HBV **protein**, which is needed for growth and repair of cells.
- There is no **fat** in white fish because the fat is stored in the fish's liver, which is removed during preparation. The fat in oily fish is unsaturated and is rich in omega-3 fatty acids. Shellfish contains a small amount of fat.
- Fish lacks **carbohydrates**, so it should be served with starchy foods like rice, potatoes and pasta.
- All fish contains the **B-group vitamins** for a healthy nervous system. Oily fish and shellfish provide **vitamins A** and **D**.
- Saltwater fish contains **iodine** and **fluoride**. Most fish are a good source of **phosphorus**, **potassium** and **zinc**. Canned fish contains **calcium** because the bones are eaten, e.g. sardines and salmon. Shellfish and sardines also have a high **iron** content.
- White fish and shellfish contain **water** so are low in calories. Oily fish has less water because it contains more fat.

Discovery Learning

Can you find out what happens to the liver oils that are removed from white fish?

Dietetic value of fish

- Fish is an important source of HBV protein for growth. It is a good alternative to meat. Include at least two portions a week, as it is important in the diet of children, teenagers and older people.
- Fish is easily digested and is ideal for children, older people and invalids.
- White fish contains practically no fat, making it ideal for those on a low-calorie diet. Oily fish is suitable for a low-cholesterol diet.

Don't Forget!
Some fish have a lot of small bones so take care to remove them during food preparation as there is a danger of choking, especially for children and older people.

- There is a wide variety of fish available and many different cooking methods can be used.
- Some fish is inexpensive but nutritious, e.g. mackerel and herring. As fish is tender, it cooks quickly and saves money, time and fuel.
- There are many different varieties of fish available but it is also available processed, e.g. canned and frozen, when not in season.
- It can be used in many different ways.

Uses of fish

- **Breakfast:** Kippers, smoked salmon, kedgeree
- **Starters:** Prawn cocktail, mussels, smoked salmon, crab claws
- **Soups:** Seafood chowder, lobster bisque
- **Main course dishes:** Baked salmon, cod and tomato tray bake, fish pie, prawn stir-fry, seafood linguine
- **Lunches:** Crab salad, seafood pasta salad
- **Sandwiches:** Open prawn, salmon and cucumber, tuna and sweetcorn
- **Snacks:** Smoked salmon blinis, prawn crackers, sushi

Don't Forget!
Some fish are in season at certain times of the year, so they are more plentiful, have a better flavour and are cheaper, e.g. cod is in season from September to March.

Guidelines for buying fresh fish

Some fish is expensive, e.g. wild salmon and lobster. Other fish is cheaper, e.g. herring and mackerel. Farmed fish is usually less expensive than wild fish. It is also important to consider the amount of waste (heads, bones and insides are discarded) as there can be up to 70% waste in fish.

Fish should be absolutely fresh – it goes stale quickly (**can you find out why?**).

- Look for:
  - bright red/pink gills
  - a seaweedy, fresh smell, no unpleasant odour
  - skin that is moist and unbroken with plenty of scales
  - eyes that are bright and bulging
  - flesh that is firm, moist and unbruised, with a close grain.
- Buy from a clean, reliable source. Fish should be stored on ice in a chilled unit in a hygienic shop with well trained, knowledgeable staff and a good turnover.
- Buy fish in season.

Discovery Learning

Why is fish 'in season' for a certain period of time? Find out why it cannot be caught all year round.

- Medium-sized fish usually have the most flavour.
- Fish are sold in a variety of cuts: as whole fish, fillets, steaks or cutlets.
- Shellfish should be heavy for their size. Crustaceans should be alive and mollusc shells should be closed or should close when touched.

Small and medium-sized fish, e.g. herring, are usually sold whole and ready to cook, which means that the head, tail, scales and insides have been removed. A larger fish, e.g. salmon, can be cut into pieces depending on the shape and size of the fish.

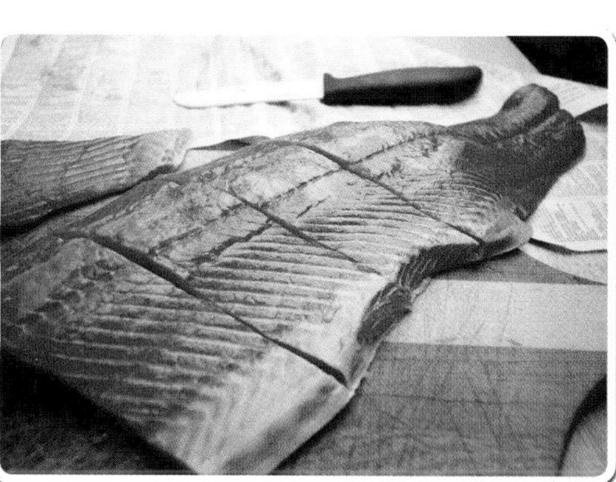

- Fillets are cut along the length of the fish.
- Cutlets are cut across the fish in the section where the gut has been removed.
- Steaks are cut across the fish and are whole pieces.
- Tailpieces come from large fish. They are usually sold and cooked in one piece.

Guidelines for buying frozen fish

Frozen fish should:

- be frozen solid
- have unbroken packets
- be used within the expiry date
- be placed in the freezer quickly
- never be refrozen

Guidelines for storing fish

Fresh fish	Frozen fish
• Remove the wrapping • Rinse in cold water • Put on a clean plate, preferably surrounded by ice, and cover loosely • Refrigerate as quickly as possible • Use as quickly as possible (within 24 hours)	• Put in the freezer as soon as possible • If fish has started to thaw do not refreeze • Use within recommended time (check use by date)

Further Investigation

For illustrated notes on skinning fish, preparing lobster and opening oysters, go to **www.bordbia.ie**, click on 'Consumer' on the top of the home page, then click on 'About Food', then on the left-hand side of the page, click on 'Fish', and then on 'Preparation'.

For helpful videos on the preparation of fish, go to **www.bbcgoodfood.com**, and search for 'How to fillet a round fish' and 'How to prepare a whole fish'.

Processing fish

Fish is a perishable food so a variety of processing methods can be used to make fish more readily available. Fish can be frozen, canned or smoked.

Frozen fish	Canned fish	Smoked fish
Cod Plaice Salmon Prawns Prepared meals	Tuna Salmon Sardines Crab	Haddock Salmon Coley Trout Herring (kippers)

Suitable methods of cooking fish

(🔗 For more information on cooking methods, see p. 119)

Frying	Deep-, shallow- or stir-fried, uncoated or coated, with e.g. batter or breadcrumbs
Baking	Whole fish, fillets or cutlets. May be stuffed or served with a sauce
Steaming	Good for delicate fish like plaice
Poaching	Fish poached in water, milk or wine, e.g. salmon; fish should never be boiled
Grilling/ barbecuing	A quick method used for fillets, cutlets or small whole fish
Stewing	In a sauce, e.g. curry
Reheating	In fish pies and cakes

Effects of cooking on fish

- Protein coagulates (sets) so fish shrinks slightly and the flesh becomes **opaque**.
- Connective tissue dissolves so fish breaks apart easily.
- Bacteria and parasites are destroyed.
- Some loss of B-group vitamins.
- If the fish is cooked in water as in poaching, some of the water-soluble minerals and vitamins leach into the cooking water. This water should be used if making a sauce.
- Overcooking results in the flesh becoming dry and rubbery.

Opaque means being firm and not transparent (see-through). Fish turns opaque as it is being cooked.

Coating	
Protects the fish flesh during cooking	Seasoned flour, egg and breadcrumbs, batter, oatmeal
Sauces	
Fish can be cooked in a sauce or the sauce can be served as an accompaniment	Hollandaise, parsley, cheese, tartare, tomato, and white wine sauces
Garnishes	
Make the dish look attractive	• Lemon or lime, slices, wedges or twists • Parsley chopped or in sprigs • Cucumber twists • Grated cheese • Tomato slices, roses or twists

Revision Questions

1. Classify fish and give three examples of each type.
2. Outline the nutritive and dietetic value of fish and fish products in the diet.
3. Compile a set of guidelines for buying, storing and cooking fish.
4. Outline the effects of cooking and processing on fish.

Eggs

Eggs are a cheap, protein-rich food. They are versatile, cook quickly and are suitable for all ages. We eat eggs from hens, ducks, geese, ostriches and quails. Eggs come in a variety of coloured shells, but that does not affect the nutritive value of the egg.

Structure of eggs

Eggs are composed of three main parts: the shell, the white and the yolk.

Don't Forget!
Due to salmonella poisoning, raw eggs should not be eaten by children, pregnant women or older people. Find out why eggs should also be quality assured.

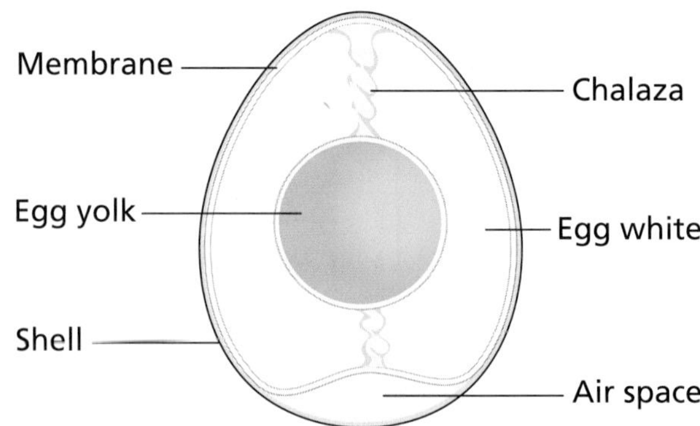

Nutritive value of eggs

- Eggs are an excellent source of HBV **protein** (13%) which is easy to digest and good for growth and repair.
- The fat in eggs is easily digested **saturated fat** (12%). The yolk is high in cholesterol.
- Eggs do not contain **carbohydrate**, so they are usually served with carbohydrates, e.g. scrambled egg on toast.
- Eggs contain the soluble **vitamins A** and **D** in the yolk and **B-group** vitamins which keep the body healthy. Eggs lack vitamin C.
- Eggs are an important source of **calcium** and **phosphorus** for healthy bones and teeth. Iron in egg yolks keeps the blood healthy.
- Most of the **water** (73%) present is in the white.

Dietetic value of eggs

- Eggs are a readily available, versatile food that can be used in a variety of sweet and savoury dishes.
- Eggs contain HBV protein so they are important in the diets of all age groups, especially lacto-vegetarians who eat dairy products and eggs. They are a good protein alternative to meat and fish.
- Eggs are cheap and nutritious, yet they are low in calories (147 kcal, mostly in the yolk), so they are good for those on low budgets.
- They contain cholesterol so they should be restricted low-cholesterol diets.
- Eggs are easily digested and are therefore good for invalids, children and older people.
- As eggs lack carbohydrates and vitamin C, include foods rich in both in the diet, e.g. serving orange juice at breakfast with poached egg on toast.

Discovery Learning

Eggs are a very nutritious food but lack vitamin C and carbohydrates. Find some egg recipes that include these missing nutrients.

Did You Know?

Nutrition guidelines recommend that a healthy person can eat up to seven eggs a week and those on a cholesterol-lowering diet can eat four to six eggs a week.

Further Investigation

Find out more about eggs and their contribution to the diet, by visiting **www.bordbia.ie**, clicking on 'Consumer', then on 'About Food'. Then, on the left-hand side of the page, click on 'Eggs'.

Uses of eggs

On their own: Boiled, poached, scrambled or fried.
Sandwiches and salads, e.g. egg mayonnaise.
Thickening, e.g. in a custard sauce, quiche and omelette.
Baking: Creating air, e.g. sponge cake, meringue.
Binding: Sticking ingredients together, e.g. burgers, fish cakes.
Coating: Protects food when frying; egg is used to stick a layer on the outside of food, e.g. breaded chicken.
Glazing: Beaten egg brushed on baked foods to make them brown and shiny, e.g. scones.
Enriching: Increasing the nutritive value of a dish, e.g. brown bread.
Garnishing: Hard-boiled egg, sliced or chopped for decoration, e.g. salad or dressed crab.
Emulsions: Egg yolk holds oil and vinegar together, e.g. mayonnaise, hollandaise sauce.
Clarifying: Egg whites used to clear jelly, stock or wine.

Discovery Learning

Can you make up a mnemonic that will help you remember the uses of eggs? Be creative!

Guidelines for selecting and buying eggs

- Buy fresh eggs in a shop with a quick turnover.
- Always check the best before date.
- Free-range eggs cost more than mass-produced eggs.
- Eggs should feel heavy for their size and have a rough shell.
- Check shells to ensure there are no cracks and breakages.
- Check carton for information, e.g. size, class and quality.

Free-range eggs come from chickens that roam freely.
Organic eggs have no artificial additives in the chickens' feed, so they tend to be more expensive (**responsible consumers, see p. 354**).

Eggs are graded by weight and quality

- Size is classified, and ranges from Small (less than 53 g) to Very Large (more than 73 g).
- Quality is decided by 'candling'.
- Extra fresh = within seven days of laying (should be removed when seven days is over).
- Class A = Best quality, small air space, good for poaching, frying and boiling.
- Class B = Large air space, staler, yolk off-centre, good for scrambling, baking, sauces.

Labelling regulations for eggs

Egg packs must contain the following information clearly written on the box.

- The **country of origin**, e.g. IE = Ireland
- The **name**, **address** and **registration number** of the **producer** or packer
- The **class/quality** of the eggs, i.e. Class A, B (Class A must indicate the farming method), e.g. free range
- The **quantity** of eggs in the pack
- **Week number** (1–52)
- Class A must show the **best before date** (must not exceed 28 days from the date of lay)
- Class A must indicate the size of the eggs
- **Storage instructions**
- **Farming method (0, 1, 2, 3):** 0 = organic; 1 = free range; 2 = barn; 3 = cage
- The **meaning of the producer code** should be explained on or inside the pack

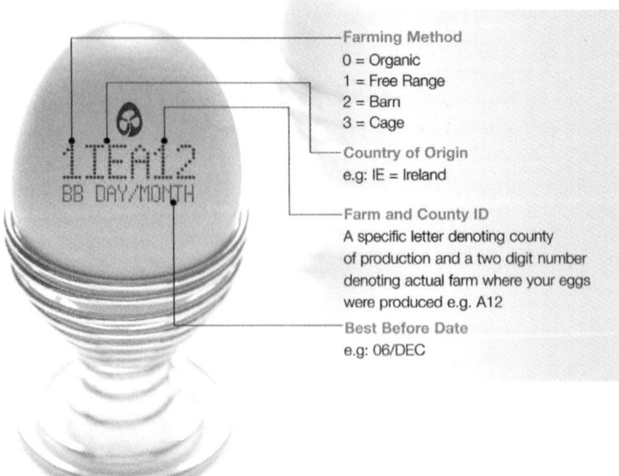

The **Quality Assurance Scheme** and new **EU legislation** state that **each individual egg must be stamped** with a code to ensure full traceability of the egg to the farm. The following codes must be stamped on each individual egg:

- **Farming method used:** 0 = organic; 1 = free range; 2 = barn; 3 = cage
- **Country of origin:** IE = Ireland
- **County and farm ID:** A letter indicates county of production, e.g. R = Roscommon, and a unique producer code, e.g. R989
- **Best before date**, e.g. BB 31/12

Storage of eggs

- Eggs should be stored in the refrigerator, e.g. the fridge door.
- Store eggs with the pointed end facing downwards (**why?**).
- Keep away from strong-smelling food (**why?**).
- Eggs should be used at room temperature so remove from the fridge one hour before use to prevent **curdling** or the shell cracking when boiling.
- Leftover egg whites can be stored in an air-tight container in the fridge.
- Leftover egg yolk can be stored covered with water in the fridge.
- Use within the recommended time.

Curdling occurs when egg protein separates from the liquid and forms lumps or grains in the mixture. This is caused by high temperature.

Effects of cooking on eggs

- Egg protein coagulates (sets), causing it to harden, e.g. boiled egg.
- If overcooked, egg white becomes tough and rubbery, yolk becomes dry and crumbly and a greenish colour occurs on the outside of the yolk of hard-boiled eggs.
- Egg white changes from **translucent** to opaque.
- Eggs shrink slightly.
- Bacteria like salmonella are destroyed.
- There is a loss of B-group vitamins.
- Too much heat causes curdling.

Translucent means almost see-though.

Did You Know?

Because of the risk of salmonella in raw eggs it is recommended that children, pregnant women and older people avoid eating products that include raw eggs like mayonnaise, unless the eggs used are pasteurised.

Tips to avoid curdling

- Use eggs at room temperature.
- Cook egg mixtures gently.
- Cool hot mixtures slightly before adding them to eggs.

Don't Forget!
Always add hot liquids to eggs, not the other way around.

Classroom-Based Assessment

Eggs are linked to CBA2 and the Practical Food Skills examination.

Cooking with eggs

When **whisking** egg whites, e.g. for meringues or mayonnaise, make sure all the eggs are fresh and that no traces of egg yolk or fat get into the egg whites or they will not whisk well.

Tips for cracking eggs

Crack each egg separately into a cup, removing any pieces of shell if there are any. Then put the eggs into the main bowl, or if the recipe requires you to separate yolks from whites, separate into two cups (check yolk does not burst, if it has, do not put into bowl with egg whites: keep separate and use in another recipe).

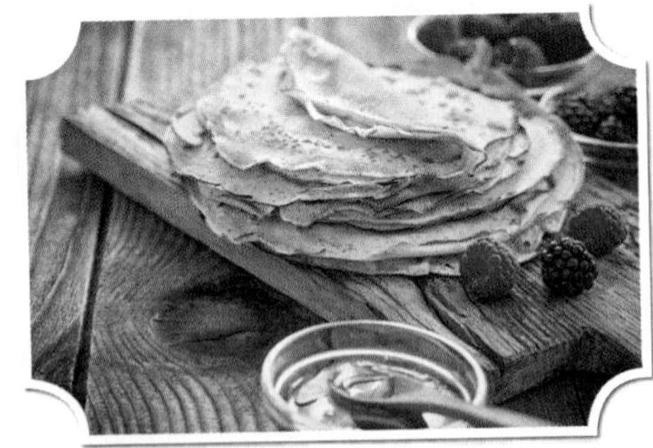

Batters are a mixture of flour, eggs and a liquid (usually milk). This mixture is beaten well to get air bubbles inside, which will make the batter rise when it is cooking (**see p. 277**). There are two types of batter:

1. **Thin batters:** Pancakes, crêpes, Yorkshire pudding
2. **Thick batters:** Coating foods, e.g. fritters

Custards

A custard is a mixture of eggs and milk, cooked gently so that the eggs thicken the milk. Custards form part of many hot and cold dishes, e.g. baked custard, crème caramel, crème brûlée and quiche.

Did You Know?

Commercial custards are made of starch. They are then coloured and flavoured to look and taste like custard.

Revision Questions

1. Assess the value of eggs and their uses in the diet.
2. Identify the culinary uses of eggs.
3. Explain how eggs are graded and labelled.
4. Compile guidelines for buying, storing and cooking eggs.
5. State the effects of cooking on eggs.

Meat alternatives

Soya beans

There are a number of different products made from soya beans on the market that can be used as high-protein alternatives to meat. Soya products are cheaper and more sustainable to produce than meat because they require less land and will grow in any climate. These products are like meat in nutritive value but contain fibre and lack saturated fat, making them healthier.

Tofu

Tofu is a white, creamy, high-protein food made by separating soya milk into curds (tofu) and whey and then pressing the curds into cubes or blocks. Tofu can be used in many ways:

- Cheese substitute in vegan pizza
- Chicken substitute in a stir-fry
- Marinated to make kebabs
- Blended with fruit into a smoothie or mousse
- Creamed with spices and herbs to make savoury dips
- Mixed with onion, garlic and herbs to form into burgers
- Coated in flour or egg and breadcrumbs
- Grilled or fried

Textured vegetable protein (TVP)

TVP is flavoured and shaped to resemble meat (as chunks, mince and steaks). TVP is usually bought dried and once **reconstituted** with water can be used in a huge variety of dishes, e.g. lasagne, spaghetti bolognese, burgers, stew and shepherd's pie. Some non-vegetarians use one-third TVP to two-thirds meat in dishes because it is healthier than using meat alone.

To **reconstitute** is to restore something (dried) to its original state (by adding water to it).

Pulse vegetables

Peas, beans and lentils are also used as meat substitutes because of their high protein content. Pulses often need soaking before use.

Nuts

Nuts are important in the diet because they are a rich source of omega fatty acids, fibre, iron and calcium.

- They include peanuts, pistachios, almonds, walnuts, cashews and pine nuts.
- They add texture and variety to recipes and meals.
- They can be used in sweet dishes, e.g. pecan pie, and savoury dishes, e.g. chicken satay.
- They are available whole, flaked, chopped and ground.
- They keep well and are easy to store.
- They are high in calories so must be restricted in low-calorie diets.
- Some people are allergic to nuts and must avoid them.

Discovery Learning

Do you know what to do if someone has an allergic reaction to nuts? It is a good idea to find out and share this information with your class.

Quorn

Quorn is a leading brand of mycoprotein food products. **Mycoprotein** is a term for protein-rich foodstuffs made from processed edible fungi. Quorn is produced both as a cooking ingredient and as a range of ready meals. It can be used for dishes such as pizza, lasagne and shepherd's pie.

Revision Questions

1. Write an informative note on soya bean products.
2. Explain what Quorn is and how it can be used in the diet.
3. Assess the value of protein alternatives in the diet.

15.10

Summary

- You need to have **two** servings from the meat, poultry, fish, eggs, beans and nuts group each day.
- **Meat** is the flesh of animals and birds and their edible internal organs (offal). It varies in flavour, composition and texture according to the type of animal, its age, breed, and feeding and rearing methods.
- Meat and poultry are a good source of **HBV protein, iron and vitamin B**. Chicken has less saturated fat than red meats. Both lack carbohydrate so should be served with carbohydrate-rich foods.
- Meat is composed of bundles of long, hollow fibres filled with meat juices containing extractives. They are held together with connective tissue. Fat cells are found between the fibres.
- **Toughness in meat** is caused by age, activity, incorrect hanging and cooking. Methods of tenderising include resting before slaughter and hanging after, mincing, beating, marinating, using meat tenderisers or slow methods of cooking.
- **Buy meat** from a clean, reliable and hygienic shop, where the meat is quality assured. Store and prepare meat safely to avoid food poisoning. During cooking the protein coagulates, some nutrients are lost, the colour changes and bacteria are destroyed. Extra care must be taken with chicken during preparing and cooking to prevent salmonella poisoning.
- Fresh meat has a **short shelf life** so it undergoes processing to extend it. It can be frozen, canned, cured, salted, smoked, dried or vacuum packed.
- There are three types of **fish**: white, oily and shellfish. Fish is an excellent source of HBV protein, vitamin B and iodine. Unsaturated fats (omega-3 fatty acids) and vitamins A and D are found in oily fish. Canned fish contains calcium.

- There are many varieties of fresh and processed fish. Some are cheap and nutritious and they can be prepared and cooked in a variety of ways.
- Buy fish from a clean, reliable and hygienic shop. It should smell of seaweed, have moist, unbroken, scaly skin, eyes should be bright, gills should be pink and the flesh should be firm. It should be stored on ice and used within 24 hours. Frozen fish should be solid, in date and stored in the freezer.
- Fresh fish has a **short shelf life** so it undergoes processing to extend its shelf life. It can be frozen, canned or smoked.
- During **cooking** the protein coagulates, the flesh becomes opaque and breaks apart easily, some nutrients are lost and bacteria are destroyed. Fish is often coated to protect it when cooking and it is often served in or with a sauce.
- **Eggs** are also a good source of HBV protein, calcium, iron and vitamins A, B and D. The fat is easily digested but is high in cholesterol. It contains no carbohydrates.
- Eggs are a cheap, versatile food that can be used in a wide variety of ways in sweet and savoury dishes.
- When **buying** eggs, they are graded according to size and class. All information about the eggs is contained on the carton in accordance with EU regulations. Store in the door of the fridge, with the pointed end downwards, and use in rotation. Use at room temperature to avoid curdling.
- During **cooking** the protein coagulates, the white becomes opaque and sets, the yolk hardens, some nutrients are lost and bacteria are destroyed. Lightly cooked eggs are easier to digest.
- Batters are either thin or thick and can be used to coat foods. A custard is a mixture of eggs and milk and can be used in sweet and savoury dishes.
- Meat alternatives come from soya beans (e.g. tofu and TVP), nuts and Quorn, which comes from a fungus. Meat alternatives are healthier than meat because they contain starch, fibre and omega fatty acids.

16 FATS, SPREADS AND OILS GROUP

Learning Outcomes 1.1, 1.2, 1.3, 1.4, 1.5, 1.6, 1.7, 1.9, 1.12, 1.13, 1.14, 1.15, 1.16, 1.17, 1.18, 1.19, 2.7

What I Will Learn

- to classify fats and oils and give examples of each type
- to identify the nutritive and dietetic value of fats, spreads and oils
- to explain how fats and vegetable oils are processed
- to compare and contrast dairy spreads
- to state the guidelines for selecting, storing and cooking fats and oils
- to state the uses of fats and oils in the diet
- to explain why foods on the top shelf of the food pyramid should be avoided

Key Words

✓ Solid	✓ Functional
✓ Liquid	✓ Spread
✓ Saturated	✓ Rendered
✓ Unsaturated	✓ Hydrogenation
✓ Margarine	

Spreads and oils provide essential fats but these are only needed in very small amounts. Choose low-fat and reduced-fat spreads and oils such as rapeseed or olive oil instead of hard margarine, lard or butter. Choose any two servings each day.

Mayonnaise and oil-based salad dressings also count towards your oil intake. Choose lower-fat options.

Don't Forget!
All oils contain the same amount of calories, so measure out the oil – don't just pour it onto the pan.

Fats are **solid** at room temperature and oils are **liquid** at room temperature. Visible fats can be clearly seen in or on food, e.g. butter, cream, fat on meat. However, other fats and oils are not clearly visible as they are combined with the food, e.g. fats in meat, cheese, eggs, milk and pastry.

Classification of fats and oils

This is done according to their source and how saturated it is.

Source	Type
Animal (saturated)	• **Suet** is raw beef or mutton fat, found around the loins and kidneys; it is used in pastries, steamed puddings and mincemeat • **Dripping** is the fat melted from beef used for roasting and frying • **Lard** is pig fat used for roasting and frying • **Dairy:** Milk, cream, butter, yoghurts and cheese • **Egg yolks** used in mayonnaise
Plant (unsaturated)	• **Vegetable oils**, e.g. maize, olive and soya beans • **Nut oils**, e.g. coconut, almond, walnut and peanut butter • **Seed oils**, e.g. sesame, sunflower and rapeseed • **Margarine**
Marine (unsaturated)	• **Oily fish**, e.g. salmon and tuna • **Fish liver oils**, e.g. cod and halibut liver oils

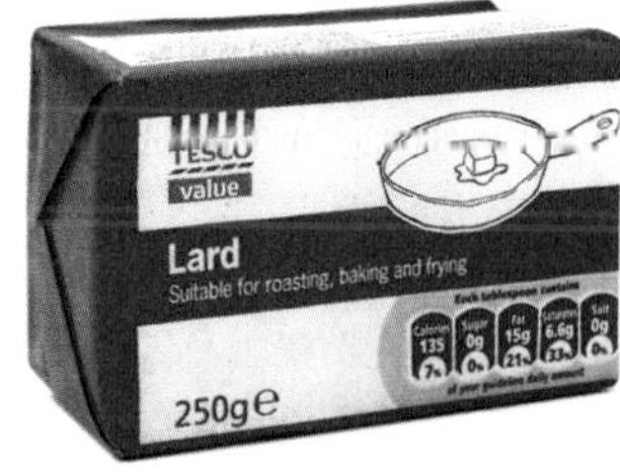

Did You Know?

Vegetable suet is available in supermarkets in Ireland. It is made from fat such as palm oil combined with rice flour. It resembles shredded beef suet, and is used as a vegetarian substitute in recipes.

Nutritive value of fats and oils

- Butter and margarine contain traces of **proteins**, while oils are usually lacking in them.
- **Fat** varies depending on type, e.g. butter (82%), oils (99.9%) and low-fat options (40%).
- **Carbohydrates** are lacking in fats and oils.
- Fats and oils are sources of **fat-soluble vitamins** A, D, E and K. The amount varies depending on the product, e.g. butter and dairy spreads contain traces of vitamin A and D, while margarine is fortified with them.
- There are trace amounts of **calcium** in butter and margarine.
- The **water** content varies according to the proportion of fat present in the product.

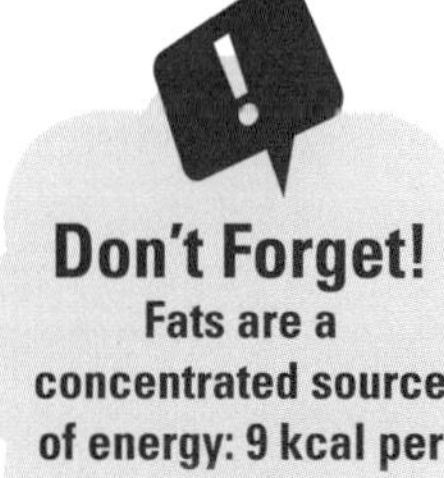

Don't Forget!
Fats are a concentrated source of energy: 9 kcal per 1 g of fat.

Dietetic value of fats and oils

(**For more information on fats, see p. 28**)

- They provide a concentrated source of heat and energy; they delay hunger because they stay in the stomach longer.
- They protect delicate organs, e.g. kidneys.
- They insulate the body in the form of adipose tissue and act as an energy reserve.
- They supply essential fatty acids and the fat-soluble vitamins A, D, E and K.
- They add flavour to food, e.g. in baking and salad dressings.

Factors that affect our choice of fats and oils

- **A person's health**: The choice of fat/oil may depend on its saturated or unsaturated fat content, e.g. butter versus low-fat spread.
- **How you want to use it**, e.g. how easy it is to spread for sandwiches, or cream in baking.
- **Flavour**: Used in salad dressings, e.g. olive or rapeseed oil. Butter is thought to have better flavour than margarine when used in cake-making.

Vegetable oils

These are obtained from a range of plants rich in oils, including:

- Cereals, e.g. corn (maize)
- Seeds, e.g. sesame, sunflower, rapeseed
- Olives
- Soya beans
- Nuts, e.g. coconuts, almonds, peanuts and walnuts

How oil is processed

Oils can be **hot pressed**, e.g. olive oil, or **cold pressed**, e.g. rapeseed oil. They differ in the following ways:

Hot-pressed oils	Cold-pressed oils
Plant material heated slightly (roasted)	Squeezed when cold
Extracts more oil	Extracts less oil
Bleached, filtered and odours removed	No additives

Further Investigation

Do you know what the difference between extra virgin and pure olive oil is? Find out online at **www.oliveoiltimes.com** and share your findings with someone else.

Did You Know?

Most good-quality oils are stored in coloured (green) glass bottles to keep them longer and filter out harmful ultraviolet (UV) rays.

Rapeseed oil

Rapeseed oil is cold pressed, so is more nutritious and contains half the saturated fat of olive oil, resulting in it being one of the healthiest culinary oils on the market. It contains no artificial colours, flavours or preservatives, and is a natural source of omega-3, -6, and -9 oils, which help to maintain normal cholesterol levels in the body, for a healthy heart and cardiovascular system.

Further Investigation

Visit the websites of the two Irish companies below for information, videos and interesting recipes.

www.donegalrapeseedoil.ie

www.secondnatureoils.com

Further Investigation

Watch the following videos on YouTube to learn more about how oil is made:
'How It's Made Vegetable Oil' (4:48)
'How Olive Oil is Made' (4:45)

Margarine

Margarine was originally developed as butter substitute. Manufacture is based on the principle of **hydrogenation**, i.e. converting liquid oils into solid fats by the addition of hydrogen gas. Margarine contains **trans fat**, which is considered by many doctors to be the worst type of fat you can eat. Unlike other dietary fats, trans fat both raises 'bad' cholesterol and lowers 'good' cholesterol.

Margarine can come in two forms:

Block margarine	Soft margarine
• Made mainly from vegetable oils but can contain marine and animal oils • High in saturated fat • Packaged in foil/waxed paper	• Contains vegetable oils, whey/buttermilk and water • High in saturated fat (but a little less so than block margarine) • Packaged in plastic tubs
Uses: Spreading, baking and frying	**Uses:** Spreading, baking and frying

Dairy spreads

A wide range of dairy spreads and butters are available to consumers. These include:

Dairy spread	Description	Examples
Low-fat dairy spreads	• Contains traces of protein • Fat (38–40%) • Low in saturates and high in monounsaturates	Dairygold Lighter Avonmore Extra Light Kerry Low-Low
Spreadable low-fat butters	• Protein (7%) • Fat (40%) • Higher in saturated fat	Connaught Gold Half-Fat
Functional dairy spreads	• Has traces of protein • No hydrogenated fatty acids • Virtually no trans-fatty acids • Contains plant stanol esters	Benecol Flora ProActiv

Functional foods can be defined as foods that provide a health benefit beyond basic nutrition. Examples of heart health foods include margarines with plant sterols or stanols, omega-3 enriched eggs and cereals with soya.

Did You Know?

By including **plant stanol ester** in the diet over a period of time, a gradual reduction in blood cholesterol levels will occur, leading to a reduction in the risk of heart disease.

Uses of fats and oils

- **Spreading**, e.g. on bread and crackers.
- **Adds flavour to food**, e.g. baking and salad dressing.
- **Improves appearance of sauces**, e.g. Alfredo sauce.
- **Prevents sticking in cooking**, e.g. shallow frying.
- **Frying:** Some vegetable oils are suitable for shallow and deep frying because of their high burning point, e.g. rapeseed oil has a high burning point of 240°C.
- **Creates emulsions**, e.g. mayonnaise.
- **Shortens:** Gives pastry its crumbly texture by inhibiting the formation of long protein strands.
- **Acts as a preservative (anti-staling)**, e.g. improves shelf life of bread and cakes.
- **Creaming,** e.g. Madeira and all-in-one mixtures.

16.6

Don't Forget!

Keep fats covered to prevent absorption of smells and flavours, and check best before dates before use.

Storage of fats and oils

Oils: Store in a cool, dry dark place.
Butter, margarine and dairy spreads: Store in the fridge.

Further Investigation

To find out more about margarine and for great baking tips and recipes go to **www.bakewithstork.com**.

Discovery Learning

If you want to cut down on the amount of oil used in cooking, Fry Light '1 Cal' sprays are useful and widely available. Visit your local supermarket or go online to find out what types of light oils are available. Present your findings to the class in a creative manner.

Foods and drinks high in fat, sugar and salt

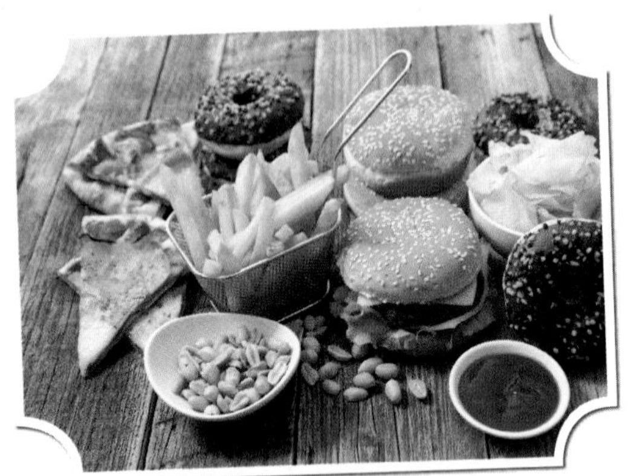

These foods should be avoided as they are high in fat, including saturated fat, sugar and salt. They may lead to obesity, heart disease, type 2 diabetes and some cancers.

Limit what you eat from this shelf to no more than one serving a day and ideally not every day. Don't be tempted to swap healthy foods for foods that are high in fat, sugar and salt. You need healthy foods in the recommended serving sizes to provide all your vitamins and minerals. There are **no** recommended servings for this group because they are not essential.

Revision Questions

1. Classify fats and oils and give two examples of each type.
2. Discuss the nutritive and dietetic value of fats and oils.
3. Classify dairy spreads and give an example of each.
4. List the culinary uses of fats and oils, providing an example in each case.

Summary

- Fats, spreads and oils provide essential fats that are only needed in very small amounts. Choose low-fat and reduced-fat spreads and oils such as rapeseed or olive oil instead of hard margarine, lard or butter.
- Choose any **two** servings each day.
- Choose plant or marine sources of saturated fats as they are high in unsaturated oils.
- Fats are **solid** at room temperature and oils are **liquid** at room temperature.
- Fats provide a concentrated source of heat and energy. They fill you up, protect delicate organs, insulate the body and act as an energy reserve. They supply essential fatty acids and the fat-soluble vitamins A, D, E and K. They also add flavour to food, e.g. baking, oils and salad dressings.
- **Vegetable oils** are obtained from a variety of plants rich in oils, including cereals (e.g. corn), seeds (e.g. rapeseed), olives, soya beans and nuts (e.g. coconuts and almonds).

- **Margarine and dairy spreads** are available too, but they can contain trans-fatty acids, which can increase cholesterol. Some spreads have extra health benefits. Read labels carefully and always be aware of portion sizes.
- **Foods and drinks high in fats**, especially saturated fats, **sugar and salt** should be avoided. They may lead to obesity, heart disease, type 2 diabetes and some cancers. Limit what you eat from this shelf to no more than one serving a day and ideally not every day.

17 FOOD PROCESSING AND LABELLING

Learning Outcomes 1.1, 1.5, 1.6, 1.7, 1.9, 1.15, 1.16, 1.17, 1.18, 1.19, 2.5, 2.7, 3.9

What I Will Learn

- to explain what a processed food is
- to understand why food is processed or preserved
- to state the aims of preserving foods
- to investigate the different methods of food preservation
- to develop a set of guidelines for home freezing
- to explain what convenience food is and give examples
- to state the advantages and disadvantages of convenience foods
- to develop a set of guidelines for buying, storing and preserving convenience foods
- to evaluate the packaging on convenience foods
- to assess the information found on food labels
- to explain what additives are and why they are used in food processing

Key Words

✓ Processed
✓ Preserved
✓ Shelf life
✓ Additive
✓ Preservative
✓ Antioxidant
✓ Emulsifier
✓ Stabiliser
✓ Freezing
✓ Canning
✓ Bottling
✓ Dehydration
✓ Irradiation
✓ Blanching
✓ Cook-chill
✓ Convenience
✓ Additive
✓ Biodegradable
✓ Recycling

Processed foods

Processing means foods are prepared in some way before being put on sale.
Preserving means treating foods to make them last longer.
Shelf life is the length of time a food remains nourishing and safe to eat.

Most foods are prepared in some way before being put on the shelf. The degree of processing varies considerably.

1. **Minimal processing** makes changes to basic foodstuffs, e.g. fruit and vegetables can be washed, peeled, sliced, juiced, frozen or dried. This type of processing can also be used to extend shelf life, e.g. milk is pasteurised.
2. **Medium processing** makes food saleable and ready for cooking and eating, e.g. milling wheat into flour or making vegetable oil from seeds and nuts.
3. Basic foods and ingredients are **highly processed** to give them added value. This type of processing takes a basic processed food and uses it to produce a food product of a higher economic value, e.g. making margarine from vegetable oil; making bread, cakes and biscuits from flour; making dairy products from milk; producing convenience meals from other processed food.

Why is food processed?

(Food groups, see p. 54)

- To extend the shelf life
- To make it safe to eat
- To save time and energy used in preparing and cooking food, e.g. cook-chill foods
- To cut down on waste
- To add variety to the diet by creating new food products, e.g. cheese, ice cream, yoghurt
- For healthier food options, e.g. Benecol drinks and Flora ProActiv butter
- To ensure a wider choice of food all year round, e.g. frozen and canned varieties of foods that are out of season
- To add nutritional value and to fortify food, e.g. breakfast cereals and supermilk

The range of processed foods includes: Milk, cheese, yoghurt, butter, margarine, spreads, flour, pasta, rice, bread, cakes, biscuits, breakfast cereals, and prepared products and meals.

Food preservation

(Food spoilage, see p. 85)

Food preservation is a form of food processing that slows down food spoilage (food going off). Food spoilage is caused by enzymes and micro-organisms (moulds, yeasts and bacteria).

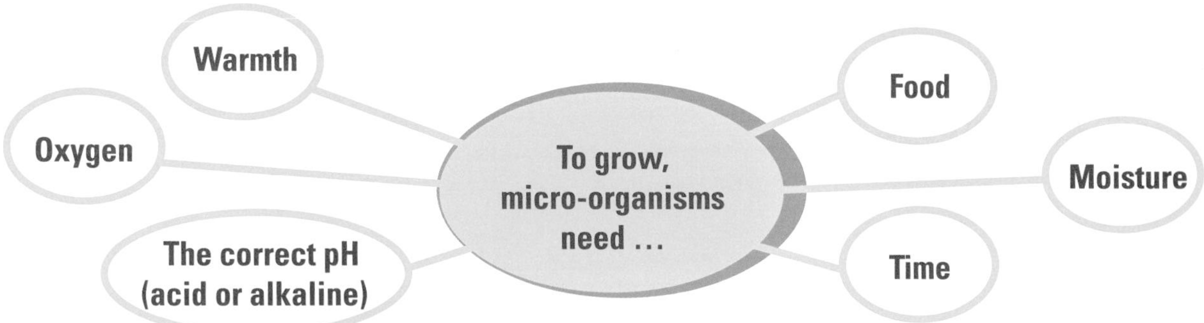

Preservation works by removing one or more of these conditions:

- **Warmth:** Refrigeration, freezing
- **Moisture:** Drying (dehydration)
- **Oxygen:** Canning, bottling

Changing the pH of food by using vinegar acts as a preservative. Using **sugar** and **salt** as preservatives also makes it difficult for micro-organisms to grow.

The aim of preservation is to:

- Kill or inactivate micro-organisms
- Prevent any new micro-organisms from entering the food
- Prevent enzyme activity which causes food to decay
- Keep the original qualities of the food, i.e. flavour, texture and nutritive value

Methods of preserving	How it works
Freezing	• Removes warmth • At very low temperatures (–18°C to –30°C) the water is changed to ice and the food is wrapped or sealed
Drying	Moisture is removed and the food is packed in airtight containers, e.g. pasta, raisins, rice, soups and breakfast cereals **Freeze-drying (AFD: accelerated freeze-drying)** can also be used: • Food is frozen, then moisture is removed and packaging is made airtight • This ensures a better retention of flavour, colour and texture, e.g. coffee
Canning/ bottling	• Removes oxygen • Food is heated to a very high temperature and is then sealed in airtight, sterilised bottles and cans, e.g. beans, jams, pickle and chutney
Using preservatives	• **Salt**, **sugar** and **vinegar** change the pH of food and act as preservatives, e.g. salted fish, jam, pickles, chutneys and relishes • The chemicals in **smoke** preserve food, e.g. smoked fish, ham and bacon • In commercial products, chemical preservatives like antioxidants are used to prevent oxygen, which makes the food deteriorate
Pasteurisation and sterilisation	Milk is heated and cooled, then stored in sterile containers
Irradiation	Energy waves are passed through the food to kill micro-organisms

To **accelerate** is to speed up, or to make it happen quickly.

Did You Know?

Irradiation kills micro-organisms and insects, inactivates enzymes, and can delay ripening or sprouting. It can also destroy some vitamins. Any irradiated food used within the EU must carry a label saying it is irradiated and carry the Radura symbol. Irradiation is used in the preservation of over 60 types of food, e.g. fruit, vegetables and cereals in 40 countries worldwide. At the moment, dried herbs, spices and vegetable seasonings are the only irradiated foodstuffs authorised across the EU.

Home freezing

The advantages and disadvantages of home freezing are listed below.

Advantages	Disadvantages
• A simple and safe method of preservation • Foods are available out of season • Adds variety to the diet • Most foods can be frozen • Freezing leftover food avoids waste • Bulk cooking and freezing saves time and fuel • Useful in emergencies • Foods retain their colour, flavour, texture and nutritive value	• Cost – and running cost – of freezer • Space needed for freezer • Rules for freezing and thawing must be followed for food safety • Defrosting the freezer takes time and effort • Can cause some damage to texture of food

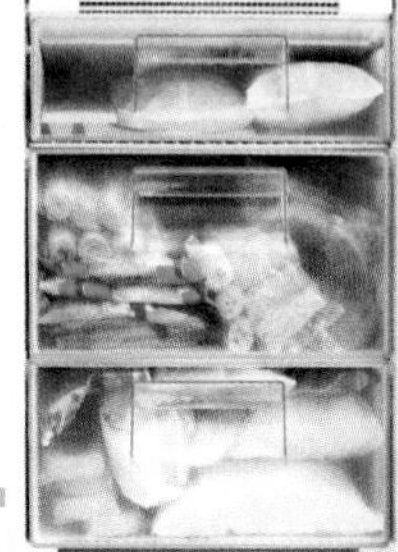

Guidelines for home freezing

Preparation	• Turn on fast-freeze button on the freezer, three to four hours before the food goes in • Only freeze one-tenth of the total freezer capacity at one time or over a 24-hour period • Choose good-quality fresh food • Cool foods well before freezing • **Blanch** vegetables first to destroy enzymes and prevent enzymatic spoilage of frozen foods • **Open-freeze** food that will stick together, then pack, e.g. berries and prawns
Packaging	• Pack in usable quantities • Seal well in packaging, removing as much air as possible • Use strong, vapour- and moisture-proof packaging, e.g. polythene freezer bags • Allow expansion room in liquid foods • Label food with name, quantity and date
Freezing	• Place in fast-freeze compartment, touching base or sides – don't overpack compartment • Leave for recommended time – up to 24 hours – then remove frozen food and place in storage sections • Open-frozen foods can now be packed into the container • Turn off fast-freeze button
Storage	• Store similar food together • Store for recommended time • Use in rotation • Keep freezer filled as it reduces running costs • Avoid opening the door unnecessarily

To **blanch** vegetables, place the prepared vegetables into boiling water for one to four minutes to inactivate enzymes. Then plunge them into cold water to stop them from cooking.

Open freezing can be done for items that could stick together, e.g. berries or sliced apple. These should be prepared as for cooking – so they are washed, peeled, cored, trimmed, etc. Lay the pieces individually on a tray, keeping them separate from each other, and freeze. Once they are frozen, pack them in a box or bag and put them back in the freezer to store for the recommended time.

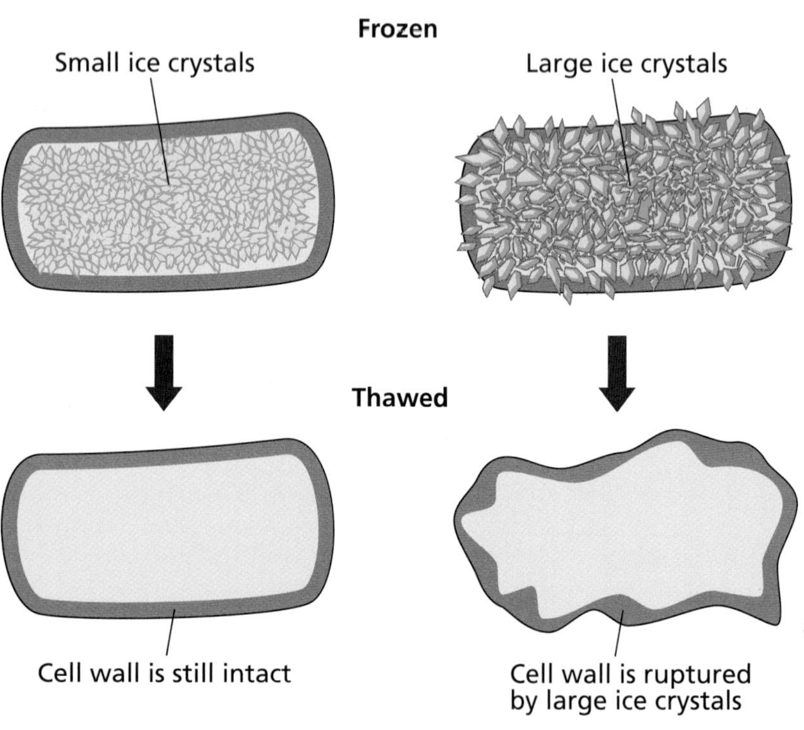

Did You Know?

Home freezing is done at –25°C and frozen food is stored at –18°C. Food is blast frozen commercially at –30°C. Fast freezing causes less damage in the cells of food and retains the texture and nutritive value of the food.

When food is frozen quickly, the ice crystals that form in its cells are small, and cause less damage to the cell wall than the large crystals formed in slower freezing.

Storage times for frozen foods

Chicken, vegetables and beef	**12 months**
White fish, cooked pastry and lamb	**6 months**
Oily fish	**4 months**
Soups, sauces and mincemeat	**3 months**
Casseroles	**2 months**
Bread	**1 month**

Don't Forget!

If you do not wrap food well, it could lead to freezer burn. This is the toughening, discolouration and drying out of food that has been exposed in the freezer. It usually occurs on protein foods such as meat and fish.

Packaging must be **airtight**, **waterproof** and **vapour-proof**.

Suitable materials for freezer packaging include:

- Polythene boxes – strong, reusable but expensive
- Polythene bags
- Foil containers
- Waxed cartons and tubs
- Margarine/ice cream tubs (**storage, see p. 103**)

Discovery Learning

Find out how to freeze a batch of vegetables and then prepare, pack, freeze and store a batch of carrots or broccoli. Come up with a recipe that will use these frozen vegetables. Share your recipes with your classmates.

Below is a chart of what foods can and cannot be frozen.

Foods that can be frozen	Foods unsuitable for freezing
• Raw and cooked meats, fish and poultry • Fresh fruit and vegetables • Reheated dishes, e.g. fishcakes and shepherd's pie • Uncooked dough and pastry • Sauces, soups, stews and savoury dishes • Breadcrumbs, stuffing, some sandwiches and packed lunches • Prepared baby foods • Advanced cooking for occasions, e.g. birthdays, Christmas, etc.	• Bananas, as they blacken • Lettuce, cucumber and salad greens, as they go limp • Whole tomatoes; tomato purée can be frozen • Whole melon or pears unless in a syrup • Milk, cream and plain yoghurt, as they separate • Whole eggs; yolks and whites can be frozen separately • Jelly and mayonnaise, as they separate • Whole potatoes; potato purée or partly cooked chips can be frozen

Other methods of home preservation include:

- **Dehydration**, e.g. Drying herbs.
- Using **heat treatments** to preserve fruit and vegetables by making jams, pickles, relishes and chutneys.

Revision Questions

1. What is a processed food?
2. Give three reasons why food is processed.
3. What are the aims of preserving foods?
4. Outline the different methods of preserving foods.
5. Compile a set of guidelines for home freezing.

• Use your workbook to revise this chapter •

Convenience foods

A number of processed foods are classified as convenience foods, e.g. frozen, canned, bottled, dried, cook-chill foods and instant or takeaway foods. Foods are partly or totally prepared so they are easier for the consumer to use, saving them time, energy and fuel. Convenience foods also include fortified, functional and novel protein foods.

Advantages and disadvantages of convenience foods

Advantages	Disadvantages
• Save time and labour, e.g. pre-chopped tinned tomatoes • Reduce fuel costs during cooking, e.g. reheating in microwave • Little cooking skills required, e.g. frozen chicken supreme and rice • Little or no waste, e.g. tinned beans • Often fortified with vitamins and minerals, e.g. milk • Often prepared in portion sizes, e.g. single or two portions, useful for people living alone • Easily stored and transported, e.g. coffee, cocoa • Large variety available, which encourages people to try new products, e.g. almond/soya milk • Consumer demands are catered for, e.g. low-fat foods • Useful for disabled or older people	• More expensive than homemade products, e.g. soup • Many contain additives such as preservatives, colourings and flavourings **(🔗 additives, see p. 227)** • Often low in fibre which is removed during processing, e.g. white rice • Often high in salt, sugar and fat, e.g. pizza • Inferior taste, colour and texture in comparison to homemade/fresh version, e.g. pasta

Passata is an uncooked tomato purée that has been strained of seeds and skins.

Classification of convenience foods

Convenience foods can be classified according to the degree of preparation required before eating.

Classification	Effect of process	Buying, storing and using
Frozen	**Nutritive value:** Similar to fresh food, but often higher in vitamins and minerals, as foods like fruit and vegetables are at their freshest when they are frozen. **Quality:** If correctly sealed and stored, appearance and flavour are similar to fresh food. **Cost:** Tend to be more expensive than fresh food, but there is no waste. **Examples of frozen products:** Meats, fish, chicken, vegetables, fruit, complete meals, desserts	**Buying:** Food should be correctly stored in the freezer and should be frozen solid. The packaging should be intact and sealed. Check expiry date. **Storing:** Put in the freezer as soon as possible or in the freezing compartment of a fridge. Store for the recommended time only. Never refreeze thawed food (**why?**). **Using:** Follow the instructions on the package as many are cooked from frozen. Thaw meat, poultry and fish in a fridge before cooking, or thaw in a microwave.
Canned/ bottled	**Nutritive value:** Some vitamins and minerals are lost during processing, or they may seep into the canning liquid. Fruit tinned in syrup is high in sugar; fish tinned in oil is higher in fat, while if brine is used there will be more sodium. **Quality:** The texture softens and the food can contain additives like colourings. **Cost:** Usually cheaper than frozen foods. As they are already cooked, they save on fuel as they only need reheating.	**Buying:** Avoid dented, rusted or bulging tins. Check date stamps. **Storing:** Store in a cool, dry cupboard. **Using:** Reheat in the canning liquid. If all the contents are not being used, remove from the tin or bottle, place in a clean container, cover and store in the fridge and use within two days. **Examples of canned/bottled foods:** Fish, vegetables, soup, fruit, jam, pickles, chutney, sauces
Dried foods	**Nutritive value:** Some loss of vitamin C. The water that is removed during drying is usually returned to the food during cooking. **Quality:** The texture and flavour is very different from fresh foods but once rehydrated it is similar. **Cost:** Cheaper than fresh versions. **Examples of dried foods:** Milk, soups, sauces, fruit, cake and bread mixes, TVP, stock cubes foods	**Buying:** Check date stamps and ensure that the packet is sealed. **Storing:** Store in a cool, dry cupboard. Use quickly once opened or store in airtight containers. **Using:** Follow the instructions on the packet. Some foods like dried soup or sauce will need water added to replace the liquid lost in drying.

Classification	Effect of process	Buying, storing and using
Cook-chill (refrigerated)	**Nutritive value:** This varies according to the product. Some contain additives, and are high in salt and refined carbohydrates. Healthier versions are lower in salt and fat and contain fibre and vitamins. **Quality:** Cook-chill foods are usually of a good quality but quantities may be small. **Cost:** They tend to be expensive.	**Buying:** Make sure they are stored correctly in the shop (**where?**). Check date stamps. **Storing:** Put in the fridge as soon as possible. Use up quickly once opened. **Using:** Use within the recommended time. Reheat thoroughly or cook according to instructions on the packet. **Examples of cook-chill foods:** Cartons or tubs of soups and sauces, quiche, lasagne, sausage rolls
Instant or takeaway food	**Nutritive value:** Varies according to the ingredients in the product. Some are balanced and nutritious, while others contain additives, refined carbohydrates, and are high in salt. **Quality:** Usually good quality. **Cost:** Some are expensive, while some (ready meals) can be good value. **Examples of instant/takeaway food:** Cakes, biscuits, chips, burgers, pizza, breakfast rolls, ready-to-cook meals, prepared salads and sandwiches	**Buying:** Make sure they are stored correctly in the shop. Check date stamps. **Storing:** Put in the fridge as soon as possible. Use up quickly once opened. **Using:** Use within the recommended time. Reheat thoroughly or cook according to instructions on the packet.

Being clever with convenience foods

- Try not to use too many convenience foods, but remember they can be useful when time is limited.
- Combine them with fresh foods, e.g. cook-chill lasagne with tossed salad.
- Use them as part of more complicated recipes to save time and effort, e.g. use a passata in pizza or a packet of cheese sauce in a lasagne.
- Always cook ready-to-cook meals according to the instructions on the label.
- Cook-chill foods must be stored carefully and reheated thoroughly.

Food packaging

Food products are packaged in order to:

- protect the food from contamination during transport and storage to ensure it arrives in peak condition
- make the food easier to transport, store and sell
- preserve food, thereby preventing waste and food spoilage
- increase the shelf life of food, thus reducing waste
- make the food more attractive to the consumer
- provide information for the consumer, e.g. use by date, nutritional information and cooking instructions

Good food packaging should be:

- Safe and non-toxic
- Hygienic
- Easy to open and reseal
- Economical to produce
- Strong and long lasting
- **Biodegradable** or **recyclable**
- Odourless
- Moisture- and vapour-proof
- Able to prevent contamination by micro-organisms
- Attractive – colours help the product stand out; the shape should be simple or striking and the image or logo should stand out

Biodegradable means that a material is capable of decomposing.

Recycling is the process of turning used waste and materials into new products. This prevents potentially useful materials from being wasted, as well as reducing energy use and pollution

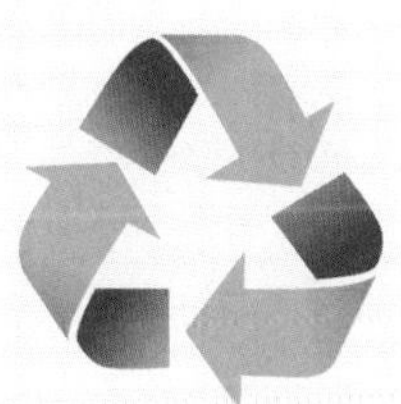

Did You Know?

If a substance enters a food indirectly, e.g. from packaging, air or careless handling, it is known as a **contaminant**.

Materials used in packaging

Metals	Advantages	Disadvantages
• Aluminium, tin, plated steel • Tin cans • Aluminium cans • Aluminium foil wrap • Foil containers • Foil bags • Aerosols	• Totally protects food by preventing the entry of gases, micro-organisms and moisture • Cans and tins are easy to stack and store • Metals can be heated, but not in a microwave (see p. 127) • Can be lacquered to prevent reaction with food	• Can be heavy, so they increase transport costs • Can be expensive to produce • Some are not recyclable

Examples of use	Environmental impact
• Fruit • Fish • Soft drinks • Butter • Takeaways • Coffee • Whipped cream	• Metal is a limited and non-renewable resource • Non-biodegradable but recyclable • Metal makes up 3.5% of domestic waste • Recycling saves raw materials and energy • The aluminium can is one of the most valuable waste materials • Recycling aluminium cans uses only 5% of the energy that would be needed to make them from scratch

To **lacquer** is to put a protective coating on inside of tin to protect the food.

Did You Know?

We each produce 344 kg of household waste annually. Can you suggest five things we can do to cut down on household waste?

Glass	Advantages	Disadvantages
• Jars • Bottles 	• Hygienic as it can be sterilised • Protects food from contaminants • Rigid containers that come in a variety of shapes, sizes and colours • Transparent and resealable • Easy to stack • Suited to heat treatments • Don't react with food • Easily moulded	• Heavy to transport • Fragile and easy to break • Expensive to make
Examples of use	**Environmental impact**	
• Mayonnaise • Olive oil • Sauces • Soft drinks • Jam • Preserves	• Glass makes up 7.5% of domestic waste • Reusable and 100% recyclable collected glass is crushed and used as a substitute for making new glass • There are numerous collection points (bottle banks) countrywide • Can be recycled many times with no loss in quality • Recycling saves energy, raw materials, production costs and landfill costs	

Did You Know?

- Energy saved from recycling one glass bottle can run a 100-watt light bulb for four hours.
- It also causes 20% less air pollution and 50% less water pollution than when a new bottle is made from raw materials.
- A modern glass bottle would take 4,000 years or more to decompose – and even longer if it's in the landfill.

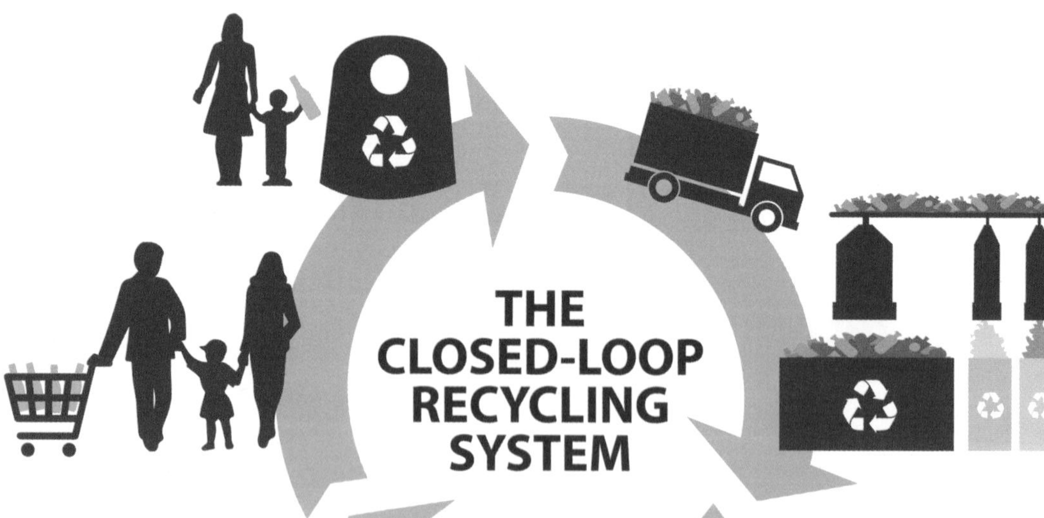

Discovery Learning

Find out some more interesting facts about recycling. Then come back and share them with the class.

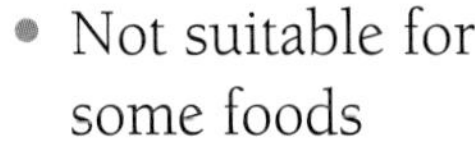

Paper	Advantages	Disadvantages
• Plain paper • Waxed paper • Waxed/laminated cardboard cartons • Greaseproof paper • Cardboard	• Biodegradable • Low in cost • Easy to open • Lightweight • Can be printed on • Waxed paper is waterproof and can be heat-sealed • Waxed cartons are suitable for sterilising (Tetra Pak)	• Not suitable for some foods • It is not easy to reseal • Plain paper is not very strong and disintegrates when wet

Examples of use	Environmental impact
• Sugar • Bread • Orange juice • Sausage rolls • Milk • Cereal boxes • Eggs	• Paper is an environmentally friendly packaging that is biodegradable and recyclable • The average household throws away 13,000 separate pieces of paper each year – most is packaging and junk mail • Recycling saves energy, conserves trees (17 trees = 1 tonne paper) and saves on disposal costs

Further Investigation

Many supermarkets in Ireland have made a commitment to reducing their waste. To find out more, visit **www.aldi.ie/waste-and-recycling** and **www.abettertomorrow-lidl.ie**.

Plastic	Advantages	Disadvantages
• Plastic cartons or boxes • PET (polyethylene terephthalate) bottles • Polystyrene • Modified Atmosphere Packaging (MAP)	• Strong and moisture-proof • Lightweight and flexible • Heat-sealable • Relatively low in cost • Suitable for frozen foods • Comes in a variety of weights, sizes, thicknesses and shapes • Can be printed on • Convenient and easy to handle	Some plastic containers/ packaging can contaminate food if heated, so food needs to be removed into another container to be heated

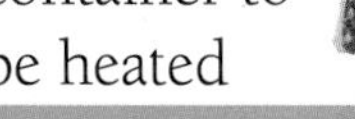

Examples of use	Environmental impact
• Dried pasta • Yoghurt • Dairy spread • Soft drinks • Takeaway food	• 120,000 tonnes of waste plastic are generated in Ireland each year • Plastic is not biodegradable and is made from crude oil which is a limited, non-renewable source of energy • A limited amount of plastic is recycled in Ireland, because the procedure is costly, time consuming and we have limited facilities • PET can be recycled as fibre • Plastic packaging litter is a major environmental hazard

Did You Know?

Plastic bags that are thrown into the world's oceans kill over a million sea creatures a year.

Did You Know?

PET stands for **polyethylene terephthalate**.

- Many drinks, food items and other consumer products are delivered in bottles or packages made from PET.
- PET makes good packaging because it's safe, strong, transparent and versatile so manufacturers like it.
- Customers choose it for its safety, light weight, resealability, shatter-resistance and recyclability.
- Up to 100% of a PET package can be made from recycled PET, and the material can be recycled again and again so it is good for the environment.
- PET can be recycled into many other new products, e.g. new bottles; fibre for carpets; fabric for t-shirts or fleece jackets; fiberfill for sleeping bags and dog beds; car parts like bumpers and door panels.

Further Investigation

To **find** how PET can be recycled into fibre, watch the video 'How Plastic Bottles are Recycled into Polyester' (5:29) on YouTube.

Consumer responsibility

To reduce the impact of packaging materials on the environment, consumers should:

- Reduce, reuse and recycle where possible
- Avoid buying products with excess packaging
- Buy loose rather than pre-packed fruit and vegetables
- Compact cartons, cans and bottles before recycling
- Compost organic packaging like cardboard and paper, as well as food waste
- Buy products in recycled packaging
- Buy in bulk or economy size to reduce packaging
- Buy concentrated detergents, softeners and deodorants
- Use cloth or other reusable bags when shopping

Did You Know?

The plastic bag levy was first introduced on 4th March 2002 at the rate of 15c per bag. Its main purpose was to reduce the consumption of disposable plastic bags by influencing consumer behaviour. It had an immediate effect on consumer behaviour with a decrease in annual plastic bag usage from an estimated 328 bags per capita to 21 bags per capita overnight.

Further Investigation

To find out more about recycling in Ireland watch the video 'Recycling Waste as a Resource' (6:35) on YouTube.

Food labels

Labels on food products are an important source of information and are controlled by Irish law, e.g. Consumer Information Act 1978 and EU Directives. The information most pre-packed foods must show is contained on the diagram below.

- Name of food and processing method, e.g. condensed milk
- Ingredients in order of descending weight – additives including flavourings and sweeteners must be included
- Quantity (%) of certain ingredients, e.g. beef in beef burgers.
- Net quantity/weight in metric (kg or litre)
- Use by date on perishables; best before date on non-perishables.
- Instructions for storage and use if necessary
- Name and address of manufacturer, packager or seller in the EU
- Place of origin if absence might mislead the consumer, e.g. Irish beef

A detailed ingredients list and nutritional information are important to all consumers, but they are especially important for those who must follow a special diet, e.g. coeliacs or diabetics, or anyone who is allergic to certain ingredients or additives, e.g. nuts, or on a low-sugar, salt, fat or cholesterol diet (**special diets, see p. 65**).

The traffic light system on labels is very simple and gives guidance on high, medium and low levels of key nutrients.

Red = high
Amber = medium
Green = low

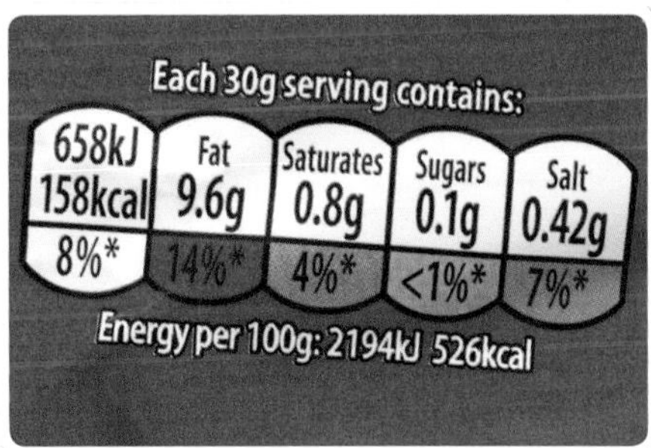

Did You Know?

When reading labels, be aware that:

- Salt can be labelled as 'sodium', 'NaCl' or 'monosodium glutamate'
- Sugar can be listed as 'dextrose' or 'maltose', etc.
- Natural or artificial colourings, flavourings and sweeteners may be used

Additives

Additives are substances put into food during processing in order to improve it in some way. They may be natural, e.g. spices or herbs, or artificial, e.g. tartrazine is a yellow colour found in sweets and soft drinks.

Additives must be tested for safety before they are used in food. Once passed, they are given an 'E' number. The number means that the additive has been passed by EU law. The amounts used in food are strictly controlled.

Food labels must state:
- The type of additive, e.g. colouring, flavouring or preservative
- The chemical name of the additive or its E number

The use of food additives must not mislead the consumer, i.e. issues related to the nature, freshness, quality of ingredients used, and they must be of benefit to the consumer.

Additives are used to:
- Improve the taste and texture of the food
- Make the food look appetising
- Preserve the food
- Ensure that the food stays safe to eat for longer to reduce the risks of food poisoning
- Make food easier to prepare

Types of additives

Additive	Example	Used in	Function
Colourings E100–E199	• Chlorophyll (E140) (green) • Caramel (E150) (brown) • Tartrazine (E102) (yellow)	• Dairy spreads • Soups and sauces • Gravy and brown sauces • Soft drinks and sweets	• Improve appearance of food • Replace colour lost in processing • Give colour to food that would be colourless otherwise • Satisfy consumer expectations
Preservatives E200–E299	• Salt • Sugar • Vinegar	• Bacon • Jam • Pickles	• Prevent food spoilage • Extend shelf life • Prevent food poisoning • Reduce waste • Ensure a greater variety of food is available out of season
Flavourings (not on E list)	• Salt, pepper, herbs, spices	• Stock cubes, cakes	• Improve or intensify taste
Sweeteners	• Sugar and honey • Aspartame (E951), e.g. NutraSweet, Canderel • Saccharine (E954), e.g. Hermesetas	• Cakes and biscuits • Low-calorie drinks and diabetic food	• To sweeten foods • Used instead of sugar
Antioxidants E300–399	• Vitamin E • Vitamin C	• Dairy spreads	• Prevent foods containing fats from spoiling (going rancid)
Emulsifiers or stabilisers E400–499	• Lecithin	• Mayonnaise	• Help oil and water to mix and stay mixed • Prevent sauces from separating
Nutritive additives	• Iron • Vitamin B	• Breakfast cereals, milk, bread	• Improve the nutritional value of food

Did You Know?

Monosodium glutamate (E621) is a flavour enhancer found in many snack foods. Artificial sweeteners make many foods sweet without adding calories. Can you find out why many people do not want to eat products containing these additives? Share what you discover with the class.

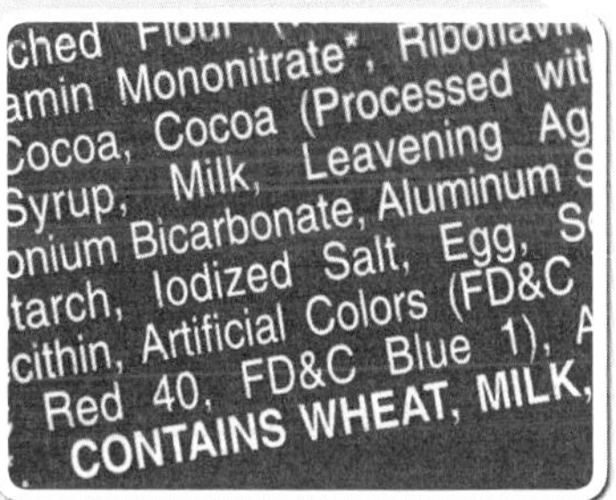

Antioxidants prevent the oxygen in air from turning fats rancid.

The advantages and disadvantages of additives

Advantages	Disadvantages
• Additives improve the colour, flavour and texture of food. • They preserve food, which prevents waste and reduces the risk of food poisoning. • They give us a wider choice of foods all year round. • They help maintain the quality of preserved food.	• Some people are allergic to certain additives (**special diets, see p. 79**). • Some additives deceive the consumer, e.g. sugar in products listed in many ways: dextrose, glucose, sucrose, etc. • Foods may contain more additives than necessary. • Possible side effects include hyperactivity in children and cancer.

Did You Know?

Genetically modified (GM) foods have had their chemical structure altered. This is done for a variety of reasons but the main aim is to produce food that is easier and cheaper to grow, as GM foods are more resistant to pesticides and the cold.

Discovery Learning

Can you find out why many people are worried about the future health risks of genetically modifying food? Share your findings with the class.

Revision Questions

1. Write an informative note on the use of convenience foods in the diet.
2. Explain why it is important to be aware of packaging while shopping for food.
3. What information must be display on a food label? Explain how this benefits the consumer.
4. Explain what additives are and why they are used in food processing.

Summary

- **Processing** means foods are prepared or altered in some way before being put on sale. **Preserving** means treating foods to make them last longer.
- **Food is processed** to extend shelf life, to make it safe to eat, to save time and energy and to cut down on waste. Food processing adds variety to the diet by creating new food products, including healthier options, to ensure a wide choice of foods all year round. It also adds nutritional value and fortifies food.
- **Preservation aims** to kill or inactivate micro-organisms, or to prevent them from re-entering the food. It also prevents enzyme activity – which causes food to decay – while keeping the original qualities of the food, i.e. flavour, texture and nutritive value.
- Food can be preserved by freezing, canning, bottling, drying and irradiation.
- To **freeze foods at home**, pre-cool the freezer (–25°C), prepare the food, make sure it is cold, wrap or seal it well and put it in the fast-freeze section of the freezer.
- The **advantages** of freezing are: it is a safe method of preservation; foods are available out of season, adding variety to the diet while remaining nutritious; most foods can be frozen; freezing leftovers avoids waste; bulk cooking and freezing saves time and fuel so it is useful in emergencies.
- **Packaging** protects food from contamination, making it easier to transport, store and sell. It prevents waste by increasing the shelf life of food and makes it more attractive to the consumer and provides essential information. Environmentally friendly packaging can be recycled or reused. Packaging must be safe, non-toxic, hygienic, strong, odourless, moisture- and vapour-proof, and should also be easy to open and reseal.
- **Convenience** foods have been processed by a manufacturer. They include frozen, canned/bottled, dried, cook-chill, instant and takeaway foods. They save time and energy and are useful in emergencies. Combining them with fresh foods improves their nutritive value. Store and use convenience foods correctly, according to the instructions on the label.
- Food labels should provide the following information: **name of food** and **processing method**, the **ingredients** in order of descending weight with the quantity (%) of certain ingredients and additives identified, **the net quantity/weight** shown in metric (kg or litre). The **use by date** is shown on perishables, and the **best before date** is on non-perishables. Food labels should also contain instructions for **storage and use** if necessary, and the **name and address** of the manufacturer, packager or seller in the EU.
- **Additives** are put in food to improve the colour, flavour and texture of the food. They can also preserve food by preventing food spoilage and food poisoning. Additives are tested for safety; they are put in foods in controlled amounts and most additives are assigned an E number.

18 PREPARING FOR FOOD LITERACY SKILLS BRIEF AND PRACTICAL FOOD SKILLS EXAM

Learning Outcomes 1.1, 1.2, 1.3, 1.4, 1.5, 1.6, 1.7, 1.8, 1.9, 1.10, 1.12, 1.13, 1.14, 1.15, 1.16, 1.17, 1.18, 1.19, 2.5, 2.7, 2.8, 2.9, 2.10

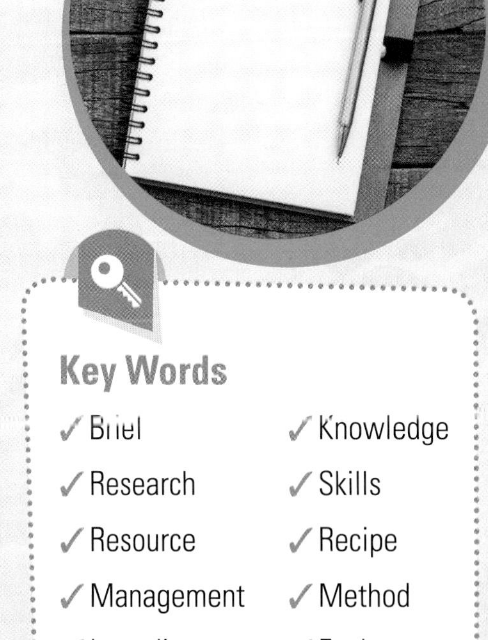

What I Will Learn

- to apply the design brief process to Classroom-Based Assessment 2: Food Literacy Skills Brief
- to conduct research using a variety of sources
- to generate a variety of ideas and possible solutions
- to analyse the requirements for the brief
- to discuss how to approach the brief with my peers and the teacher
- to use technology, as appropriate, in the preparation and cooking of food
- to demonstrate a range of cooking principles and techniques
- to apply sustainable resource management practices
- to apply safe and hygienic practices in food handling, preparation, storage and serving
- to demonstrate culinary and creative skills in preparation, implementation and presentation
- to evaluate and reflect on the task when completed

Key Words

- ✓ Brief
- ✓ Research
- ✓ Resource
- ✓ Management
- ✓ Ingredients
- ✓ Equipment
- ✓ Knowledge
- ✓ Skills
- ✓ Recipe
- ✓ Method
- ✓ Evaluate

During the first two years of Junior Cycle Home Economics you will be provided with many opportunities to:

- Plan, prepare, cost and evaluate healthy and nutritious individual and family meals and snacks, considering any individuals with diet-related diseases or special dietary considerations.
- Apply safe and hygienic practices in food handling, preparation and storage and apply a range of cooking principles and techniques in the preparation of healthy individual and family meals incorporating budgetary considerations and using available technology.
- Investigate the impact of our food choices from an ecological and ethical perspective, while applying sustainable practices to the selection and management of food and material resources.

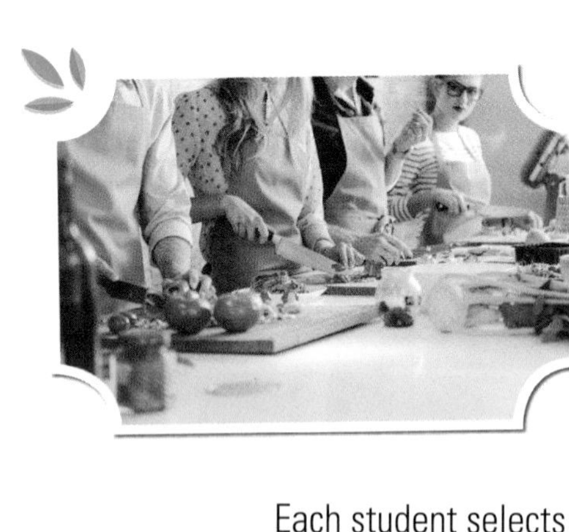

- Compare common foods used in food preparation and how they affect the nutrition and sensory quality of the product and interpret the information found on food packaging and labels to help you evaluate commercial and homemade food products.

At the beginning of year three, you will carry out your second Classroom-Based Assessment: Food Literacy Skills Brief, which will be assessed by your teacher and reported on to your parents.

Don't Forget!
Links are made to CBA2 and the Practical Food Skills examination throughout this book.

Each student selects a brief from a list of briefs issued each year by the State Examinations Commission (SEC). It is directly linked to the Practical Food Skills examination (students use the same brief for both), which may include, but is not limited to, options from the following broad areas:

- Healthy family meals to reflect the current healthy eating guidelines, e.g. low in sugar, salt and fat; high in fibre, fruit and vegetables (**nutrition, see p. 16; healthy eating guidelines, see p. 56)**
- A special dietary consideration or a diet-related disease (**special diets, see p. 65)**
- A particular stage of the lifecycle (**balanced diet, see p. 53)**
- Healthy school lunches (**meal planning, see p. 95; lunches, see p. 133)**
- A healthy homemade alternative to a commercial or takeaway meal (**healthy eating, see p. 56; consumer choices, see p. 349)**
- Resourceful cookery (**food preparation, see p. 107; cooking food, see p. 117)**
- A food enterprise or farmers' market product/s (**recipe modification, see p. 111; packaging, see p. 222; labelling, see p. 227)**
- Ethnic cookery (**meal planning and culture, see p. 15)**

Don't Forget!
Diet-related diseases include chronic diseases such as obesity, diabetes, cardiovascular disease, osteoporosis and dental disease.

Don't Forget!
Special dietary considerations include those which regard people who are advised to, or choose to deviate from population dietary recommendations. This could be for both medical, e.g. coeliac disease, food allergies, food intolerance, inflammatory bowel disease and non-medical reasons, e.g. vegetarian diets, religious or cultural reasons.

The Classroom-Based Assessments will provide an opportunity for students to:

- Research information using a range of methods
- Analyse data and evidence to make informed value judgements and decisions
- Organise information and plan logically
- Communicate clearly and effectively

- Collaborate with others on tasks
- Reflect on their own learning

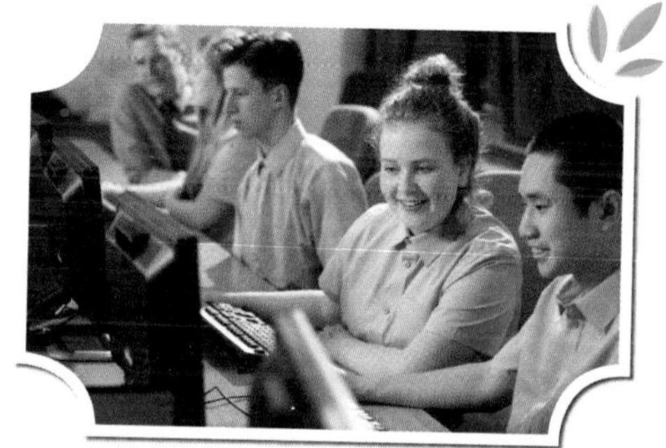

The Design Brief Process

The Design Brief Process is an open brief which is used to outline the requirements of a particular task. The DBP is ideally cyclical and reflective and may involve the following stages:

- Defining the task
- Investigation and research
- Generating ideas and developing possible solutions
- Presenting ideas to others for feedback
- Refining the design
- Production
- Evaluation

You will then use the Design Brief Process to:

- Research from a variety of sources, e.g. books, magazines, online, visits to shops, etc.
- Analyse the brief to help generate ideas and possible solutions.
- Plan for the requirements for the brief and for the Practical Food Skills examination.
- Discuss your thoughts on how to approach the brief with your classmates and teacher.

Let the information below guide you to complete your CBA2:

Design Brief Process	How to do this
Defining the problem/task	• You need to examine what the brief is really asking you to do. You must **identify the problem** to be solved. • The best way is to write out the brief on a page, then using a highlighter or coloured pen **underline all of the key words**. These describe what needs to be done. • Look up the definitions for these words, particularly the ones you do not understand. **Now re-write this brief** in your own words. • List the **requirements** of the design; ask yourself what must be done to satisfy the brief. • Examine the wording to see if there is a **theme**. How might this be included so that it will not look like an add-on or afterthought? • Has the dish to suit any particular **age group** or **special dietary consideration**? What are the nutritional requirements of this particular age group or diet? • At this stage you should reflect on your **cooking skills**, the **ingredients** available locally and the equipment you have in your school, as well as the **time** available to you to complete the task.

Design Brief Process	How to do this
Investigation/ research	Now that you have a good understanding of the problem, it's time to start looking for the answers. **Show evidence at all stages of this work**, and look for inspiration in books, magazines, etc. Produce a bibliography. • Look for recipes that meet the brief. Use a variety of **research** methods, e.g. textbook, magazines, online, etc. Acknowledge all sources of information. • Are your dishes/menus **suitable**? Justify your choices, terms of nutrition, sustainability and cost. • **Ask your teacher** what they think of your findings and if you are stuck, they will help you get back on track.
Generating ideas	Choose your solution to the brief: • Name **three dishes/menus** you intend to prepare. • They must show a **link with your analysis and research**. • Remember **these are possible solutions to the brief**.
Developing possible solutions	• **Evaluate** each dish/menu idea: discuss out why they are or are not fully meeting the brief, and whether or not you like them. • Do they meet the **budgetary or time constraints** imposed?
Presenting ideas to others for feedback	• At the end of this section, **you must ensure that your recipes/menus meet the brief**. • Justify your choices, look at other students' choices, identify any pitfalls and **discuss your ideas** with them. • Ask your teacher for advice also!
Final solution	• **Take on board the feedback** of your classmates and teacher and decide on your final menu. • **Present** your CBA2: Food Literacy Skills report in a creative way, e.g. as a computer presentation, poster or factsheet.

Final examination

The final examination will consist of a **Practical Food Skills** examination and a **written** examination, which are each allocated 50% of the marks available.

Practical Food Skills examination

The Practical Food Skills examination will be one hour and thirty minutes long, with an additional thirty minutes of preparation time prior to the start of the practical examination.

It is an individual examination and will be completed by the end of year three.

It is based on your chosen brief from CBA2, after reflection and feedback, and you will be asked to demonstrate your culinary and creative food literacy skills by preparing, serving and evaluating healthy nutritious dishes to meet the requirements of the brief by:

- using technology, as appropriate, in the preparation, implementation and evaluation
- demonstrating a range of cooking principles and techniques
- applying sustainable resource management practices
- applying safe and hygienic practices in food handling, preparation, storage and serving
- demonstrating culinary and creative skills in preparation, implementation and presentation

Preparation in advance

Reflect on feedback from your CBA2 and **produce a task sheet**, to include:

- a list of ingredients
- a list of equipment
- what you plan to do in the preparation time
- the order of work and time plan
- what costs are involved
- nutritional information

Preparation time on day (30 min)

Preparation time is very important, so use the following guidelines to help you make the most of it:

- Wash your hands, tie back your hair (including long fringes), put on an apron, and remove any jewellery and nail varnish.
- **Take out your equipment** – including serving dishes – and set the table.
- **Remove all the food** from tins, plastic bags and containers and place in bowls, plates, etc.
- **Weigh the ingredients** and place on plates, in ramekins, etc.
- **Wash** any fruit and vegetables, but do not peel or chop them yet.
- Make a **stock**, if needed.
- **Grease tins** and line them if necessary.
- **Put the oven on**, but do not set the temperature.

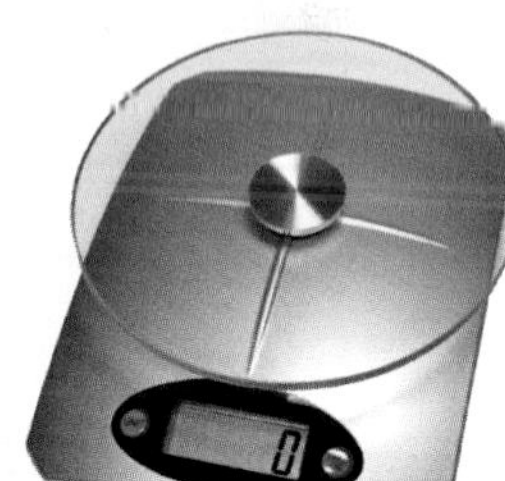

Don't Forget!
Weigh out your ingredients carefully, because if they are not in proportion it may affect the consistency and texture of the finished dish.

Production

Before cooking

- **Prepare all ingredients** before you start to cook.
- Make sure you know the **correct method** for preparing/chopping each fruit or vegetable.
- Keep your fingers '**curled in**' when chopping vegetables for safety.
- Chop fruit and vegetables into **equal-sized pieces** to ensure even cooking.
- Prepare each fruit and vegetable separately and peel onto a plate for **composting**.
- Use a **separate chopping board and knife for meat**, and place on a separate plate to prevent cross-contamination.
- Use the **correct techniques** (e.g. mix, beat, whisk, cream) and **equipment** (e.g. spoon, whisk, electric blender, food processor) to **combine** ingredients.

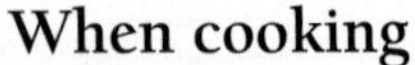

When cooking

- Always have a **side plate and wooden spoon** beside the cooker, and never leave the wooden spoon in the saucepan while cooking.
- **Preheat** the oil or butter before adding onion or meat (3–4 or medium flame).
- Cook rice, potatoes or pasta on the back rings, and meat and sauce on the front rings.
- Use the **correct cooking method and temperature**:
  - Simmering: on a low heat (1–2 or low flame), resulting in a gentle ripple of bubbles.
  - Boiling: on a medium heat (3–4 or medium flame), resulting in bubbles breaking rapidly on surface.
- Keep the **handles** of saucepans turned in.
- For baking, **be familiar with your oven**, as each one heats up differently.
- Be seen to **adjust the temperature** of your oven – it shows that you are familiar with the cooker.
- Always **wipe the top and the sides** of a dish before putting it in the oven.
- Be seen to **taste your dish** with a teaspoon (do not double dip!) and season with salt and pepper while cooking.
- When **making a sauce** (especially a roux), the key is to measure flour, fat and liquid accurately. If a sauce is too thick, add stock or water; if too thin, add blended cornflour.
- Handle food as little as possible.

Don't Forget!
Using small appliances in the kitchen can cut down on preparation.

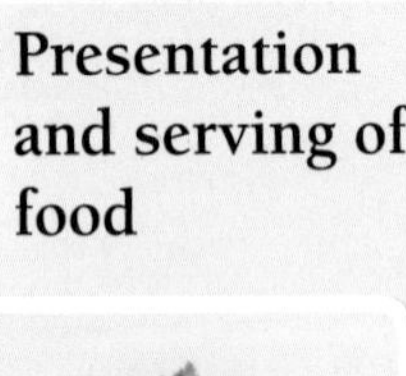

Presentation and serving of food

- When your dish is ready, **serve it while it is hot**.
- Use **suitably sized serving dishes** and don't overfill the plate.
- Use pot stands, wire trays, etc. and a large serving spoon (not a wooden one) to serve.
- If a drink or whipped cream is ready before serving, **cover and refrigerate** until serving.
- **Garnish savoury dishes and decorate sweet dishes** – choose as appropriate and keep things small and neat. Wipe the plate clean before serving.
- Remember to check that you have all the components of dishes **ready and on the table**. Place a small bowl of warm water and tasting cutlery on the table for the examiner. Finally, place your **menu card** on the table.
- When you are ready, **call the examiner** – never taste in front of the examiner.

Washing up

- **Scrape** the dishes and **pile** them neatly to the left of the sink.
- Fill the sink or basin with **hot soapy water**; never wash under a running tap, as this wastes water.
- Wash in the following order: **glass**, **crockery**, **cutlery**, **metal** (you may have to soak the last).
- **Drain dishes** to the right of the sink.
- **Dry dishes** thoroughly with a clean tea towel and place on the table.
- **Call the examiner** to inspect the dishes before putting them away.

Don't Forget!
Hygiene and safety are very important so always be aware of this when preparing, cooking, serving and storing food.

Evaluation

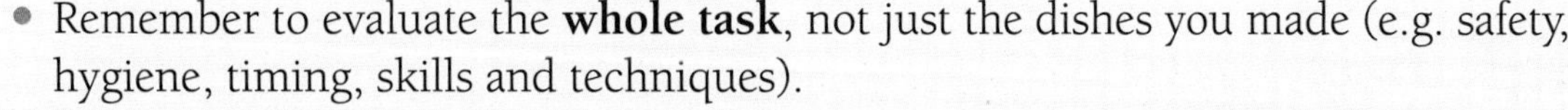

- Remember to evaluate the **whole task**, not just the dishes you made (e.g. safety, hygiene, timing, skills and techniques).
- Pay attention to **specific aspects** of the assignment (e.g. nutrition, dietary restrictions, costings, sustainability etc.).
- Be as **descriptive** of your dish as possible, and **give a reason** for your comments, e.g. 'the scones were golden brown due to the glaze' or 'the sauce was lumpy – I should have kept stirring as it was thickening'.
- **Use key terms** from your descriptive word bank. Avoid using vague words like 'nice', 'lovely', 'good', 'disgusting' or 'horrible'.
- Always suggest a **modification** for the next time – this shows your ability to critically analyse your work.
- If something went wrong, what did you do to sort it out? What could you do to **improve** the next time?

Don't Forget!
Allow 10–15 minutes to complete your evaluation towards the end of the practical examination.

There are a variety of recipes in the next chapter to help you prepare for your CBA2 and the Practical Food Skills examination – these can be used as-is or modified to meet the brief.

At the end of year three, you will sit a written examination of one-and-a-half hours' duration.

19 RECIPES

Learning Outcomes 1.2, 1.3, 1.4, 1.5, 1.6, 1.7, 1.17, 1.18

Here are a selection of recipes that can be used or modified for use in practical classes or for CBA2 and the Practical Food Skills examination.

Revision Toolkit

Cost all your dishes and try to modify them to make them healthier or to meet the needs of a person with a particular diet. It is a good idea to do a cost comparison between shop bought and homemade products in order to make better food choices.

Breads and scones

High-fibre bread

Ingredients

200 g wholemeal flour
150 g plain flour
¼ tsp salt
¼ tsp bread soda
25 g oatmeal
25 g wheatgerm
1 dsp brown sugar
50 g butter or margarine
350 ml buttermilk
1 dsp pinhead oatmeal (for top of loaf)

Method

1. Preheat the oven 200°C/fan 180°C/Gas Mark 6 and grease a loaf tin.
2. Sieve the plain flour, bread soda and salt into a bowl. Add the wholemeal flour, oatmeal, wheatgerm and sugar. Mix well.
3. Rub in the butter or margarine, make a well in the centre and add the buttermilk. Mix to a soft, wet consistency.
4. Place in loaf tin, cut a cross over the top and sprinkle with pinhead oatmeal.
5. Bake in the oven for 40–45 mins until it's golden brown and makes a hollow sound when tapped on the base.
6. Cool on a wire tray and use within a day or two.

Serve cold, sliced, with butter.

White soda bread

Ingredients

450 g plain white flour
1 level tsp bread soda
1 level tsp cream of tartar
1 level tsp salt
1 tbsp caster sugar (optional)
25 g butter
250 ml of buttermilk
1 egg

Method

1. Preheat the oven to 200°C/fan 180°C/Gas Mark 6, and flour a baking tray.
2. Sieve the flour, bread soda, cream of tartar and salt into a bowl. Add sugar, if using.
3. Rub in the butter until it resembles breadcrumbs.
4. Mix the egg with the milk and add to dry mixture to form a soft dough.
5. Turn onto a floured surface and knead gently until smooth on the base. Turn the smooth side up.
6. Cut a cross over the top and place on the floured tray.
7. Bake in the oven for 40–45 mins until it's golden brown and makes a hollow sound when tapped on the base.
8. Cool on a wire tray and cover with a dry tea towel to give a soft crust.

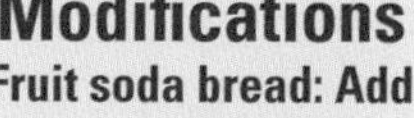

Modifications

Fruit soda bread: Add raisins or sultanas to dry ingredients before adding liquid.

Serve with butter and jam.

Banana and walnut bread

Ingredients

150 g coarse wholemeal flour
150 g self-raising flour
4 tbsp rapeseed oil
1 level tsp cinnamon
3 tbsp honey
2 tbsp hot water
2 eggs
2 large bananas
50 g walnuts chopped

Method

1. Preheat the oven to 180°C/fan 160°C/Gas Mark 4, and lightly grease and line the base of a 900 g loaf tin.
2. Place the flours, cinnamon and chopped nuts into a bowl and mix together.
3. In a separate bowl beat the oil, honey, water and eggs together. Peel and mash the bananas and stir into this mixture. Add this wet mix to the dry ingredients and stir until smooth.
4. Place in loaf tin and make a cut lengthways down the centre of the loaf.
5. Bake in the oven for 60 mins or until well risen and firm to touch.
6. Cool on a wire tray.

Serve sliced, warm or cold with butter.

Savoury tomato and olive bread

Ingredients

225 g plain flour
200 g porridge oats
1 tsp bread soda
500 g tub of fat-free natural yoghurt
1 level tsp salt
2 tbsp finely chopped sun-dried tomatoes
8–10 olives chopped
1 tsp dried basil or freshly chopped basil leaves

Method

1. Preheat the oven to 180°C/fan 160°C/Gas Mark 4, and lightly grease a 900 g loaf tin.
2. Sieve the flour and bread soda. Mix in the oats, chopped olives, salt, sun-dried tomatoes and basil.
3. Put the yoghurt into a large mixing bowl. Stir in the dry ingredients until the mixture is well combined and forms a thick dough.
4. Place in the loaf tin, and smooth the top with the back of spoon dipped in cold water.
5. Place in the centre of oven and bake for 40–45 mins until risen and golden brown.
6. Leave in the tin for five mins then turn onto a wire tray to cool.

Serve warm, sliced and dipped in basil pesto.

Aromatic flat breads

Ingredients

200 g plain flour
1 tsp ground cumin
1 tsp ground coriander
Pinch of salt
A little water, to bind

Method

1. Sieve the flour, salt and spices into a bowl; add water slowly to make dough.
2. Heat a frying pan and add a little oil.
3. Roll out and flatten pieces of the dough and put on the hot pan; turn after a minute when browned.

Serve with the soup or curry.

Tea scones

Ingredients
225 g self-raising flour
125 ml milk (approx)
Vegetable oil
Pinch of salt
25 g butter or margarine
25 g golden caster sugar (optional)
1 egg

Method
1. Preheat the oven to 200°C/fan 180°C/Gas Mark 6, and flour a baking tray.
2. Sieve the flour and salt into a bowl.
3. Rub in the butter or margarine until resembling breadcrumbs; stir in the sugar if used.
4. Beat the egg into the milk reserving a little; stir into the mix a little at a time to form a soft dough.
5. Turn onto a floured surface and knead gently until smooth on the base. Turn the smooth side up.
6. Roll out lightly to 2.5 cm and cut out using a cutter (small or medium) dipped in flour.
7. Place on the floured tray.
8. Glaze with any remaining egg and milk.
9. Bake in the oven for 15 mins until golden brown.
10. Cool on a wire tray.

Serve in a basket with butter and jam, or as a treat with jam and cream.

Modifications
Fruit scones: Sultanas, raisins, mixed fruit or cherries may be added to the dry ingredients before adding the liquid.
Wholemeal scones: Mix 125 g coarse wholemeal flour and 125 g of self-raising flour, then follow the method above.

Healthy heart scones

Ingredients
200 g self-raising flour
50 g oatmeal
75 g mixed fruits
1 tsp baking powder
Pinch of salt
25 g sugar
75 g soya butter
Zest of 1 orange
175 ml buttermilk or rice milk
1 egg

Method

1. Preheat the oven to 190°C/fan 170°C/Gas Mark 5, and line a tray with greaseproof paper.
2. Sieve the flour, salt and baking powder into a bowl, then stir in the oatmeal and sugar.
3. Rub in the soya butter, then stir in the fruit and zest.
4. Beat the egg into the milk reserving a little; stir into the mix to form soft dough.
5. Spoon equal size blobs of mix onto the tray, brush with the reserved milk mix.
6. Bake for 25–30 mins until golden.

Serve warm with a low-fat spread.

Modifications
Substitute the mixed fruit with fresh blueberries or raspberries or use a low-fat dairy spread rather than soya butter.

Cheese and chive scones

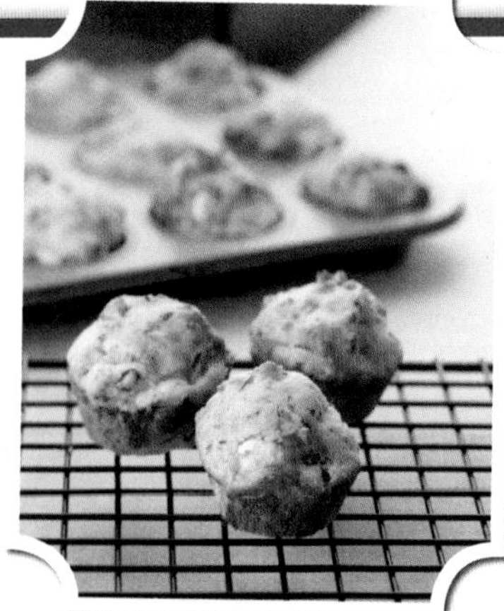

Ingredients

300 g plain flour
1 small courgette
1 tsp golden caster sugar
1 level tsp bread soda
Pinch of salt
125 g grated cheddar cheese
3 tbsp chives, chopped
150–300 ml buttermilk
1 beaten egg and sesame seeds, to glaze

Method

1. Preheat the oven to 200°C/fan 180°C/Gas Mark 6, and lightly dust the tray with flour.
2. Grate the courgette onto kitchen paper and squeeze to remove moisture.
3. Sieve the flour, sugar, salt and bread soda into a bowl, add grated cheese and chopped chives, and mix well.
4. Mix in the courgette and enough buttermilk to make a soft dough.
5. Put the baking tray into the oven to preheat.
6. Turn onto a floured surface and knead gently until smooth on the base. Turn the smooth side up.
7. Roll out lightly to 2.5 cm and cut out using a cutter (small or medium) dipped in flour.
8. Place on the preheated tray glaze with beaten egg and sprinkle with sesame seeds.
9. Bake in the oven for 15–20 mins until golden brown.
10. Cool on a wire tray.

Serve warm with butter or cold with relish and ham.

Rock buns

Ingredients

225 g self-raising flour
75 g caster sugar
½ tsp cinnamon
1 tsp baking powder
125 g unsalted butter, cut into cubes
150 g dried fruit
1 free-range egg
2 tbsp milk
1 tsp vanilla extract
A little icing sugar, to dust

Method

1. Preheat the oven to 180°C/fan 160°C/Gas Mark 4, and line a tray with greaseproof paper.
2. Mix the flour, sugar and baking powder in a bowl and rub in the cubed butter until the mixture looks like breadcrumbs, then mix in the dried fruit and cinnamon.
3. In a clean bowl, beat the egg and milk together with the vanilla extract.
4. Add the egg mixture to the dry ingredients a little at a time and stir with a spoon until the mixture just comes together as a thick, lumpy dough.
5. Spoon equal size blobs of mix onto the tray. Leave space between them as they will flatten and spread out to double their size during baking.
6. Bake for 15–20 mins, until golden brown. Remove from the oven, allow to cool for a couple of minutes then cool fully on a wire tray. Dust with icing sugar.

Modification
For a healthier option, use 125 g plain flour with 100 g wholemeal flour.

Buns and bars

Queen cakes

Ingredients
175 g self-raising flour
125 g golden caster sugar
125 g butter or margarine
2 eggs
2 tbsp cold water

Method
1. Preheat oven to 200°C/fan 180°C/Gas Mark 6.
2. Line a bun tin with paper cases.
3. Sieve the flour, and put it in a bowl with the sugar, butter or margarine, eggs and water.
4. Beat all the ingredients together with an electric mixer or wooden spoon until the mixture is smooth.
5. Put a heaped dessertspoonful of the mixture into each bun case.
6. Place in the oven on the top shelf and bake for about 15 mins until golden brown.
7. Cool on a wire tray. When cold, decorate as you like with your favourite toppings.

To decorate
Glacé Icing/melted chocolate or buttercream icing (see below)
- **Sprinkles**
- **Glacé cherries or grated lemon zest**
- **Small sweets**

Glacé Icing

Ingredients
125 g icing sugar
15 ml warm water

Method
1. Sift the icing sugar into a bowl and gradually add the warm water until the icing becomes thick enough to coat the back of a spoon. If necessary, add more water (a drop at a time) or icing sugar to adjust the consistency.
2. It can be coloured using food colouring, adding a drop or two at a time until it is the shade you want.

Melted chocolate

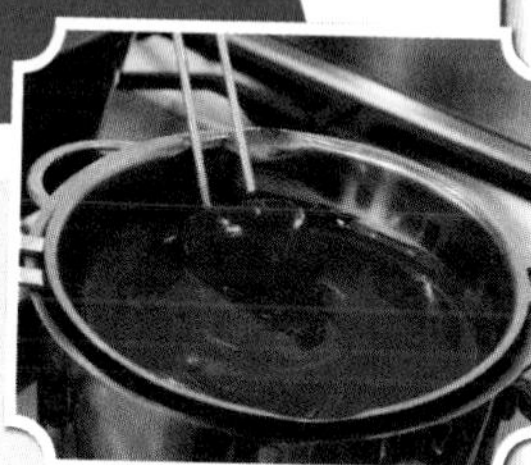

Ingredients
150 g dark, milk or white chocolate

Method
1. Break up the chocolate into a dry bowl.
2. Bring about 5 cm of water to a simmer in your saucepan.
3. Put the heatproof bowl on top of the saucepan.
4. Stir chocolate occasionally as it softens until you have just a few small un-melted chunks. Remove bowl from the heat; the residual heat will melt the rest.

Discovery Learning
When melting chocolate, make sure that the water doesn't touch the bottom of the bowl or get into the chocolate. Why is this important?

Cupcakes

Ingredients

125 g self-raising flour
125 g golden caster sugar
125 g butter or margarine
2 eggs
A few drops of vanilla essence

Method

1. Preheat the oven to 180°C/fan 160°C/Gas Mark 4.
2. Line cupcake tin with paper cases.
3. Beat the butter/margarine and sugar together until light and fluffy. Beat in the vanilla essence.
4. Beat in the eggs a little at a time with a little sieved flour, until it is combined.
5. Put heaped spoonfuls of the mixture into each bun case.
6. Place in the oven on the top shelf and bake for about 15–20 mins until golden brown.
7. Cool on a wire tray.
8. When cold, decorate with buttercream and your favourite toppings.

Buttercream icing

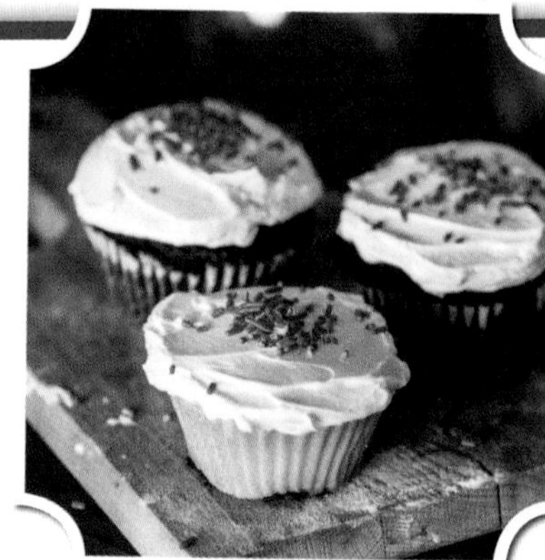

Ingredients

125 g butter (at room temperature)
225 g sieved icing sugar
A few drops of vanilla essence
Selection of food colourings
Sweets (optional)

Method

1. Beat the butter, icing sugar and vanilla essence together until smooth and creamy.
2. Divide the icing into separate bowls for each colour you want to use, and gradually add the colouring, mixing well until the right colour is achieved.
3. Pipe or swirl icing onto each cupcake. Top with a sweet, fruit, sprinkles, or whatever else takes your fancy

Coconut buns

Ingredients

200 g self-raising flour
Pinch of salt
75 g margarine
75 g caster sugar
1 egg
50 g desiccated coconut
3–4 tbsp milk
Warmed jam and desiccated coconut, to decorate

Method

1. Preheat the oven to 200°C/fan 180°C/Gas Mark 6.
2. Sieve flour and salt into a bowl.
3. Rub in margarine until mixture resembles breadcrumbs.
4. Stir in sugar and coconut and mix well.
5. Beat egg. Add a little milk and pour this into the centre of mixture, adding enough to make a stiff dough.
6. Using a spoon and fork, pile into 12 cakes on a greased baking tray.
7. Bake in oven for about 20 mins.
8. Put warmed jam and coconut onto two separate plates.
9. Dip buns into the warm jam, then into the coconut.

Berry granola bars

Ingredients

200 g porridge oats
100 g butter
100 g sunflower seeds
50 g sesame seeds
50 g chopped walnuts
3 tbsp honey
100 g light muscovado sugar
1 tsp ground cinnamon
100 g dried cranberries, cherries or blueberries or a mix

Method

1. Preheat the oven to 170°C/fan 150°C/Gas Mark 3. Butter and line the base of an 18 × 25 cm roasting tin.
2. Mix the oats, seeds and nuts in the tin, then toast in the oven for 5–10 mins.
3. Meanwhile, heat the butter, honey and sugar in a pan, stirring until butter is melted.
4. Add in the toasted oat mix, cinnamon and dried fruit. Stir until all the oats are well coated.
5. Tip into the tin, press down lightly, then bake for 30 mins.
6. Cool in tin, then cut into 12 bars.

Serve for breakfast, a snack or as part of a lunch.

High-energy cereal bars

Ingredients

150 g puffed rice cereal
150 g rolled oats
50 g Cheerios
50 g honey
50 g peanut butter
25 ml coconut oil
Pinch of sea salt (optional)
50 g dark chocolate, chopped (optional)

Method

1. Grease and line the base of a 9-inch square cake tin with two pieces of greaseproof paper (one placed horizontally and one vertically to aid lifting the bars out of the tin).
2. In a large mixing bowl, put in puffed rice, rolled oats, and Cheerios and toss to combine.
3. Put the honey, peanut butter, salt (if using) and coconut oil into a saucepan. Stir continuously until mixture is smooth.
4. Combine the honey/peanut butter mixture with the cereals in a large mixing bowl. Mix gently until all the cereal is coated evenly. Add chocolate if using. It will be very sticky!
5. Pour the mixture into the prepared tin, spread it out with a wet rubber spatula (right into the corners!) into an even layer and press down firmly.
6. Place the tin in the freezer for about 20 mins or until firm.
7. Lift the bars from the tin, using the greaseproof paper and place them on a chopping board. With a sharp knife or pizza cutter, slice the square into six rows and then slice them in half to make 12 bars.
8. Wrap the bars individually in plastic wrap. Store in an airtight container in the refrigerator for up to a week, or in the freezer for up to a month.

Serve for breakfast, as a snack or as part of a lunch.

Lining a loaf tin

Muffins and biscuits

Fruity muffins

Ingredients

225 g plain flour
2 tsp baking powder
2 large eggs
50 g butter, melted
175 ml skimmed milk
100 ml runny honey
140 g fresh blueberries
140 g dried apricot, chopped
140 g sultanas
85 g dried cranberries
1 tsp grated orange zest
1 tsp ground cinnamon

Method

1. Preheat the oven to 200°C/fan 180°C/Gas Mark 6, and very lightly butter or line a 12-hole muffin tin.
2. Sieve the flour and baking powder into a bowl.
3. In another bowl, lightly beat the eggs, then stir in the melted butter, milk and honey.
4. Add to the flour with the remaining ingredients. Stir quickly to combine – it's fine if there are some lumps left.
5. Spoon the mixture into the muffin tin. Bake for 20–25 mins until well risen and pale golden on top.
6. Leave in the tin for a few minutes before turning out.
7. When cool, they'll keep in an airtight tin for two days, or can be frozen for up to a month.

Serve for breakfast, in lunch boxes or as a tasty treat.

Oaty muffins

Ingredients

200 g wholemeal flour
50 g rolled oats (plus extra for sprinkling)
1½ tsp baking powder
1½ tsp bicarbonate of soda
150 ml natural low-fat yoghurt
50 ml rapeseed oil
2 large eggs
100 g puréed apples
1 ripe banana, mashed
4 tbsp clear honey
1½ tsp cinnamon
100 g blueberries
2 tbsp mixed seeds
1 tsp of vanilla extract

Method

1. Preheat oven to 180°C/fan 160°C/Gas Mark 4. Line a 12-hole muffin tin with 12 large muffin cases.
2. In a jug, mix the eggs, yoghurt, oil, apple purée, banana, honey and vanilla.
3. Put the remaining ingredients, except the seeds, into a large bowl, add a pinch of salt and mix to combine.
4. Pour the wet ingredients into the dry and mix until you get a smooth batter.
5. Divide the batter between the cases.
6. Sprinkle the muffins with the extra oats and the seeds.
7. Bake for 25–30 mins until golden and well risen and a skewer inserted into the centre of a muffin comes out clean.
8. Remove from the oven, transfer to a wire rack and leave to cool. These can be stored in a sealed container for up to three days.

This is a great recipe for using leftover fruit, especially overripe bananas. If you have any apples left over, stew them and freeze them in large ice cube trays until you need them.

Modifications

Any of these ingredients or combination of them can be used in place of those in the recipe: dried cranberries, diced fresh apple, walnuts and raisins, dried mixed berries, dried apricots, pecans, ground almonds, desiccated coconut and fresh or frozen raspberries.

Serve for breakfast, in a lunch box or as a healthy snack.

Chocolate chip cookies

Ingredients

150 g self-raising flour
75 g porridge oats
125 g butter, at room temperature
1 egg
1 tsp vanilla essence
125 g light muscovado sugar
100 g milk chocolate chips

Method

1. Preheat oven to 190°C/fan 170°C/Gas Mark 5. Lightly grease two baking trays.
2. Cream the butter and sugar until smooth.
3. Add the egg and vanilla essence and continue to mix.
4. Stir in the sieved flour, oats and chocolate, and mix to a stiff texture.
5. Spoon the mixture onto the baking trays, leaving enough space to allow for spreading.
6. Bake for 10–15 mins until beginning to turn brown.
7. Cool for 2–3 mins on baking tray, then transfer to a wire tray to cool completely.
8. When cooled store in an airtight container for up to three days.

Modifications
Exchange milk chocolate chips for dark or white chocolate or substitute cranberries for chocolate.

Serve as a treat with a glass of milk, tea or coffee.

Shortbread

Ingredients

125 g plain flour
50 g cornflour
125 g butter, at room temperature
50 g caster sugar

Method

1. Preheat oven to 160°C/150°C/Gas Mark 3. Lightly grease an 8-inch sandwich tin.
2. Cream the butter and sugar together until smooth with an electric mixer or a wooden spoon.
3. Add the sieved flour and cornflour and mix gently until a dough is formed.
4. Form dough into a ball with your fingertips and knead lightly if required.
5. Press into a sandwich tin and prick around the top of the dough with a fork.
6. Bake in preheated oven for about 20 mins or until a pale golden colour.
7. Allow to cool in tin for 5 mins, cut into triangles, then transfer to a wire tray to cool.
8. When cold, store in an airtight tin.

Modifications
Shape into round biscuits, and sandwich two together with cut strawberries and whipped cream to make 'strawberry shortcake', or serve with a scoop of ice cream as a dessert.

Serve as a treat with tea or coffee.

Cakes and tray bakes

Sponge cake

Ingredients

75 g self-raising flour
75 g caster sugar
3 eggs
A few drops of vanilla essence

Filling:
Strawberry jam
150 ml whipped cream
Icing sugar, to dust

Method

1. Preheat the oven to 200°C/fan 180°C/Gas Mark 6. Grease and line the base of two small sandwich tins with greaseproof paper.
2. Crack the eggs into a large bowl, add in the sugar and whisk with a balloon whisk or electric mixer until the mixture thickens and holds a figure of 8 on the surface, then add in the vanilla essence.
3. Sieve the flour and fold it into the thickened mixture using a metal spoon.
4. Pour into the prepared tins and bake for 15 mins.
5. When baked, cool on a wire tray.
6. Once cold, spread one sponge with whipped cream and the other layer with warmed strawberry jam. Sandwich them together and dust the surface of sponge with sieved icing sugar.

Modifications
Use other flavoured jams or fill with fresh berries and cream.

Serve with fresh cream or ice cream.

Crunchy flapjacks

Ingredients

150 g porridge oats
75 g brown sugar
100 ml golden syrup
125 g crunchy peanut butter
1 tsp vanilla essence
75 g sultanas
75 g puffed rice cereal

Method

1. Lightly grease a swiss roll tin, or line tin with greaseproof paper.
2. Put the brown sugar and syrup into a saucepan over a medium heat until just boiling, then remove from the heat.
3. Stir in the peanut butter and vanilla essence and mix until smooth.
4. In a large bowl, mix together the oats, sultanas and puffed rice. Pour the saucepan contents over the cereals and mix well.
5. Press into the prepared tin using the back of a damp spoon. Allow to cool, then cut into squares.
6. Wrap in greaseproof paper to keep fresh and crunchy.

Modifications
Replace the sultanas with chopped cherries or apricots.

Serve as a snack or part of a school lunch.

Carrot cake

Ingredients

225 g self-raising flour
50 g muscovado sugar
125 g sultanas
150 g grated carrot
25 g chopped walnuts
Zest of 1 orange
3 eggs
175 ml rapeseed oil
½ tsp cinnamon
¼ tsp mixed spice
Pinch of bread soda
Frosting:
225 g cream cheese
375 g sieved icing sugar
1 tsp vanilla extract
Chopped walnuts, to decorate

Method

1. Preheat oven to 150°C/fan 140°C/Gas Mark 2. Line a 6-inch deep cake tin with a double layer of greaseproof paper.
2. Put sugar, sultanas, walnuts, carrots and orange zest into a bowl.
3. Beat the eggs and oil together and stir into the carrot mixture.
4. Sieve the flour, cinnamon, spices and bread soda together and add to the other ingredients.
5. Gently stir all ingredients well together.
6. Pour into a prepared tin and smooth down. Bake for 1 hour.
7. Test the cake by lightly pressing the centre; it should spring back and the top should be golden brown. Alternatively, insert a skewer or knife and if it comes out clean, the cake is baked.
8. Leave in tin for 15 min, then transfer to wire tray to cool.
9. For the frosting, beat all the ingredients together until smooth and creamy. Spread on top of cake and sprinkle with chopped walnuts to decorate.

Serve with cream or ice cream.

Pastry

Apple tart

Ingredients

225 g plain flour
125 g margarine (frozen)
150 ml cold water (approx.)
4 cooking apples, peeled, cored and sliced
A little sugar, to sweeten apples
Icing sugar, to dust (optional)

Method

1. Preheat oven to 200°C/fan 180°C/Gas Mark 6. Grease an ovenproof plate or foil plate.
2. Sieve flour into a bowl. Grate the frozen margarine into the flour.
3. Using a knife, mix the grated margarine into the flour. Add water a little at a time and mix to a soft dough with the knife.
4. Turn onto a floured board and knead lightly. Divide the pastry in half.
5. Roll out half the pastry to the size of an ovenproof plate.
6. Arrange apples on the pastry. Sprinkle with sugar to sweeten.
7. Roll other piece of pastry to cover the apples.
8. Dampen edge of base pastry with cold water to seal. Seal the edges by using the back of a knife to form a crust.
9. Put a cut on top of pastry to allow steam to escape and bake for 25–35 mins.

Modifications
Use strawberries to sweeten the apples, so reducing amount of sugar used.

Serve hot or cold with cream, fromage frais, custard or ice cream.

Mince pies

Ingredients

250 g plain flour
Pinch of salt
25 g ground almonds
25g icing sugar
175 g butter
1 large egg
1 tbsp lemon juice
500 g mincemeat

Method

1. To make the pastry, sieve the flour, salt and icing sugar into a bowl. Stir in the ground almonds. Chop or coarsely grate the cold butter and rub this into the dry ingredients. A food processor may be used for this.
2. In a small bowl, whisk together the egg and lemon juice. Add this to the dry ingredients and mix together to form a smooth dough. Knead gently on a floured board, cover with cling-film and refrigerate until required.
3. To make the mince pies, leave the pastry at room temperature for approximately 20 mins. Roll out thinly on a floured board. Using a round 3-inch fluted cutter, cut out circles of pastry (makes approx. 36).
4. Use the pastry circles to line the bases of shallow patty tins. Place a heaped teaspoon of mincemeat into each pie. Cut out star shapes and place over the mincemeat and bake in a preheated oven at 190°C /fan 170°C/Gas Mark 5 for 10 mins. Allow to cool on a wire tray.

Serve warm or cold with lightly whipped cream or crème fraîche. Decorate with a dusting of icing sugar or thin glacé icing.

Quiche Lorraine

Ingredients

200 g plain flour
100 g butter or margarine (frozen)
Pinch of salt
A little cold water

Filling:
4 back rashers
2 eggs
50 g grated cheese
4 mushrooms, sliced
1 onion, diced
200 ml milk
Salt and pepper

Method

1. Preheat oven to 220°C/fan 200°C/Gas Mark 7, and grease a flan dish.
2. Make the pastry: Sieve the flour and salt into a bowl, then grate and rub in butter or margarine until the mixture resembles fine breadcrumbs.
3. Add the water and mix to a stiff dough.
4. Roll out the pastry and line a flan dish.
5. Bake blind for 15 mins (see below), and then turn the oven down to 190°C/fan 180°C/Gas Mark 5.
6. Make the filling: de-rind and cut the rashers, then sauté with onion and mushrooms.
7. Beat the eggs, add seasoning and stir in the milk.
8. Grate some cheese onto the pastry base, add sautéed ingredients, pour on the egg mixture and sprinkle remaining cheese on top.
9. Bake for 30–40 mins until mixture is set.

How to bake blind

Line pastry case with baking paper and fill with dried beans, rice or pastry weights. Bake in a preheated oven at 220°C for 10 mins. Carefully remove paper and weights and bake for a further 5–10 mins or until pastry is golden and dry. This prevents the pastry becoming soggy when the filling is added.

Serve hot or cold in wedges with a side salad, garnished with tomato slices and parsley.

Savoury lunch slices

Ingredients

225 g plain flour
125 g butter or margarine (frozen)
Pinch of salt and pepper
Cold water

Filling:
- 5 finely chopped scallions
- 125 g cooked ham, cut into cubes
- 225 g cheddar cheese, grated
- 6–8 baby tomatoes, sliced
- 100 g spinach (wilted)
- 150 ml milk
- 2 eggs
- Salt and pepper
- 25 g parmesan
- 8–10 fresh basil leaves

Put spinach leaves into warm oil and turn until they **wilt** (soften). Season the wilted spinach with salt and pepper and nutmeg.

Method

1. Preheat oven to 190°C/fan 170°F/Gas Mark 5.
2. Sieve flour and salt and pepper into a bowl, grate in the butter/margarine and rub in until it resembles fine breadcrumbs.
3. Add sufficient water to make a soft dough. Turn onto a lightly floured board and gently knead.
4. Roll out pastry and use to line a 28 × 18 cm Swiss roll tin.
5. Place scallions, ham and cheese and wilted spinach (see below) into the pastry. Arrange tomato slices on top.
6. Beat eggs and milk together and add salt and pepper.
7. Pour gently into pastry. Sprinkle with Parmesan and torn basil.
8. Bake for 20 mins or until golden brown and set.
9. Cut into slices.

Modifications

You can add vegetables like mushrooms, peppers, spinach or sweetcorn. Chicken or turkey can be used also.

Serve hot or cold with a green salad. These slices are ideal for a packed lunch or quick snack.

Sausage rolls

Ingredients

200 g plain flour
100 g margarine or butter (frozen)
1 tbsp finely chopped fresh parsley
Salt and pepper
Cold water

Filling:
- 200 g sausage meat
- 75 g breadcrumbs
- 1 small onion, finely chopped
- 1 tbsp tomato ketchup
- 1 tsp mixed herbs

A beaten egg and a handful of sesame seeds, to top (optional)

Make breadcrumbs by hand by running bread up and down a medium-sized grater; alternatively, use a food processor with a slicing blade.

Method

1. Preheat oven to 220°C/fan 200°C/Gas Mark 7. Lightly grease two baking trays.
2. Sieve flour and salt and pepper into a bowl, grate in the butter/margarine and rub in until it resembles fine breadcrumbs, and add in chopped parsley.
3. Add sufficient water to make a soft dough. Turn onto a lightly floured board and gently knead.
4. Roll out pastry into a rectangle, and cut in half lengthwise.
5. Place sausage meat, chopped onion, breadcrumbs, ketchup and mixed herbs into a bowl and mix well together. Divide the mixture in two and roll out into two long sausages that are the same length as the pastry.
6. Place a roll of sausage meat in the centre of each rectangle of pastry, and roll the pastry around the sausage. Dampen the cut edges of the pastry with a little water. Press lightly with a fork to seal. Glaze with a little beaten egg and sprinkle with sesame seeds, if using. Cut the roll into pieces 5–10 cm in length.
7. Place on the greased tray and bake for 10 mins, then reduce the heat to 190°C/fan 170°C/Gas Mark 5 and bake for 15 mins more.

Serve hot or cold with salad, or coleslaw. These are ideal for a packed lunch or quick snack.

Soups

Vegetable stock

Ingredients

2 onions
2 carrots
2 sticks of celery
1 leek
½ parsnip
1 bouquet garni
1 clove of garlic
Pinch of nutmeg
100 g (4–5) large mushrooms
2 litres of cold water

How to make and use a bouquet garni
A bouquet garni is a bunch of herbs, e.g. a bay leaf, two cloves, parsley, peppercorns and a blade of mace, which are tied together in a piece of muslin and infused into a liquid to give flavour. It should be removed before serving. A commercial bouquet can be bought in a sachet like a tea bag and popped into stocks or soups.

Method

1. Prepare vegetables – wash peel and chop roughly.
2. Put them into saucepan with, nutmeg, the bouquet garni and water. Bring to the boil and then simmer for 45–60 mins. Strain and use as required, or cool and store in fridge. This stock can also be frozen.

Red lentil soup

Ingredients

200 g red lentils
2 litres chicken or vegetable stock
1 large onion, roughly chopped
2 cloves of garlic, chopped
3 large carrots, roughly chopped
Salt and pepper
Pinch of chilli flakes (optional)

Method

1. Wash peel and chop the carrots; peel and chop the onions and garlic.
2. Place all the ingredients into a large saucepan and bring to the boil.
3. Simmer gently for 20 mins.
4. Liquidise and season, adjusting the consistency with a bit of water if it is too thick.

Serve with brown bread.

Farmhouse vegetable soup

Ingredients

500 g of mixed vegetables (1 carrot, 1 leek, 1 celery stick)
25 g margarine or butter
1 onion
1 potato
800 ml vegetable stock
1 tbsp vegetable oil
25 g flour
1 bouquet garni
Salt and pepper

Method

1. Prepare vegetables: Wash, peel and dice carrot, potatoes, onion, and slice celery.
2. Wash and chop the leek and put into salted water to clean, then drain through a colander.
3. Heat the oil in a large saucepan and gently fry onion and potatoes.
4. Add carrot, celery and leek and fry gently. Season with salt and pepper.
5. Stir in the flour to absorb fat; gradually stir in the milk.
6. Add stock and bouquet garni and bring to the boil stirring continuously.
7. Cover saucepan and simmer gently for about 40 mins.
8. Remove the bouquet garni and purée until smooth using a hand blender or a liquidiser.
9. Heat through until piping hot

Garnish with chopped parsley and a swirl of cream, and serve with wholemeal or soda bread.

Mushroom soup

Ingredients

600 g mixed mushrooms
1 onion
2 sticks of celery
3 cloves of garlic
A few sprigs of fresh flat-leaf parsley
1 tbsp olive oil
1.5 litres chicken or vegetable stock
75 ml single cream
Sea salt and black pepper
6 slices of ciabatta bread
A little olive oil

Method

1. Clean and finely slice the mushrooms.
2. Peel and finely slice the onion, celery and garlic and finely chop the parsley.
3. Heat a splash of olive oil in a large saucepan over a medium heat, add the onion, celery, garlic and mushrooms, pop the lid on and cook gently until softened.
4. Add the stock into the pan and bring to the boil, then turn the heat down to low and simmer for 15 mins.
5. Season to taste with sea salt and black pepper, remove 2–3 tbsp mushrooms and leave aside as garnish, then purée with a hand blender or liquidiser until smooth.
6. Pour in the cream, bring just back to the boil, then turn off the heat.
7. Heat up a griddle pan, brush ciabatta with olive oil and heat it on pan for 4–5 mins until golden on each side.
8. Spoon the soup into bowls.

Garnish with mushrooms and chopped parsley, and serve with the toasted ciabatta.

Starters

Smoked salmon and prawns, with lime vinaigrette and horseradish cream

Ingredients

4 slices smoked salmon
10 large cooked prawns peeled but tails left on
Sauce:
- 1 tbsp crème fraîche
- 1 tsp horseradish

Salt and pepper

Salad:
- 2 handfuls of small leaf salad
- juice and zest of 1 lime
- 1 tsp clear honey
- ½ tsp finely grated fresh root ginger
- 2 tbsp light olive oil

Method

1. Mix the crème fraîche with the horseradish and a little salt and pepper.
2. Lay the smoked salmon and prawns on two plates, then top with a dollop of the horseradish cream.
3. For the dressing, whisk the lime juice and zest with the honey, ginger, then whisk in the oil.
4. Toss the salad in most of the dressing and pile on top. Drizzle the remaining dressing around the plate and serve.

Serve with wholemeal or soda bread.

Tuna fishcakes

Ingredients

160 g tin of tuna in brine
200 g cold mashed potatoes
1 scallion, diced and fried
1 tsp mustard
Salt and pepper
1 beaten egg
25 g flour
50 g breadcrumbs
1 tbsp vegetable oil

Method

1. Gently stir the cooked scallion and drained tuna through the mashed potatoes.
2. Add the mustard and season well.
3. Shape into patties and add flour, egg and breadcrumbs.
4. Fry in hot oil until golden and hot through.

Serve with a crisp green salad.

Bruschetta

Ingredients

1 small ciabatta loaf or
 1 large baguette
1 clove garlic
Rock salt or table salt
4 tbsp virgin olive oil
Topping:
 3 very ripe tomatoes
 Salt and black pepper
 Fresh herbs

Method

1. Peel tomatoes for topping and chop very finely.
2. Peel garlic, and cut in two.
3. Preheat the grill or use pop-up toaster. Cut bread into thin slices on the diagonal and toast.
4. Rub a little garlic over one side of each slice. Drizzle with olive oil and sprinkle with a little rock salt/table salt.
5. Top with tomatoes and season with salt and pepper. Garnish with fresh herbs.

Serve as a hot snack or starter and serve straight away.

Warm bacon and crouton salad

Ingredients

1–2 slices thickly cut, sliced
 pan bread
2 tbsp olive oil
3–4 rashers
1 small head cos lettuce
2–3 spring onions
50 g Parmesan or pale
 cheddar cheese
6 cherry tomatoes
Fresh parsley or coriander
Dressing:
 1 tbsp balsamic vinegar or
  white wine vinegar
 ½ tsp Dijon mustard
 3 tbsp virgin olive oil
 1 clove garlic

Method

1. Preheat oven to 180°C/fan 160°C/Gas Mark 4.
2. Cut bread into 1 cm cubes for the croutons and put into freezer bag with oil. De-rind and snip rashers into small strips, add to bag, and toss to coat.
3. Spread croutons and rashers on baking tin, and bake for 15–20 mins until crisp. Drain and cool on kitchen paper.
4. Wash lettuce, spin, dry, tear leaves into edible pieces. Wash and peel spring onions, chop up finely into small pieces with a scissors. Make shavings from cheese using a potato peeler or grater. Wash and chop parsley/coriander; wash and halve tomatoes.
5. For the dressing, whisk all dressing ingredients together or shake in a screw-top jar.
6. Place the lettuce in a bowl, toss with the croutons, bacon, cheese and onion, and dress to taste just before serving.

Garnish with a few cherry tomatoes, and serve on individual plates as a starter with fresh crispy rolls or french bread.

Modifications

Goats' cheese salad

Use all the ingredients in the recipe for *Warm bacon and crouton salad*, but leave out the Parmesan. Use 150 g goats' cheese and thin circles of baguette for bread.

1. Preheat oven to 180°C/fan 170°C/Gas Mark 4.
2. Cut the bread into thin circles, divide the goats' cheese into 12 thin slices, and put some cheese onto each piece of bread. Place on a baking tray. Add de-rinded and snipped rashers. Bake for 15 minutes until the rashers are cooked, the bread is toasted and the cheese is melting. Then continue as above.

Warm chicken, bacon and crouton salad

Use all the ingredients in the recipe for *Warm bacon and crouton salad*, but leave out the cheese. Use a large chicken fillet, cut into small strips, stir fry the chicken in a little oil to cook through, and stir in 1 tsp light soy sauce. Place the lettuce in a bowl, and add the chicken, bacon and croutons. Then continue as above.

Main course dishes

Spaghetti Bolognese

Ingredients

400 g lean minced beef
2 tbsp olive oil
2 streaky rashers
1 onion
1 clove garlic
1 tsp dried basil or oregano
1 tin chopped tomatoes
2 tbsp tomato purée
Salt and black pepper
100 g mushrooms, chopped
1 carrot, diced or grated
200 g cooked pasta
Fresh Parmesan cheese
Fresh parsley or basil

Did You Know?
Bolognese sauce is also called 'ragu'.

Method

1. Peel onion and halve lenghtways. Slice, first following the lines on onion, and then slice into fine dice.
2. Crush garlic and use scissors to cut rashers into short strips.
3. Heat oil in saucepan and then gently soften bacon, onion and garlic for 5 mins. Add diced/grated carrot and chopped mushrooms.
4. Turn up the heat, add meat and cook to develop flavour, stirring all the time. Add remaining ingredients and chop tomatoes if necessary.
5. Bring to a simmer and stir. Reduce heat, cover and simmer gently for 20–25 mins.
6. Thin with 1–2 tablespoons water or stock if the sauce is too thick; if too thin, boil with the lid off until it thickens.
7. Taste and add more seasoning if necessary.

Serve hot with pasta, freshly tossed salad and garlic bread, and garnish the dish with chopped fresh herbs and grated fresh Parmesan (or other hard Italian cheese).

Lasagne

Ingredients

Ragu, made to the recipe above
12 sheets of lasagne

Cheese sauce:
- 25 g flour
- 25 g butter
- 375 ml milk
- Salt and pepper
- 100 g grated Parmesan or cheddar cheese

Method

1. Preheat oven to 180°C/fan 160°C/Gas Mark 4. Grease large baking dish.
2. Make roux cheese sauce: Melt the butter, add the flour and cook for 1 min over a gentle heat. Remove from the heat and gradually add the milk, mixing well between each addition. Season with salt and pepper. Return to the heat and stir continuously until it boils, then reduce heat and simmer until it thickens – about 2–3 mins. Add in half the cheese and stir until it melts. Set aside.
3. Spread a layer of Bolognese sauce over the base of the dish, cover with lasagne sheets, pour a layer of cheese sauce over the pasta, then layer the ragu, pasta and sauce again until used up.
4. Sprinkle the remaining cheese on top and bake for 30–40 mins.

Garnish with tomato and parsley, and serve with green salad and garlic bread.

Ham, spinach and ricotta cannelloni

Ingredients

12–14 cannelloni tubes
500 g ricotta cheese
100 g toasted pine nuts
1 kg fresh spinach
100 g diced ham

Sauce:
- 1 litre milk
- 1 onion
- 1 bay leaf
- 50 g margarine
- 50 g flour
- 75 g Parmesan

Method

1. Put the milk, onion and bay leaf on to infuse.
2. Wilt the spinach, and chop up, then chop the pine nuts.
3. Beat the ricotta, add the ham, nuts and spinach, season well.
4. Stuff the cannelloni tubes and lay in a shallow greased dish.
5. Make a roux from the margarine and flour; slowly pour in the infused milk.
6. Pour the white sauce over the cannelloni and sprinkle with the Parmesan.
7. Bake for 35–40 mins in a medium hot oven until bubbling and golden.

Garnish with chopped basil or parsley, and serve with garlic bread and a side salad.

Tagliatelle à la carbonara

Ingredients

200 g diced smoked bacon
50 g butter
150 ml stock
3 eggs plus 2 yolks
150 ml cream
100 g Parmesan cheese
400 g tagliatelle
1 tbsp olive oil
Salt and pepper

Method

1. Cook the tagliatelle in plenty of boiling water.
2. Fry the bacon in the olive oil until golden, add half the butter and the wine, and simmer for a few minutes.
3. Beat the eggs, yolks, cream and Parmesan.
4. Add the cooked pasta to the smoked bacon mixture and toss to coat the pasta.
5. Stir the egg mix into the hot pasta which will cook the egg.
6. Stir in the remaining butter and season.

Garnish with chopped parsley and serve in bowls with crusty bread.

Chicken stir-fry

Ingredients

4 chicken fillets
2 carrots
1 pepper (any colour/½ each of 2 colours)
8 spring onions
6 button mushrooms
1 small onion
100 g mangetout
2 tbsp sunflower oil
2 cm piece fresh root ginger
1 tbsp honey
3 tbsp soy sauce
1 tbsp fresh lemon juice
½ tsp cornflour
300 ml fresh vegetable stock
1 clove garlic

Method

1. Peel and chop ginger. Place ginger, honey, soy sauce and lemon juice in a bowl for the marinade.
2. Chop the chicken and leave in the above marinade for 10–15 mins or longer if time allows.
3. Wash and slice all vegetables.
4. Heat oil and fry chicken pieces for 5 mins, stirring all the time.
5. Add the carrots next, as they take the longest to cook.
6. Add all the remaining vegetables, stirring all the time.
7. Blend the cornflour into the leftover marinade sauce, then mix the marinade into the stock.
8. Pour the stock into the saucepan and stir everything well.

Garnish with spring onions and cucumber slices, and serve with rice or egg noodles.

Modifications

You can substitute beef, lamb, pork or fish for the chicken. Most vegetables can be used in a stir-fry or curry, including baby corn, broccoli or cauliflower. Nuts and seeds can add variety too and are a good protein substitute for vegetarians.

Did You Know?

Marinating is the process of soaking foods in a seasoned (spices/herbs), often acidic, liquid (lemon, lime, vinegar) before cooking to tenderise the meat and add flavour.

Chicken fajitas with guacamole

Ingredients

4 free-range chicken breast strips
2 tbsp olive oil
Salt and pepper
1 tbsp sweet smoked paprika
2 medium red onions
1 red pepper
1 yellow pepper
½ bunch of fresh coriander
8 tortilla wraps
Guacamole:
- 10-12 mixed colour cherry tomatoes
- 1 fresh red chilli
- 2 ripe avocados
- 1–2 limes

A few sprigs of coriander
Chunky fresh salsa and natural yoghurt or soured cream, to serve

Method

1. Add the chicken strips to a bowl with olive oil, ½ lime juice, salt, pepper and the paprika. Toss to coat, then leave to one side to marinate for 10–15 mins.
2. Peel and finely slice the onions, de-seed and finely slice the peppers and chop the coriander leaves, discarding the stalks.
3. Place a large frying pan on a high heat, add a splash of olive oil, the onion and peppers and cook for around 5 mins, or until slightly softened.
4. Add the chicken and cook for a further 5–10 mins or until golden and cooked through, stirring occasionally.
5. Meanwhile, make the guacamole. Roughly chop the cherry tomatoes. De-seed and finely chop the chilli, then finely chop a handful of the coriander leaves. Halve and de-stone the avocados, then squeeze the flesh onto a board, discarding the skins and stones. Squeeze over the juice of 1½ limes, then chop and mash everything together. Season to taste.
6. Once the chicken is golden and cooked through, season to taste, then scatter over the remaining coriander leaves.
7. Warm the wraps according to packet instructions, then take to the table along with the chicken and vegetables, guacamole and bowls of fresh chunky tomato salsa and yoghurt so everyone can build their own.

Beef burritos

Ingredients

500 g minced beef
2 tbsp olive oil
2 onions, finely chopped
6 garlic cloves, crushed
1 tbsp tomato purée
2 tins chopped tomatoes
2 tbsp wine vinegar
5–6 chilli peppers, finely chopped
2 tsp paprika
2 tsp cumin
2 tsp chilli powder
50 g grated cheddar cheese
100 g sour cream
Salt and pepper

Method

1. Preheat oven to 180°C/fan 160°C/ Gas Mark 4.
2. Fry mince until brown.
3. Heat oil in large pan, fry onions, chillies and garlic for 5–6 mins.
4. Stir in spices and remaining ingredients.
5. Add in mince and simmer for 20–30 mins to thicken.
6. Heat tortillas in the microwave for about 30 seconds.
7. Fill tortillas with chilli, sour cream, cheese and salsa.
8. Place in oven for 10 mins.

Serve with rice or salad.

Simple chicken curry

Ingredients

4 chicken fillets
1 onion
6–8 button mushrooms
½ red pepper
½ green pepper
1–2 tbsp vegetable oil
25 g margarine
25 g flour
1 small onion
1 tbsp curry powder
1 tbsp tomato purée
½ small cooking apple
375 ml chicken or vegetable stock
1 tbsp chutney
2–3 drops lemon juice
Salt and pepper

Method

1. Make the sauce: Melt the fat, and fry onion until soft. Add flour and curry powder, stirring all the time, and cool slightly before gradually adding the stock, stirring all the time. Bring to the boil, add purée, apple, lemon juice, chutney and seasoning. Set aside.
2. Wash, peel and slice all vegetables.
3. Dice chicken into cubes and sear the surface.
4. Add chicken and vegetables to curry sauce and simmer for 30–40 mins.

Garnish with parsley and toasted almonds (optional) and serve with boiled rice.

Did You Know?

There are many accompaniments that can be served with curries. These include sliced tomato or cucumber, poppadoms, naan bread, mango chutney, crème fraîche, toasted flaked almonds, sliced banana tossed with lemon juice or raita.

Raita

Grate 10 cm of cucumber. Discard the juice. Mix with 125 g natural yoghurt, 2 tsp fresh mint or 1 teaspoon dried mint, a pinch of sugar and salt. Garnish with paprika. Serve as a sambal with curry dishes.

Chicken risotto with pesto and rocket

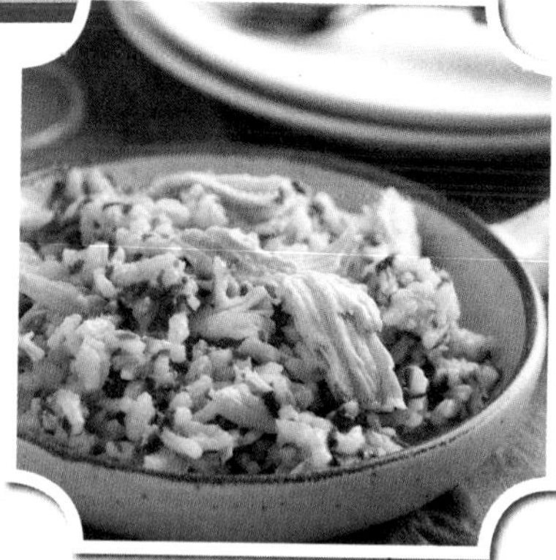

Ingredients

- 3-4 chicken fillets, cut into strips
- Salt and pepper
- 2 tbsp flour
- 4 tbsp olive oil
- 2 cloves of chopped garlic
- 1 finely chopped onion
- 200 g risotto rice
- 1 litre hot chicken stock
- 2 tbsp pesto
- 1 tbsp pine nuts

Method

1. Season the chicken and toss in the flour, and set aside.
2. Heat the oil and fry the onion and garlic until soft and translucent, add the rice and fry briefly.
3. Add a spoon of the stock stirring until evaporated, then add the stock a ladle at a time, stirring until absorbed before adding the next ladle.
4. When the rice is cooked to a creamy consistency, stir in the pesto and pine nuts; keep warm.
5. Fry the chicken to golden and stir into the risotto.

Garnish with rocket leaves and Parmesan shavings.

Chicken satay

Ingredients

- 2 chicken fillets, cut into strips
- 1 onion
- 1 pepper
- 1 courgette
- 6–8 mushrooms
- 50 g bean sprouts
- Crushed garlic, ginger and chilli (to taste)
- Soya sauce
- 2 tbsp crunchy peanut butter
- 50 g cashew nuts
- A little oil
- 80 g brown rice

Method

1. Heat the wok to very hot, add the oil and coat the pan.
2. Throw in the seasoned chicken strips, then the vegetables and garlic, ginger and chilli.
3. Add some soya sauce and the peanut butter, followed by a dash of water to form a sauce. Finally, stir in the cashews.
4. Cook the brown rice in a large pot of boiling salted water for 20–30 mins.
5. Rinse in cold water and drain, and if necessary reheat in the microwave.

Cooking quinoa and bulgur wheat

1. Rinse the quinoa/bulgur wheat thoroughly, then put in a saucepan and cover with hot stock by at least 5 cm.
2. Simmer until stock is absorbed and the grains are tender (you may need to add more stock during cooking).
3. Fluff the grains with a fork before serving.

Quinoa stuffed baked peppers

Ingredients

2 peppers, cut in half
1tbsp oil
1 chopped onion
100 g quinoa
250ml vegetable stock
50 g chopped mushrooms
50 g chopped courgette
1 clove chopped garlic
50 g chopped smoked bacon
75 g grated cheese
Shredded basil

Method

1. Preheat the oven to 200°C/Gas Mark 6.
2. Cook the quinoa in stock for 10–15 mins.
3. Cut the peppers in half and de-seed.
4. Fry the onion, garlic, courgette, mushrooms and bacon.
5. Add the cooked quinoa and basil.
6. Spoon into the pepper and sprinkle with cheese.
7. Bake for 30 mins until soft.

Serve as a starter, main course or an accompaniment.

Spiced bulgur wheat with prawns

Ingredients

200 g bulgur wheat
500 ml chicken stock
2 cloves garlic
1 chilli
100 g king prawns
1 diced spring onion
1 diced pepper
6–8 cherry tomatoes

Method

1. Cook the bulgur wheat in the hot stock.
2. Fry the onion, garlic, pepper and chilli.
3. Add the prawns and cherry tomatoes.
4. Stir in the bulgur wheat.

Garnish with chopped parsley and lemon wedges and serve with crusty bread.

Crispy baked hake with tartar yoghurt sauce

Ingredients

4 hake fillets (175–200 g each), skinned and boned
25 g butter, melted
75 g of stale breadcrumbs
20 g finely grated cheese
1 tbsp chopped parsley leaves
40 g plain flour
1 egg, lightly beaten
Salt and pepper
Yoghurt tartar sauce:
- 150 g Greek-style yoghurt
- 1 tsp Dijon mustard
- 1 tbsp capers, drained and finely chopped
- 1 small gherkin, finely chopped
- 1 tbsp chopped parsley leaves

Method

1. Preheat oven to 200°C/fan 180°C/Gas Mark 6.
2. Line a large baking tray with greaseproof paper and brush with a little of the melted butter.
3. Place the breadcrumbs in a shallow dish with the grated cheese and parsley. Place the flour and egg in separate shallow dishes.
4. Season the hake with a little salt and black pepper. Dip the hake, one piece at a time, into the flour, shake off the excess, then dip into the egg and finally into the breadcrumbs mixture. Place on the baking tray. Brush the remaining melted butter over the top and sides of the fish. Place in the oven and bake for 15 mins or until cooked through.
5. Meanwhile make the yoghurt tartar sauce: Place yoghurt, mustard, capers, gherkin, parsley, salt and pepper in a small bowl. Mix well to combine.

Serve the sauce with the crispy hake, tender stem broccoli or wilted spinach and sautéed baby potatoes.

Hot Thai fish cakes

Ingredients

400 g fish (salmon and cod or hake fillet)
1 clove garlic
Grated zest of 1 lime or lemon
2 slices white bread
2 tsp red curry paste
1 tbsp Thai fish sauce *(nam pla)*
1 egg
Oil for frying

Method

1. Peel the garlic, grate the zest from the lime or lemon, and cut the bread into pieces.
2. Wash, skin and remove bones from fish, put into processor with the egg, bread, zest, curry paste, fish sauce and garlic. Blend until smooth and turn onto a plate.
3. Heat the oil. Wet hands and form the fish paste into eight even-sized cakes.
4. Place directly onto pan. Fry on both sides until golden and cooked through. Drain on kitchen paper.

Garnish with coriander leaves and serve on a bed of noodles or with a side salad.

Pizza

Ingredients

450 g strong white flour
1 tsp sugar
Pinch of salt
1 x 7g sachet of fast-acting yeast
300 ml warm water (1 part boiling to 2 parts cold)
1 tbsp olive oil
Tomato sauce:
- 1 tbsp oil
- 400 g tin chopped tomatoes
- 1 onion, finely chopped (optional)
- 1 garlic clove, crushed
- 1 tsp fresh herbs (basil, thyme, parsley, etc.) or ½ teaspoon dried mixed herbs

Suggested Toppings: Cheese (mozzarella and/or grated cheddar or goats' cheese), slices of pepperoni or chorizo, sliced ham, shredded cooked chicken, peppers, mushrooms, sweetcorn, rocket, etc.

Method

1. Make the dough by putting the flour, sugar, salt and yeast into a large bowl. Add the oil to the warm water and pour into the dry ingredients. Mix together to form a dough.
2. Turn the dough onto a floured surface and knead for 7–10 mins, until dough is smooth and elastic. This can be done in half the time by using dough hooks in an electric mixer. Return to bowl and cover loosely with a tea towel. Leave in a warm place to prove until doubled in size – about 45 mins to 1 hour.
3. Meanwhile, make the sauce: Heat the oil in a pan, add the onion and gently fry until soft. Add the tomatoes, garlic and herbs and bring to the boil. For a smooth sauce, this may be blitzed in a food processor.
4. The sauce should be thick enough to coat the back of a spoon. If it needs thickening, bring it to the boil and reduce for few minutes to thicken.
5. Preheat oven to 200°C/fan 180°C/Gas Mark 6.
6. When dough is ready, dust a board, flour and roll out to a round. The size depends on the thickness and the number of pizzas you wish to make.
7. Place pizza on baking tray. Spread with a little of the tomato sauce, then the cheese and the toppings of your choice.
8. Bake for about 10–15 mins depending on the thickness of the pizza, until the pizza is golden underneath and the topping is bubbling on top.

Accompaniments

Sweet potato wedges

Ingredients

2–3 sweet potatoes cut into wedges
A little olive oil
Salt and pepper
Thyme

Method

1. Preheat the oven to 200°C/fan 180°C/Gas Mark 6.
2. Toss the wedges in the oil, season well and spread on a baking sheet.
3. Bake for about 30 mins until brown around the edges.

Serve as a side for a fish, or meat dish.

Modifications
Ordinary potatoes can be used; par-boil them for 5 mins before baking to crisp them up more.

Green salad

Ingredients

1 head of lettuce or 1 packet of mixed leaves
3 scallions
½ small cucumber
½ small green pepper
Parsley or other fresh herbs

Method

1. Wash and dry lettuce. Arrange in a salad bowl.
2. Wash and chop scallions, de-seed and wash green pepper and slice into fine strips. Wash and slice cucumber.
3. Arrange nicely in a bowl, sprinkle with chopped parsley or other herbs.

Toss in French dressing just before serving.

French dressing

Ingredients

1 tbsp white wine vinegar
Salt and pepper
1 tsp Dijon mustard
3 tbsp groundnut oil
1 garlic clove, crushed

Method

1. Mix white wine vinegar with salt and pepper in a jar with a tight-fitting lid.
2. Put the lid on and shake until the salt has dissolved.
3. Add Dijon mustard and shake again, then add the oil and garlic and shake once more.
4. Serve over salad or new potatoes or French beans.

Avocado, apple and walnut salad

Ingredients
2 avocado pears
1 red apple
Lemon juice
50 g chopped walnuts
Baby salad leaves
Dressing:
- 2–3 tbsp lemon juice or wine vinegar
- Pinch of salt, sugar and pepper
- ½ tsp mustard
- 6 tsp sunflower oil

Method

1. Make the dressing: Mix the lemon juice or vinegar with seasonings in a bowl with a whisk. Add in the oil gradually while whisking until the dressing thickens.
2. Cut the avocados in half using a stainless steel knife, and remove the stones.
3. Remove flesh from each avocado in one piece using a tablespoon and cut the flesh into dice. Put in a bowl and sprinkle with lemon juice.
4. Chop walnuts into small pieces. Wash and core the apple, dice and add with walnuts to the avocados.
5. Add the dressing, mix gently, and check the seasoning. Fill into the avocado shells and arrange each half on a plate.

Garnish with lettuce leaves, sliced tomato and cucumber, and serve with grilled, baked or roasted meats.

Warm potato salad

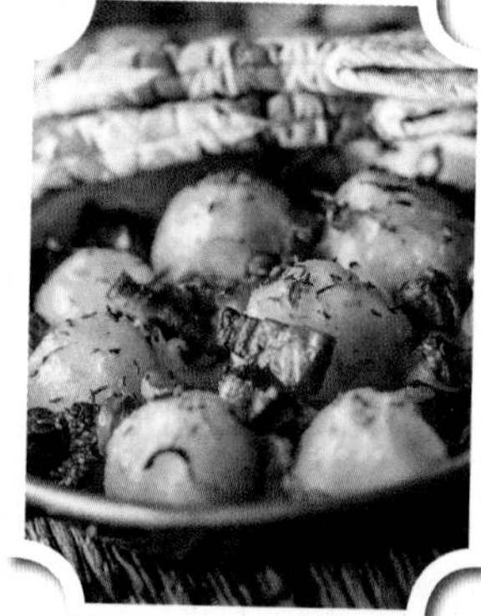

Ingredients
400 g baby potatoes
4 rashers
Dressing:
- 1 small red onion
- 1 scallion
- 1 tbsp cooking oil
- 1 tbsp honey
- 3 tbsp cider vinegar
- 2 tsp cornflour
- 3 tbsp water
- 2 tbsp fresh dill, chopped

Method

1. Scrub and wash potatoes (no need to peel), cut into quarters, and cook in boiling salted water until soft. Drain well.
2. Grill the rashers until crispy and cut into small pieces with scissors.
3. Peel, chop and dice onion and scallion and sauté in oil until soft.
4. Blend cornflour, vinegar and water and add to the onion mixture. Bring to the boil and cook until thickened.
5. Add the honey and chopped dill.
6. Mix with warm potatoes and rashers and pile into serving dish.

Garnish with fresh dill or flat leaf parsley.

Sauces

Sauces add flour and texture to a dish; here is a selection of sauces that can be used and adapted to suit many recipes.

Mayonnaise

Ingredients

2 free-range egg yolks
1 tsp Dijon mustard
1 tbsp lemon juice or vinegar to taste
300 ml sunflower oil
½ tsp salt and pepper

Method 1: Using an electric beater

1. Place the egg yolks, mustard and lemon juice or vinegar in a mixing bowl. Mix at high speed for 20 secs.
2. With the motor running, add the oil in a very thin stream, stopping slowly when ⅓ has been added. Beat well, and continue adding the oil slowly until the mayonnaise becomes very thick.
3. Add salt and pepper to taste.

Method 2: Using a balloon whisk

1. Whisk the egg yolks, mustard and lemon juice or vinegar for 1 min until light and creamy.
2. Add the oil 1 teaspoon full at a time, whisking continously – this is important.
3. After ⅓ of the oil has ben added and the mayonnaise is very thick, you can add the oil more quickly but beat vigorously in between each addition. Add salt and pepper to taste.

Store in a screw-top jar in the fridge.

Coleslaw

Ingredients

1 small white cabbage
1 large carrot
1 small onion (optional)
1 apple (optional)
Lemon juice
50 g mayonnaise
Salt and pepper

Method

1. Wash the cabbage, quarter, remove the stalk and shred finely.
2. Wash top and tail and grate the carrot.
3. Wash and core apple, dice and toss in lemon juice to prevent browning.
4. Peel and grate the onion.
5. Place all ingredients in a bowl, mix in mayonnaise until all vegetables are coated and chill until required.

Hollandaise sauce

Ingredients

2 free range egg yolks
1 tbsp lemon juice
75 g butter

Method

1. Melt butter.
2. Using a liquidiser, blend egg yolks and lemon juice for 10 secs at the slowest speed.
3. Pour butter onto the running blades drop by drop. Season well. Keep warm, covered, in a bowl over hot water. It will thicken a little more, but can be thinned with a little water stirred in.

Serve with salmon, eggs (see below) or vegetables like asparagus.

Eggs Benedict

Ingredients

4 free-range eggs
3 tbsp of white wine vinegar
2 toasting muffins
4 slices of Parma ham
1 batch of hot hollandaise sauce

Method

1. Bring a deep saucepan of water to the boil, and add the vinegar. Break the eggs into four separate ramekins. Split the muffins, toast them and warm some plates.
2. Swirl the water briskly to form a vortex and slide in an egg. It will curl round and set to a neat round shape. Cook for 2–3 mins, then remove with a slotted spoon.
3. Repeat with the other eggs, one at a time, re-swirling the water as you slide in the eggs. Spread some sauce on each muffin, scrunch a slice of ham on top, then top with an egg. Spoon over the remaining hollandaise and serve at once.

Fresh tomato sauce

Ingredients

1 onion
1 garlic clove
1 carrot (optional)
1 tbsp olive oil
300 g fresh tomatoes or
  1 can chopped tomatoes
1 rounded tsp flour
150 ml water
1 tbsp tomato purée
1 tsp dried oregano
½ tsp sugar
Salt and pepper

Method

1. If using liquidiser/processor, chop vegetables roughly. If not, wash and chop tomatoes finely. Smash garlic, peel and crush. Peel onion and carrot, grate on large holes of grater.
2. Heat oil, sauté onion, carrot and garlic until soft (about 5 mins).
3. Add flour and stir for 1 min. Remove from the heat.
4. Slowly stir in the liquid and tomatoes and all other ingredients.
5. Cover and simmer for 20 mins. Liquidise until smooth.
6. Taste the sauce, correct seasoning and serve.

Serve with 50 g diced mozzarella, stirred into the sauce to melt just before serving. Pour over hot pasta and top with basil leaves.

Barbecue sauce

Ingredients

Use the ingredients for *Fresh tomato sauce* but omit carrot. Add the following:
1 tsp mustard
2 tsp brown sauce
1–2 tsp honey
1 tsp brown vinegar

Method

1. Make as for *Fresh tomato sauce* (omitting carrot).
2. Add all extra ingredients at step 5.

Serve hot or cold with barbecued, grilled, or baked meats, fish or vegetables.

Sweet and sour sauce

Ingredients

Use the ingredients for *Fresh tomato sauce* and add the following:
1 tsp soy sauce
1 tsp sugar
1 tsp cider vinegar
100 g crushed pineapple

Method

1. Make as for *Fresh tomato sauce* (omitting carrot).
2. Add all extra ingredients at step 5.

Serve hot or cold with barbecued, grilled, or baked meats, fish or vegetables.

Smoothies

Smoothies can be made with a wide variety of fruit and veg combined with milk, juice, yoghurt and enriched with oats, seeds and peanut butter. Experiment and see what you like!

Banana and peanut butter smoothie

Ingredients
1 banana
1 tbsp crunchy peanut butter
½ pint of skimmed milk
Sprinkle of seeds

Method
1. Put all the ingredients in a blender and whizz until smooth. Ice can be added to make it thicker and colder, more like a slushie.
2. This makes an excellent lunch/snack drink, as it can be made in advance and put in a shaker.

Fruits of the forest smoothie

Ingredients
¼ pint skimmed milk
¼ pint juice
Frozen berries (handful)

Method
1. Blend as above. This will be thick and chilled.

Strawberry kiwi smoothie

Ingredients
125 ml cold apple juice
1 ripe banana, sliced
1 kiwi, peeled and sliced
5 strawberries
1 dsp honey
6–8 ice cubes

Method
1. Blend as above. This will be thick and chilled.

Desserts

Chocolate mocha mousse

Ingredients

100 g dark chocolate (70%)
2 whole eggs
4 egg whites
1 tbsp Camp Coffee

Method

1. Melt the chocolate in a bowl over a pot of boiling water; allow to cool slightly.
2. Beat the whole eggs with the coffee before beating into the chocolate.
3. In a separate bowl whisk the egg whites to a soft peak.
4. Fold into the chocolate mix.
5. Pour into glasses and chill. Decorate with whipped cream and grated chocolate.

Serve with fresh fruit.

Apple and strawberry crumble

Ingredients

100 g flour
50 g muesli
75 g margarine
75 g brown sugar
½ tsp cinnamon
3 large cooking apples
5–6 strawberries
Juice of ½ lemon

Method

1. Preheat the oven to 190°C/fan 170°C/Gas Mark 5, and grease the pie dish.
2. Wash the apples, core, peel and slice. Hull and slice the strawberries.
3. Layer slices into the dish and sprinkle with half the sugar.
4. Cut lemon in half and squeeze over the apples.
5. Sieve the flour into the bowl.
6. Rub in the margarine with your fingertips until it resembles fine breadcrumbs.
7. Mix in the muesli and the rest of the sugar.
8. Cover the sliced apples and strawberries with crumble mixture.
9. Bake in the oven for 30–35 mins until the top is crisp.

Serve with custard, cream or ice cream.

Modifications

You can use a variety of fruit combinations: rhubarb, pear and chocolate chip, apple and blueberry …

Gooey chocolate cake

Ingredients

100 g self-raising flour
100 g caster sugar
Pinch of salt
25 g cocoa
50 g melted margarine or butter
1 egg
4 tbsp milk
1 tbsp vanilla extract
Sauce:
100 g brown sugar
25 g cocoa
150 ml water

Method

1. Mix together flour, caster sugar, salt and cocoa.
2. Add melted margarine or butter, egg, milk and vanilla extract to above mix. Stir well to combine and place in microwavable bowl (sides should be at least 5 cm higher than the batter as the cake will rise).
3. Make sauce by combining brown sugar with the remaining cocoa and the water. Sprinkle on top of batter mix.
4. Warm water for 30 secs and tip on top of cake gently. Use a fork to gently prick a few holes in batter to allow some water to seep into it.
5. Cook on high in microwave for 5 mins.

Serve with ice cream or custard.

Strawberry cheesecake

Ingredients

Base:
200 g digestive biscuits, crushed
100 g butter

Filling:
1 pack cream cheese
1 packet strawberry jelly
1 tin strawberries
Carton cream
3 tbsp caster sugar
2 egg whites
1 strawberry yoghurt

Method

1. Make the base by melting the margarine and adding the crushed biscuits. Press into a loose-bottomed tin.
2. Drain the juice from the strawberries, use 100 ml of this to melt the jelly.
3. Beat the cheese, sugar, yoghurt and strawberries together.
4. Whip the cream.
5. Whisk the egg whites.
6. Add the cooled jelly to the cheese mixture; add in the cream.
7. Fold in the egg whites.
8. Pour over the base. Leave to set for around 4 hours.

Batters

Batters can be used in a variety of ways in sweet and savoury dishes.

Type	Ingredients	Use
Thin	100 g flour, pinch of salt, 1 egg and 250 ml milk	Pancakes, crêpes, Yorkshire pudding
Thick (coating)	100 g flour, pinch of salt, 1 egg and 125 ml milk	Coating fish, sausages, fritters

Method

1. Sieve flour and salt into a bowl.
2. Make a well in the centre and drop in egg and a little milk, mix with a wooden spoon or whisk, and add the milk a little at a time, whipping until you have a smooth batter.
3. If possible, leave to stand for 30 mins.

To make pancakes …

4. Lightly grease the frying pan and heat.
5. Pour in 2–3 tablespoons of batter.
6. Lift the pan and tip it to spread the batter.
7. Cook until the batter is set on top and brown underneath.
8. Turn and brown the other side.

Pancakes can be served with a sweet (e.g. stewed apple, cinnamon and cream, ice cream and chocolate sauce, fresh berries and maple syrup) or savoury (e.g. chicken and mushroom in a white sauce, smoked salmon and crème fraîche, ham and cheese) filling.

Bread and butter pudding

Ingredients

25 g butter, plus extra for greasing
10 thin slices of bread
50 g sultanas
2 tsp cinnamon powder
350 ml whole milk
50 ml double cream
2 free-range eggs
25 g granulated sugar
Nutmeg, grated, to taste

Method

1. Preheat the oven to 180°C/fan 160°C/Gas Mark 4, and grease a 1-litre pie dish with butter.
2. Cut the crusts off the bread. Spread each slice on one side with butter, then cut into triangles.
3. Arrange a layer of bread, buttered-side up, in the bottom of the dish, then add a layer of sultanas. Sprinkle with a little cinnamon, then repeat the layers of bread and sultanas, sprinkling with cinnamon, until you have used up all of the bread. Finish with a layer of bread, then set aside.
4. Gently warm the milk and cream in a pan over a low heat to scalding point. Don't let it boil.
5. Crack the eggs into a bowl, add three-quarters of the sugar and lightly whisk until pale.
6. Add the warm milk and cream mixture and stir well, then strain the custard into a bowl.
7. Pour the custard over the prepared bread layers and sprinkle with nutmeg and the remaining sugar and leave to stand for 30 mins.
8. Place the dish into the oven and bake for 30–40 mins, or until the custard has set and the top is golden brown.

Serve with ice cream, whipped cream or warm custard.

Further Investigation

If you want more recipes look them up online on some of the following websites:

www.odlums.ie
www.easyfood.ie
www.lidl-recipes.ie
www.donalskehan.com
www.rte.ie/recipes
www.potato.ie
www.bbcgoodfood.com
www.bbc.com/food/cuisines

Strand 2
Responsible Family Living

Section 1: The Efficient Home

20 THE FAMILY

Learning Outcomes 1.6, 1.7, 1.9, 2.1, 2.2, 2.3, 2.4, 2.5, 2.11, 3.7, 3.8

What I Will Learn

- to identify different types of families
- to describe the changes that have occurred in families in Ireland in recent years
- to consider the factors that influence family life
- to identify the basic needs of a child and adolescent
- to discuss the functions of the family
- to explore the roles and responsibilities of each family member
- to discuss family relationships and the importance of good communication
- to identify the causes of conflict within the family
- to explain how to deal with conflict within the family
- to determine what is required to provide a safe and nurturing home environment

Key Words

✓ Family
✓ Adoption
✓ Divorce
✓ Relationship
✓ Custom
✓ Nuclear
✓ Extended
✓ Blended
✓ Lone-parent
✓ Cohabiting
✓ Functional
✓ Dysfunctional
✓ Rights
✓ Responsibilities
✓ Roles
✓ Adolescence
✓ Peer
✓ Gender
✓ Stereotyping
✓ Equality

Most people grow up in a **family**, which is a group of people who are related by blood, marriage, or some other connection, e.g. adoption or fostering. They usually have a close relationship and share the same name and home. In this section we will study the relationships, customs, behaviour patterns and social problems that are a part of modern family life. The family unit can vary from culture to culture. Even within Ireland, there are many types of families.

Adoption means to legally bring another person's child up as your own.

Divorce is the ending of an existing legal marriage. It leaves the divorced couple free to remarry.

Types of family

Nuclear family: Consists of two parents and their child or children living in the same house.

Extended family: Consists of two parents, children and other relatives, such as grandparents, aunts and uncles. Many of these people live together in one home or near each other.

Lone-parent family: Consists of a mother or father who may be unmarried, separated, divorced or widowed, along with their child or children.

Blended family: When partners have children from previous relationships and they all live together as one family. The partners may also have more children together.

Some of the social changes that have occurred in the 21st century have had a major impact on family life. These include recent changes in relation to family law, the decreasing of the influence of the Church and multicultural influences.

Did You Know?

According to the 2016 Census, Ireland has the lowest divorce rate in the European Union, but the numbers of divorced people in Ireland actually increased from 87,770 in 2011 to 103,895 in 2016. However, it does represent a lower increase than was recorded between 2006 and 2011.

Did You Know?
A total of 1,147 same-sex marriages have taken place in Ireland (April 2017) since the marriage-equality legislation came into effect in November 2015.

- The **decrease of the influence of the Church** and **multicultural influences** have led to couples cohabiting (living together without being married) and an increase in birth rates outside of marriage. It has also led to changes in the law:
  - The **Divorce Act (1996)** allowed couples to divorce in Ireland. This has led to an increase in **lone-parent** and **blended** families.
  - The **Marriage Act (2015)** allowed same-sex couples to marry, which has led to a new **nuclear** family structure with same-sex parents.
- The **cost of living** during the recession had led to more people cohabiting and raising their children rather than getting married. Due to financial pressures and other factors, many adult children are living at home with their parents for longer.
- Nowadays, many couples **relocate** or move away from their extended family to find work, etc. Raising children can be more difficult without a family support network – it can also lead to social isolation.

Factors that influence family life

No two families are alike, be they happy or unhappy, employed or unemployed, rich or poor. There are a huge range of influences on the family, which impact on the family unit, making life difficult or helping them to survive.

Social influences	• More women are working outside the home • Fathers are more involved in raising children • Higher rates of divorce and marriage breakdown • Fewer children in families • A better education system has improved employment prospects • Increased leisure time allows more quality time to spend on family activities
Economic influences	• Higher income leads to a better standard of living for some families • Unemployment or high cost of living – some families have financial problems • Many families are dependent on social welfare • Childcare and education are big expenses for some families
Cultural influences	• Family background and traditions • Race and religion • Living in a rural or urban area • Local traditions, such as music or sport • Social media and peer pressure have a major influence on teenagers

What children and teenagers need:
- Nourishing food
- Proper clothing
- To be kept safe and protected
- Love and affection
- To live in a healthy environment
- A stimulating environment in which to develop
- Loving and consistent guidance and discipline

Functions of the family

A functional family will provide for all **physical**, **emotional**, **social** and **educational** needs of family members. A dysfunctional family will only provide some of these needs.

Physical needs	• Food • Clothing • Warmth • Shelter – a place to live in • Protection from danger • Providing care when a member is sick
Emotional needs	• Love • Comfort • Security • Understanding
Social needs	• Personal relationships with family members • Social skills to enable them to cope with life
Educational needs	• Encouragement and support with schoolwork • Providing a stimulating environment • Conversation • Reading stories to children

Did You Know?

The Irish Society for the Prevention of Cruelty to Children (ISPCC) runs a confidential helpline for children and teenagers called Childline. It also runs a programme ('4me') aimed at 13- to 18-year-olds who are at risk of abusing drugs and alcohol, or who are involved in anti-social behaviour.

Childline: (01) 676 7960

Parenthood

- Parents have a duty and **responsibility** to provide for their children's needs.
- Some parents find this difficult, especially if there are problems such as marital breakdown, financial worries, addictions or health problems.
- Some parents, often through no fault of their own, fail to provide for their children's needs.
- The state can provide help through social services.
- No matter what type of family they are born into, every child has certain **rights**.

A **right** is something a person is entitled to.
A **responsibility** is something for which a person is accountable (they should or must do it).

Rights and responsibilities of children and adults

Children/adolescents' rights	Children/adolescents' responsibilities
Children and adolescents have a right to: • Love and understanding • Grow up in the care of their family, where possible • Live in a healthy environment • Receive an education • Protection from cruelty and neglect	Children and adolescents should: • Show respect for others • Obey parents and people in authority • Learn how to behave in society • Be cooperative and dependable in the home • Participate well in school

Adolescence is the period of time during which a child is developing from a child to an adult.

Siblings are your brothers and sisters.

Adolescents who behave **responsibly**:
- Have good relationships with **siblings**, parents and grandparents
- Are good role models for younger children
- Are reliable friends and a positive influence on their peers
- Are aware of the needs of others in their community

Adults' rights	Adults' responsibilities
Adults have the right to: • Work • Vote • Avail of consumer rights • Sign legal documents • Marry	Adults should: • Provide for their family's needs • Show respect for others • Set reasonable boundaries (rules) for younger members of the household • Show respect for all family members • Behave appropriately in society and set a good example • Be aware of the needs of others in their community

Relationships and roles within the family

A **relationship** is the interaction between people. The first relationships we form generally occur within the family. In a good relationship, we get along and communicate well with each other. If family relationships are good, it is usually easier to form relationships outside the family unit.

There are different types of relationships within the family:

- Ideally, **parent and parent** relationships should be close and loving. Parents should share equal responsibility for the family.
- **Parent and child** relationships should be affectionate and respectful. Children should be able to trust their parents. Parents should set reasonable boundaries for their children and be consistent and fair when disciplining their children.
- Relationships between **siblings** should be close and caring. Equal treatment by parents will reduce friction and jealousy between siblings.
- The **grandparent and grandchild** relationships should also be caring and respectful.

A **role** is the way we are expected to behave in relationship.

Family roles

A family is made up of individual people who are expected to behave in a particular way, according to their position. Each person in the family has a different role to play.

Peers are people who are a similar age or who have the same interests.

Children and adolescents' roles

- Children are expected to behave in a way that is appropriate for their age group.
- Their roles gradually change as they become adolescents – they are expected to become more responsible and independent. The influence of friends and **peers** often becomes stronger than the influence of family.

Parents' roles

In the past, fathers and mothers had very separate roles. The father usually earned money, was in charge of discipline and made all the major decisions in the home. He had very little to do with running the home or with childcare. The mother usually stayed at home and looked after the children and the house. Nowadays, these roles are not as clearly defined and there is more equality between fathers and mothers. Parents' roles include caring for the needs of their child or children, disciplining them, providing for them financially and being their first educators.

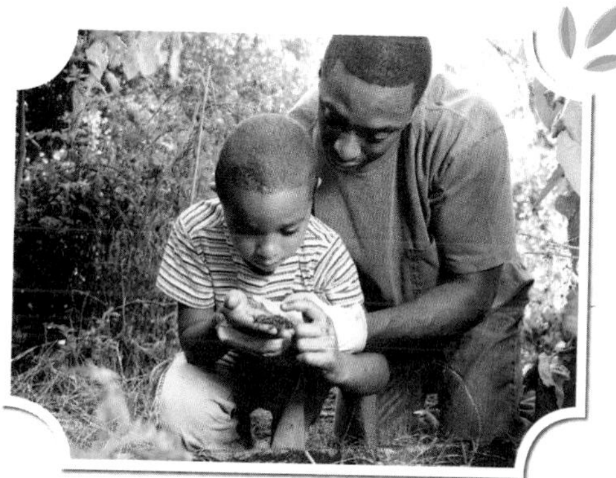

Gender/sex roles

- **Gender**, or sex, means being male or female. Males and females are expected to act in a particular way according to their gender. **Gender roles** are learned from those around us as we grow up, such as parents, our environment and the media. Traditionally, males were expected to behave in a particular way, e.g. be strong and brave, and females in another way, e.g. be gentle and caring. In modern society this is changing – it is acceptable for both men and women to have traits that were traditionally considered either feminine or masculine, e.g. assertiveness (traditionally masculine) and sensitivity (traditionally feminine).
- The equal treatment of males and females is called **gender equality** or **gender equity**. People are often **stereotyped** according to their sex, e.g. 'all childminders are female'. Males and females have a right to equal treatment at home, in school, in their community and in work. **Gender inequality/inequity** occurs when males or females are treated unfairly. Gender inequality can cause unhappiness and a loss of self-esteem.

Stereotyping is a fixed and oversimplified image or idea of how a particular person or group behaves, e.g. 'boys don't cry', 'all Americans are loud'.

Communication

Communication is how we relate to one another.

- Communication is the most important part of all relationships. If there is no communication, there can be no relationship.
- Communication can be verbal, through talking, or non-verbal, where there is no talking but feelings are communicated through facial expressions, gestures and body language.
- When we meet people for the first time, we make a lasting impression with our appearance and by the way we communicate.
- Being a good listener is also an important communication skill.

To be a **good communicator**:

- Speak clearly
- Look people in the eye
- Listen attentively

Conflict

Everyone has disagreements with other people from time to time. Conflict can only be resolved by communicating with the other person or people.

In a family, there can often be areas of conflict, especially between teenagers and their parents because of **role confusion**, with each side seeing the situation differently, e.g. a parent feels they have a responsibility to keep their child safe, while the teenager feels they should be more independent.

Causes of conflict

- Teenagers want more freedom, and they begin to question rules that they accepted as children.
- Peer groups become very important during adolescence and can have more influence than parents.
- External influences such as social media and underage drinking can cause great distress and conflict.
- Romantic relationships can also cause conflict with parents because parents may not be prepared to deal with such changes in their child's relationships.

Dealing with conflict effectively

- Good communication between teenagers and their parents is essential in order to deal with conflict.
- House rules should change as children get older and more responsible.
- Parents and teens need to **empathise** with each other.
- Avoid confrontation. It is important to take time to calm down and become less emotional and angry.
- Both parents and teenagers need to compromise (give and take) – this is the best way to solve conflict.

CHILL when communicating with another person: Communicate Honestly, show Interest, Listen and know when to Leave well enough alone.

To **empathise** means to understand how another person feels.

Revision Questions

1. Identify four different types of family structure.
2. Describe four changes that have occurred in families in Ireland in recent years.
3. Suggest some ways in which family life may be affected either in a positive or a negative way.
4. Discuss the functions of the family.
5. Describe the role and responsibilities of adults.
6. What are the main causes of conflict between adolescents and parents in the family?
7. What is required to provide a safe and nurturing home environment?

Summary

- A **family** is a group of people related to each other by blood, marriage or some other connection, e.g. adoption. Different types of families include nuclear, extended, lone-parent and blended families.
- Changes in 21st-century family life include an increase in cohabiting couples and in lone-parent and blended families. There are also more same-sex nuclear families, and adult children are living at home for longer.
- **Factors that influence family life** include **social factors**, e.g. women working, divorce and marriage breakdown; **cultural factors**, e.g. race and religion; and **economic factors**, e.g. unemployment and the cost of childcare.
- **Functions of the family** include providing for physical and educational needs, caring for family members and allowing them to develop socially.
- **Rights of the child** include the right to love and understanding, to grow up in the care of their family, where possible, to live in a healthy and safe environment and to receive an education. They should also be protected from neglect and cruelty.

- A **child's responsibilities** include showing respect, obeying rules and learning to behave in society. Adolescents should be cooperative and dependable in the home, and should participate well in school.
- A **relationship** is the interaction between people. Family relationships include parent and parent relationships, parent and child relationships and relationships between siblings.
- **Communication** is how we relate to one another and is the most important part of all relationships. If there is no communication, there can be no relationship.
- A **role** is the way we are expected to behave in a relationship. A parent's role is to care for and provide for their children. Children's roles change gradually as they become adolescents.
- **Gender**, or sex, means being male or female. **Gender inequality/inequity** occurs when people are treated differently because of their gender.
- Everyone has **conflicts** or disagreements with other people from time to time. Conflict can only be solved by communicating with the other person or people, avoiding confrontation, showing empathy and compromising.

21 MANAGING RESOURCES

Learning Outcomes 1.2, 1.4, 1.5, 1.6, 1.15, 1.16, 2.4, 2.5, 2.7, 2.8, 2.9, 2.10, 2.11, 2.12, 2.13, 3.6, 3.7, 3.8, 3.9

What I Will Learn

- to explain what management is
- to identify the resources that are available to us
- to determine the qualities required to be a good manager and apply these qualities to the management of the home
- to use a management system
- to develop a work plan for cleaning the home
- to identify sources of income
- to discuss family expenditure
- to state the advantages of budgeting
- to create a budget
- to explore buying on credit
- to explore the advantages of saving
- to discuss why a home filing system is important

Key Words

✓ Management ✓ Resources ✓ Sustainable ✓ Qualities ✓ Ergonomics ✓ Budget ✓ Income ✓ Expenses ✓ Debt ✓ Salary ✓ Wages ✓ Gross ✓ Net ✓ Statutory ✓ Voluntary ✓ Deductions ✓ Tax credit ✓ Mortgage

Managing resources

Management is the skilful use of resources to achieve a goal. A **resource** is anything that can be used to help perform a task. A good manager will plan and use resources efficiently without waste.

The resources available to a manager include:

- **Human Resources:** people with their knowledge, skills, time and energy
- **Money**, which is used to buy other resources like food, equipment and commodities, e.g. cleaning agents
- **Environmental resources:** air, water, oil, electricity and gas
- **Community resources:** schools, hospitals, libraries and community centres

Home management is the efficient running of the home. It is usually performed by one or both parents with the help of other family members.

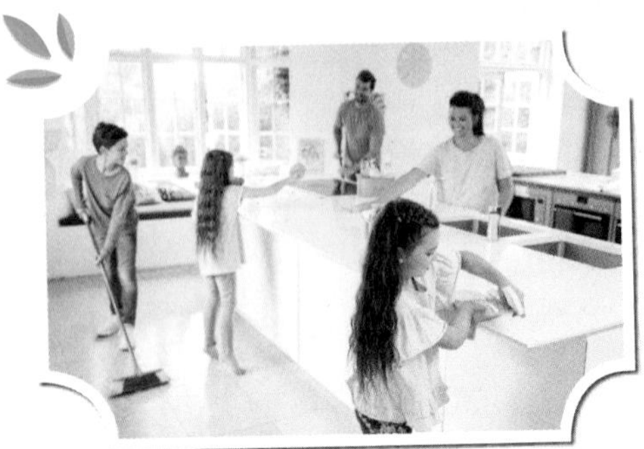

The **aim** of home management is to provide a healthy, safe and happy home environment for the family, where everything runs smoothly and without stress. When a home is run efficiently, money is not wasted, the home is kept clean, laundry is done and the family eats healthily.

All family members should be involved in the running of the home, as home management involves many tasks including budgeting, meal planning, childcare, shopping, cooking, cleaning, laundry, gardening and maintenance.

Management systems

All management systems involve decision making. Managing a home involves the following steps:

1. **Make a decision and set goals:** Decide on what you need to do or want to achieve, e.g. making family meals for a week.
2. **Identify the resources** you will need to complete the task, e.g. human energy, knowledge and skills, time, ingredients, equipment, cleaning agents, cloths and hot water.
3. **Plan:** Check what is in the fridge and presses, make a shopping list and draw up a work plan.
4. **Take action:** Put the plan into action, e.g. go to shop, store ingredients, prepare, cook and serve the meals each day.
5. **Evaluate:** Ask yourself a number of questions.
   - Are you happy with the result?
   - What went well and why?
   - Were the resources suitable?
   - Were the resources used efficiently and nothing wasted?
   - What would you do differently and why?

   You can use what you learn from this task to inform future decisions.

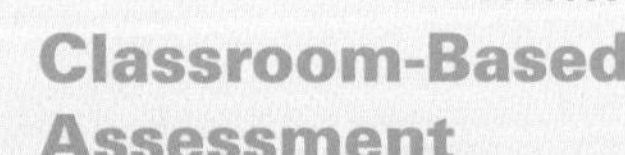

Classroom-Based Assessment

This section can be linked to CBA2 and the Practical Food Skills examination.

Cleaning management

To ensure good hygiene standards in the home, you need:

- A clean supply of water and efficient drainage
- To disinfect sinks, toilets and drains regularly
- Good ventilation and heating to prevent dampness
- Good lighting that shows dirt
- Rooms and surfaces that are easy to clean
- Careful waste disposal
- Hygienic people in the home (see p. 84)

Keeping a house clean can be time consuming if it not managed well, so a good cleaning routine is essential.

- Start by listing all the jobs that need to be done.
- Divide them up according to how often they have to be done, e.g. daily (making beds, washing dishes), weekly (changing the bed linen) or occasionally (washing the windows, trimming hedges).
- Divide the jobs between household members according to how much free time a person has, and their abilities, e.g. a young child can tidy up their toys and older children can make their beds and wash dishes.
- Make sure two or three weekly jobs are done every day, and that one occasional job is done every week.
- Organise tasks in a logical order, e.g. taking out the ashes before you sweep or dust (**why?**).
- Try out the routine, and adapt it if necessary.

Don't Forget!
Keep all your cleaning equipment and agents together in one cupboard (why?).

When cleaning, the correct equipment and cleaning agents are needed, as well as human resources like skills, time and energy.

Cleaning equipment

Cloths
Including tea towels, polishing cloths, microfibre cloths, sponges and wire scrubbers

Brushes and mops
Including sweeping, scrubbing, toilet and dishwashing brushes. These come in a variety of fibres, shapes and sizes

Basins and buckets
Needed for carrying water

Vacuum cleaner
An electrical appliance to lift dirt and dust quickly

Steam cleaner
An electrical appliance that uses steam to deep clean surfaces

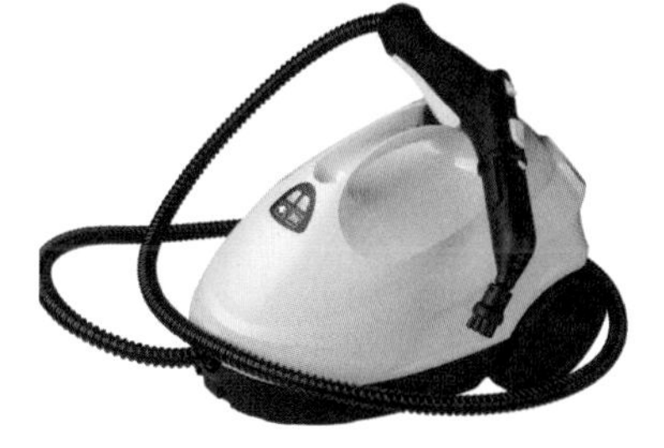

Gloves
To protect your hands during cleaning, especially for dirty jobs

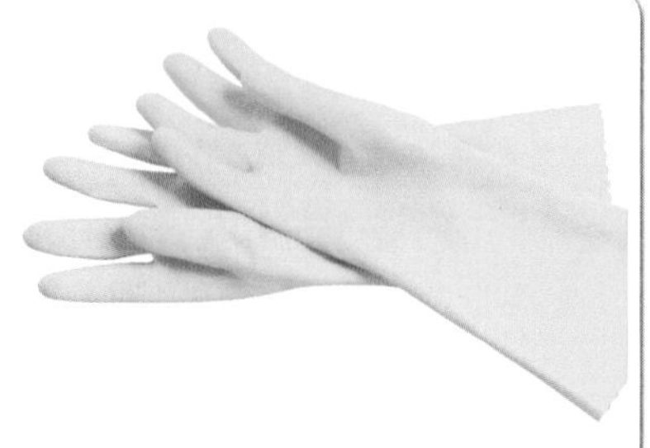

Don't Forget!
Cleaning agents are dangerous chemicals so store in a safe place if there are children in the home.

Your choice of cleaning agent is important too. Consider:

- How safe the product is
- Ease of use: the time and energy involved in using the product is important
- Has it got a pleasant smell?
- The product's effectiveness
- The product's cost and its packaging (**why is this important?**)
- Versatility: can the one product be used for many cleaning jobs?

Discovery Learning
Find out what to do if a child swallows a household cleaning agent, and explain what to do to at least one other person in your class.

Cleaning agents		
Water		Used hot to wash and cold or warm to rinse
Detergent		Used to remove dirt and grease, e.g. washing up liquid, washing detergent, dishwasher detergent
Bleach		Used to remove stains and kill germs
Polish		Used to shine metal, glass, floors and furniture
Abrasive		Used when friction is needed to remove grit or grime, e.g. cream cleaners, steel wool pads
Disinfectant		Kills germs
Multipurpose cleaning agents		Can be used on a variety of work surfaces, e.g. chrome, worktops, glass and cookers

Discovery Learning
Did you know that you can make your own 'green' cleaners using common kitchen ingredients? Find out how to make as many green cleaners as you can.

Don't Forget!

When using cleaning agents:
- **Follow the manufacturer's instructions carefully**
- **Rinse thoroughly**
- **Protect your skin**
- **Store all of them in one cupboard away from children, or use child locks**

Sequence of work when cleaning a room:

Tidy → Sweep → Dust → Vacuum → Wash → Polish

Revision Toolkit

Can you come up with a mnemonic to help you remember this sequence of work?

Ergonomics is the study of the efficiency of people in the workplace. It involves planning the layout of equipment and the sequence of tasks so the least amount of time and energy is used.

Guidelines for cleaning household equipment

- Protect yourself: cover hands and clothes and surrounding area
- Gather cleaning equipment and agents and bring them to the item to be cleaned
- Dismantle the piece of equipment and wash removable parts separately
- Use a mild cleaning agent first but if needed use a stronger alternative
- Work from top to bottom and towards yourself (**why?**) when cleaning a large appliance
- Rinse and dry thoroughly
- Polish surfaces
- Tidy up the area, and put away the cleaning equipment and cleaning agents

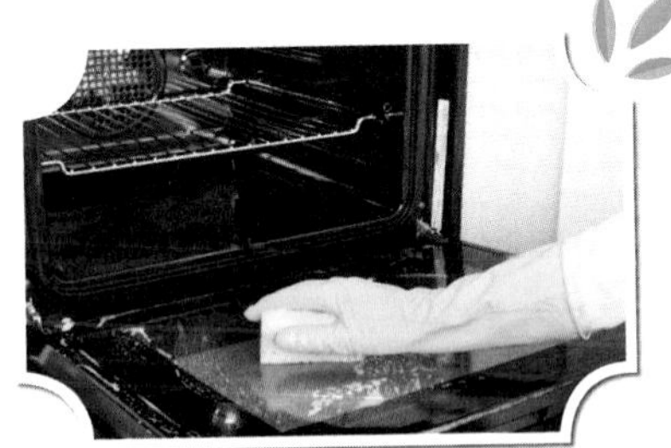

Shopping for electrical appliances

Technology, especially in electrical appliances, has made our personal and family life easier, as it cuts down on time taken to complete jobs, so freeing people up to spend more quality time together as a family. Electrical appliances can be classified as follows:

Type of appliance	Examples
Large appliances	Cookers, refrigerators, freezers, dishwashers and washing machines
Small appliances with a motor	Liquidisers, blenders, food processors and mixers
Small appliances with a heating element	Toasters, irons and kettles

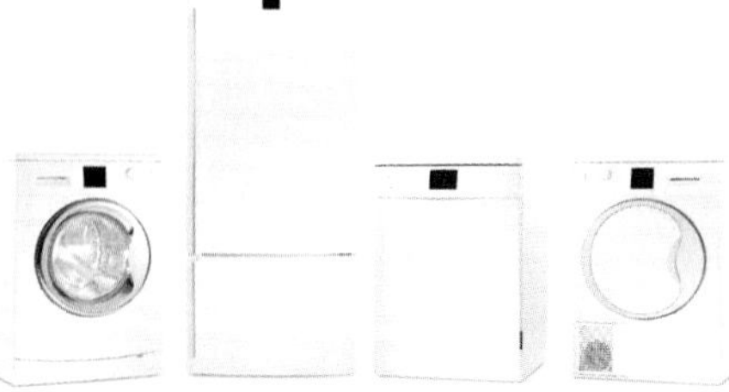

Discovery Learning

Can you identify four ways household appliances and technology have improved life for the modern family? Share your findings with the class.

Don't Forget!

Measure the space for the appliance before you leave home, and bring a measuring tape with you to check size of the appliance in the shop.

The wise consumer will consider the following when buying appliances:

Cost	Initial cost, delivery charges, installation and running charges
Energy	Energy efficiency
Size	Size based on space available and number in family
Brand	Brand name – is it reliable? How would you find out?
Quality	Has it got any safety symbols or quality marks?
Care	How easy it to assemble, use, and to take apart and clean?
Features	Has it got any additional features like timers and lights?
Guarantee	Has it got a guarantee and a good aftersales service? Check what it covers and if servicing done locally.

Revision Questions

1. Define 'management'.
2. List the resources that are available to us for running a home.
3. Describe the qualities a good manager should have.
4. Outline the steps in a managerial decision making process.
5. What is a green cleaner and why would you use one?
6. List four points to consider when buying a new washing machine.

Money management

CROSS-CURRICULUM BUSINESS STUDIES

Money is an important resource in every family, so money management is an important skill to have. It involves managing money wisely so that you can meet all your expenses. Planning a budget is a good example of money management:

- **Identify your goal:** Your goal is to divide up your income to ensure there is enough for paying all your expenses.
- **Identify your resources:** Usually money, time and skills.
- **Plan:** On paper or on screen, work out your income and expenses, then allocate a percentage of income to each expense so that all your expenditure is covered.
- **Take action:** Put the plan into action.
- **Evaluate:** Did the budget work? Were you able to cover all your expenses? If not, you will have to change your budget.

Discovery Learning

What skills will you need to have when managing money? Identify these skills and in pairs discuss why each is needed.

Benefits of managing your money

- You will know where your money is going and whether you are spending more than you can afford.
- It will give you peace of mind and a sense of control.
- It can help you to avoid debt problems, prepare for emergencies, save money and achieve your future goals.

Wages refers to weekly payment for doing a job.
Salary refers to fortnightly or monthly payments for doing a job.
Debt is money that you owe and have to pay back.

A plan for spending money and saving money is called a **budget**. Creating a budget involves dividing up **income** and allowing a certain amount towards each expense and saving, to avoid going into debt.

Income

Most households have a regular weekly, fortnightly or monthly income, in the form of a wage or salary, a pension, social welfare payments or interest on savings.

Discovery Learning

Find out what type of payment a person can get if they are unemployed, disabled or sick.

However, not all the money we earn is ours to spend. Some goes to the state to pay for running the country. This is our **tax liability** and is a compulsory deduction from our wages or salary.

Gross income is the total amount earned before deductions are made. **Net** income is a person's take-home pay – the amount left after deductions have been taken out. **Statutory deductions** are compulsory (must pay) and **voluntary deductions** are optional. **Tax credits** refer to the part of an income that is not taxed.

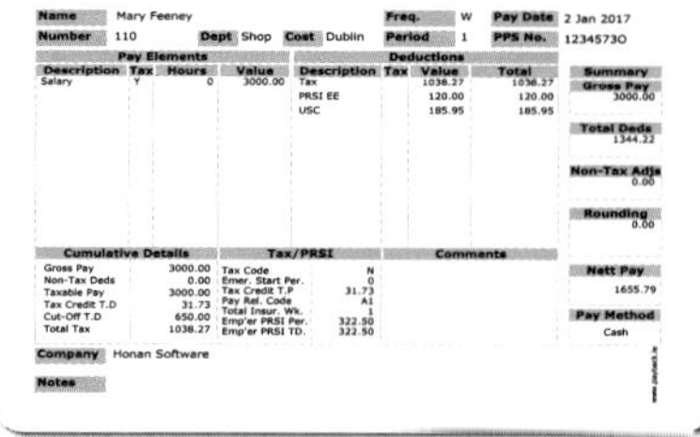

Name: Mary Feeney | Freq.: W | Pay Date: 2 Jan 2017
Number: 110 | Dept: Shop | Cost: Dublin | Period: 1 | PPS No.: 12345730

Pay Elements				Deductions			
Description	Tax	Hours	Value	Description	Tax	Value	Total
Salary	Y	0	3000.00	Tax		1038.27	1038.27
				PRSI EE		120.00	120.00
				USC		185.95	185.95

Summary	
Gross Pay	3000.00
Total Deds	1344.22
Non-Tax Adjs	0.00
Rounding	0.00
Natt Pay	1655.79
Pay Method	Cash

Cumulative Details		Tax/PRSI		Comments
Gross Pay	3000.00	Tax Code	N	
Non-Tax Deds	0.00	Emer. Start Per.	0	
Taxable Pay	3000.00	Tax Credit T.P	31.73	
Tax Credit T.D	31.73	Pay Rel. Code	A1	
Cut-Off T.D	650.00	Total Insur. Wk.	1	
Total Tax	1038.27	Emp'er PRSI Per.	322.50	
		Emp'er PRSI TD.	322.50	

Company: Honan Software
Notes:

Deductions

Statutory deductions

- **Income tax – Pay As You Earn (PAYE)** is deducted by the employer and goes to the state to pay for services.
- **Pay Related Social Insurance (PRSI)** goes towards paying people if they are ill or unemployed.
- The **Universal Social Charge (USC)** is a government tax on income.
- **Pension contributions** can be compulsory in some jobs.

Voluntary deductions
- **Private health insurance**, e.g. Irish Life Health, Laya
- Trade union fees, e.g. SIPTU, TUI
- Pension payments

Net income is a person's take-home pay, the amount left after deductions have been taken out.

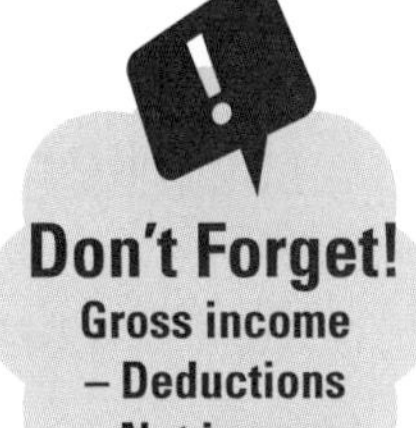

Don't Forget!
Gross income
– Deductions
= Net income

Expenses

Expenses differ from person to person depending on age or what stage their family is at, e.g. a young person working and living in an apartment will have different expenses from a family with two school-going children.

Needs are things we cannot do without, things we must have to survive and live, e.g. food, water, clothing, shelter and warmth.

Wants are things we would like to have but do not need to survive, e.g. holidays and expensive cars.

Essential expenditure money is used for essentials (needs), e.g. mortgage, food.
Discretionary expenditure money is to be spent on non-essential personal choices (wants), e.g. holidays.

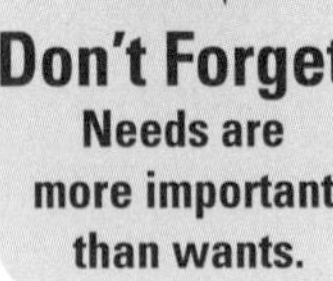

Don't Forget!
Needs are more important than wants.

Family expenses

- Rent or mortgage
- Food
- Household expenses, e.g. electricity, heating, water, cleaning agents
- Education and childcare
- Travel, e.g. car repayments, tax, insurance, NCT, petrol, servicing, bus fares
- Clothing
- Entertainment, e.g. newspapers, internet connection, TV licence, going out, holidays
- Medical expenses, e.g. dentist, doctor, health insurance, medicines
- Emergencies, e.g. unexpected costs
- Savings

Budgeting

Family budgeting is a responsible job, so should be shared between the adults in the family. It should be flexible to allow for changes in family circumstances, e.g. loss of a job or the arrival of a new baby. Families should be careful not to take on too many commitments or buy a lot on credit, because this can cause financial stress and hardship.

There are three steps to budgeting:
1. Calculate income
2. List expenses
3. Allocate a percentage of income to each expense

A budget should be designed specifically to suit the individual or family in question. It must be reviewed regularly and adjusted if necessary (**consumers, see p. 345**).

Sample budget based on a net income of €600 per week for a family with one child

Expense	%	€ per week
Rent or mortgage	20%	€120
Food	20%	€120
Household expenses	15%	€90
Education and childcare	10%	€60
Travel	10%	€60
Clothing	5%	€30
Entertainment	5%	€30
Medical expenses	5%	€30
Emergencies	5%	€30
Savings	5%	€30

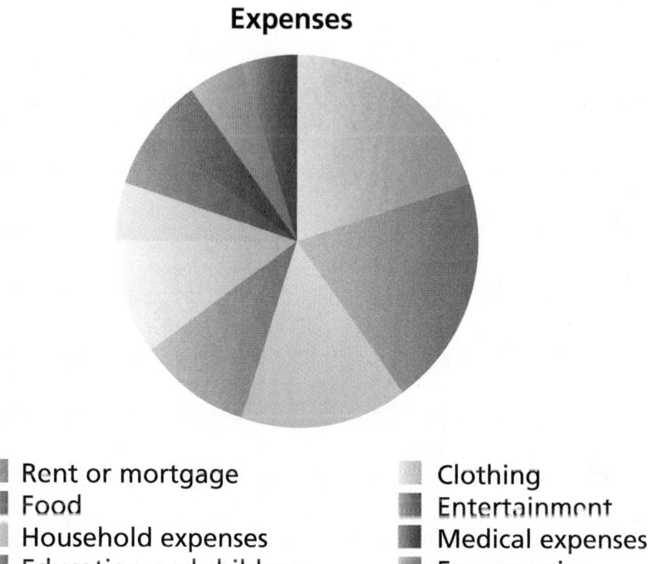

Expenses for a single young worker would be different, as many young people share houses and the expenses involved, and do not have education or childcare to pay for. A retired older couple could have no rent or mortgage to pay.

Advantages of budgeting

- Makes you feel more secure – fewer financial worries
- A budget allows you to plan for major bills
- There is less chance of overspending and impulse buying
- Areas of overspending are identified quickly
- Sets a good example for children
- Allows for saving

Impulse buying means buying something on the spur of the moment.

The Money Advice and Budgeting Service (MABS) is funded and supported by the Citizens Information Board. It helps families and individuals who are having money problems.

Credit or saving?

Credit is a way of borrowing money. It means 'buy now, pay later'. Buyers borrow money to buy goods and pay it back later usually with interest. Often it is used to buy large items like houses and cars but can be used to buy consumer goods like furniture or electrical goods, if the buyers do not have the money to pay for them immediately.

- Credit costs more than paying cash. The credit company or bank charges the borrower interest to cover the cost of borrowing which can be expensive.
- You must be over 18 to get credit.
- If a family take on too many credit commitment it can be dangerous because if circumstances change they may not be able to make repayments. The item may be repossessed, i.e. taken back.

Discovery Learning

Find out what a mortgage is, and the difference between a bank loan and an overdraft. Share your findings with the class.

Did You Know?

The Consumer Credit Act 1995 protects the consumer in all credit agreements.

Forms of credit

- **Hire purchase**: This is an agreement whereby a person hires goods for a period of time, by paying instalments, and will own the goods at the end of the agreement if all instalments are paid.
- **Bank overdraft**: This is when a bank arranges to allow the customer to spend more than is in their account, up to an agreed amount, without paying interest.
- **Loan**: A loan is the lending of money from a bank, building society or credit union to an individual or organisation. This loan is paid back in instalments with interest over a set period of time.
- **Credit card**: A credit card is a payment card issued to an individual so they can pay for goods and services based on the cardholder's promise to pay the credit card company or bank back the amount (plus other agreed charges). Pay off fully when billed to avoid interest.

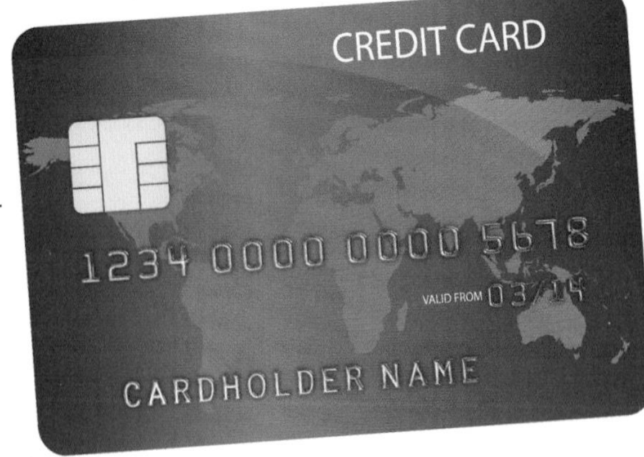

Credit	
Advantages	**Disadvantages**
• Buyer has the use of the goods immediately • Credit is necessary for large items such as houses or cars (**why?**) • It is good for the economy, as it encourages buying, therefore increasing employment • Buyer avoids having to carry large amounts of money	• High interest makes items more expensive • There is a danger of having too many credit repayments, leading to debt • It encourages impulse buying and overspending • Goods can be repossessed if repayments are not made

Saving

Savings means putting a certain amount of money aside each week or month. If you want to buy a computer or go on holiday, put aside a little from your budget each week until you have enough to pay for it with cash.

Savings	
Advantages	**Disadvantages**
• Money is generally safe and secure • Savings earn interest • It avoids impulse buying and overspending • Good example for children • Cash buyers pay less	• You have to wait until you have enough money

Where can you save?

- Bank
- Building society
- Credit union
- Post office

To choose the best option, consider the:

- Interest rate
- Ease of withdrawal
- Safety
- Extras, such as free banking

Discovery Learning

It is never too early to start saving, so investigate a suitable saving scheme for a teenager and feed your choice back to the class.

Have a home filing system

To be a good money manager, it is essential to have a home filing system, so important documents like bills, receipts, guarantees, insurance policies and pay slips are stored safely and can be easily found when needed. Bank statements can be monitored and spending adjustments made if necessary, e.g. past and present electricity or fuel usage can be monitored. A filing cabinet, accordion file or a sectioned box could be used. You can also use online folders, as many bills and receipts are emailed now and consumers can get discounts for paperless billing.

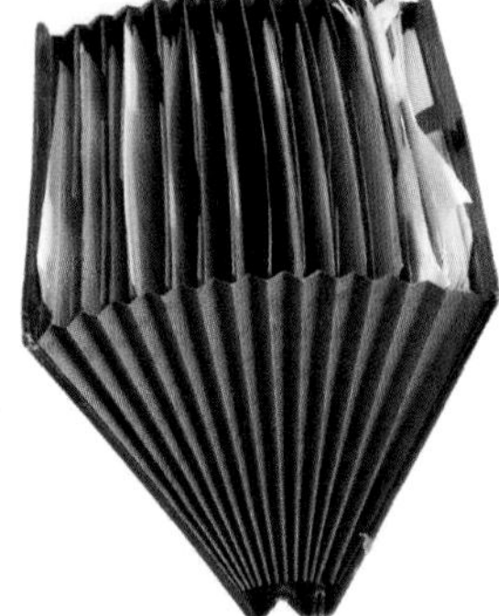

Revision Questions

1. Explain the term 'budget'.
2. Identify three sources of income.
3. Discuss what expenses a family might have.
4. State the advantages of budgeting.
5. Explain how to plan a budget.
6. Which is best: to buy on credit or to save to buy? Why?

Summary

- **Management** is the skilful use of resources to achieve a goal. A resource is anything that can be used to help perform a task. A good manager will plan and use resources efficiently without waste.
- **Home management** is the efficient running of the home. It is usually performed by one or both parents, with the help of other family members. The aim of home management is to provide a healthy, safe and happy home environment for the family where everything runs smoothly and without stress. When a home is run efficiently, money is not wasted, the home is kept clean, laundry is done and the family eats healthily.
- A **management system** involves making a decision and setting goals, identifying the resources, planning, action and evaluation.
- An **efficient cleaning routine** is essential in a home. Plan ahead and use sustainable products and efficient equipment.
- **Money management** means managing your money wisely so that you can pay all your expenses and avoid debt.

- A **budget** is a plan for spending and should be planned using a management system.
- Remember that gross income minus deductions is **net income**. **Statutory deductions** include PAYE, PRSI and USC. **Voluntary deductions** include health insurance and union fees.
- **Expenses** include housing, food, household expenses, childcare, entertainment and savings.
- **Credit** means buy now and pay later. Overdrafts, mortgages, hire purchases and credit cards are **forms of credit**.
- **Savings options** include banks, building societies, credit unions and the post office.
- A **home filing system** will help you keep track of all your expenditure and is a way of storing important documents so that you can easily access them.

Section 2: Designing a Sustainable and Safe Home

22 DESIGNING A SUSTAINABLE HOME

Learning Outcomes 1.5, 1.16, 2.4, 2.5, 2.6, 2.7, 2.8, 2.9, 2.10, 2.12, 3.6, 3.7, 3.8, 3.9

What I Will Learn

- to explain the term 'shelter'
- to differentiate between a house and a home
- to assess the different types of housing available
- to identify the factors that influence our housing choices
- to consider design features and the principles of design when decorating a room
- to create an interior design plan for a variety of rooms to include an annotated floor plan
- to identify the steps to follow when decorating a room
- to discuss the services provided to the home
- to create a sustainable home environment

Key Words

✓ Shelter	✓ Form	✓ Rhythm
✓ Accommodation	✓ Shape	✓ Traffic flow
✓ House	✓ Line	✓ Gas
✓ Community	✓ Colour	✓ Electricity
✓ Statutory	✓ Texture	✓ Lighting
✓ Voluntary	✓ Pattern	✓ Heating
✓ Amenities	✓ Principles	✓ Insulation
✓ Home	✓ Balance	✓ Ventilation
✓ Design	✓ Emphasis	✓ Water
✓ Function	✓ Proportion	

Revision Toolkit

Use as many of these words as often as you can in sentences to improve your vocabulary use and to become more familiar with them.

Shelter

Shelter is a basic human need. From the earliest times, humans have made shelters to protect or shield themselves from the weather and other dangers.

Types of shelter vary with climate and other conditions, for example, in colder climates, a well-insulated house is needed for warmth and for protection from wind, rain and snow. In warmer climates, houses are needed for protection from intense heat and tropical storms.

Shelter can come in the following forms:

House	Houses can be two, three or four storeys (floors) high. They can be single-storey, e.g.: • A **bungalow** (a single-storey house) • A **dormer** (a single-storey house with rooms in the roof space) Houses can also be: • **Detached** (not attached to another house) • **Semi-detached** (sharing a wall with one other house) • **Terraced** (in a row of attached houses)
Flat or apartment	• A **self-contained living area** in a larger building, e.g. a converted house • A small complex or a high-rise block that contains similar units • These vary in size and design
Bedsit	• One room is divided into living and sleeping areas for a single person
Sheltered housing	• Groups of specially designed houses or apartments where older people or those with disabilities can live on their own but with certain shared facilities • There is usually a caretaker or supervisor living on site too
Residential housing	• Where groups of people live in one building, e.g. student accommodation or a nursing home
Mobile home	• These include caravans, pre-built mobile homes, boats or tents • They can provide permanent or temporary accommodation

Accommodation is a room, group of rooms, or building in which a person or people may live or stay.

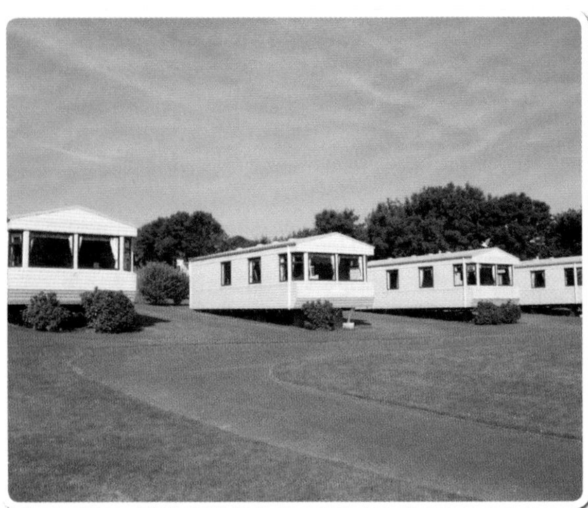

Housing choice

Our choice of housing is influenced by:

- **Location:** Where the house is located, i.e. rural (in the country) or urban (in a city); its proximity to work, schools, shops and amenities, or to the surrounding community.
- **Cost:** People are restricted by the amount of money they can afford to spend.
- **Size:** The number and size of rooms should be suitable for the number of people in the family.
- **Style:** The design and layout of the house must appeal to the family, e.g. modern or traditional.
- **Special needs:** Some accommodation needs to be adapted to meet the needs of the individual, e.g. wheelchair user.
- **Availability:** The availability of housing is also important as there may be a housing shortage in some areas, e.g. cities.
- **Energy efficiency:** An energy-efficient home has good insulation, uses sustainable materials and has an environmentally friendly energy and heating system.

Amenities are useful and desirable leisure features in a local area, e.g. parks, walks, beaches, playgrounds, sports fields, cinemas, swimming pools and leisure centres (resource management, see p. 289).

Very few people live exactly where they want to. Some people choose to live and work in the countryside, while others prefer to live near other people in villages, towns and cities, which provide a sense of community. Many people want to live near their work to save time and money travelling. It is also useful to live near schools, public transport and shops.

A **community** is a group of people who live together in a local area. Each community has its own services and **amenities**. Some community **services** are statutory (provided by the state) and some are **voluntary** (provided by volunteers).

Statutory services	Schools, health centres, social services, libraries, An Garda Síochána, post offices
Voluntary services	Youth clubs, sports clubs, active age groups, mother and toddler groups, St Vincent de Paul, book clubs, and musical and drama groups

Discovery Learning

Find out what services and amenities are in your local area. Design an information leaflet on at least three of these services and amenities and present your findings to the class.

House or home?

A house becomes a home when it is occupied by people and their possessions. It becomes more than a shelter – it provides for all our needs, making it a comfortable and safe place to live.

A home provides for our:

- **Physical needs:** Food, warmth, shelter and clothes.
- **Emotional needs:** Love, security, protection and privacy. A home must protect more vulnerable family members, such as babies, young children and older people.
- **Social needs:** Learning to interact with others, communicate, share and co-operate.

However, a family's needs are constantly changing, so homes must adapt too (**functions of the family, see p. 283**).

Revision Questions

1. Define the term 'shelter'.
2. Explain the difference between a house and a home.
3. Identify the different types of housing available.
4. Discuss the factors that influence our housing choices.
5. List five services or amenities a young family might want close by their home.

House design

Houses, clothes, furniture, cars and equipment have all been designed by someone. A **design** is a plan or sketch for the making of something. A good design is functional, attractive, safe, durable and environmentally friendly (**textiles, see p. 383**). In this section we will look at design of the home, i.e. room planning and interior design.

The features of good design include:

- Function
- Form, including shape and line
- Colour
- Texture
- Pattern

Classroom-Based Assessment

This section is linked to CBA1.

Function

Function is arguably the most important feature of design. If an object does not fulfil its function, it is badly designed, e.g. an uncomfortable chair.

There are a number of features consumers look for in relation to function:

- Comfort
- Safety
- Durability
- Easy to maintain
- Easy to use

Don't Forget!
Some objects in the home do not have a practical function – they are used purely for their aesthetic or decorative value. Can you give some examples of these items?

Form

This refers to the shape and line of an object.

Shape is the outline of an object. The four basic shapes are squares, rectangles, triangles and circles. Many objects in our home are based on these shapes.

Vertical lines make things look taller.

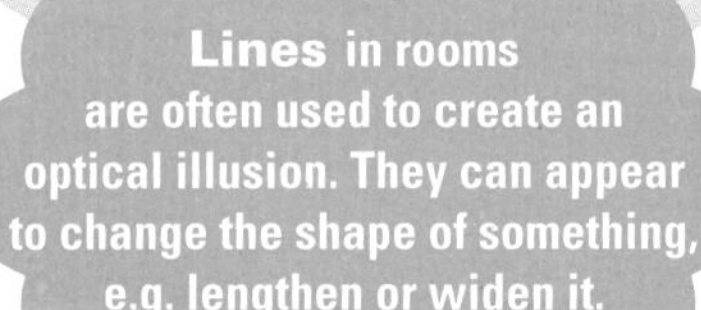

Lines in rooms are often used to create an optical illusion. They can appear to change the shape of something, e.g. lengthen or widen it.

Horizontal lines make things look wider.

Curved lines suggest movement but are also gentle and relaxing.

Diagonal lines suggest movement but are more dramatic.

Colour

Colour is an important design feature that can affect the atmosphere in a room, and even people's emotions.

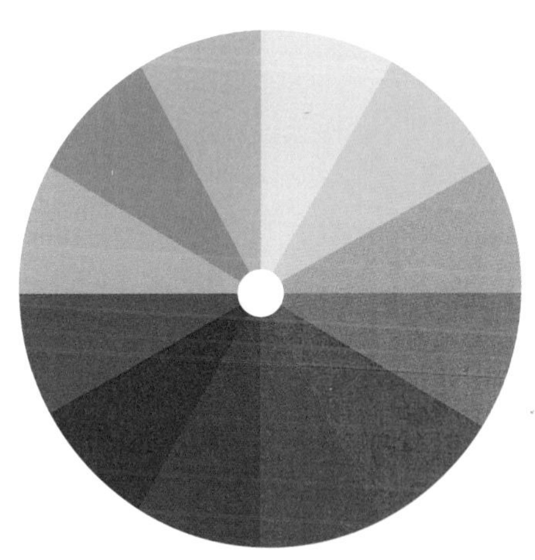

- **Primary colours:** Red, yellow and blue are known as primary colours because you cannot mix them from other colours. All other colours are mixes from primary colours.
- **Secondary colours:** Orange, green and purple are mixed from equal amounts of two primary colours.
- **Tertiary colours** are created by mixing a primary and a secondary colour, e.g.:

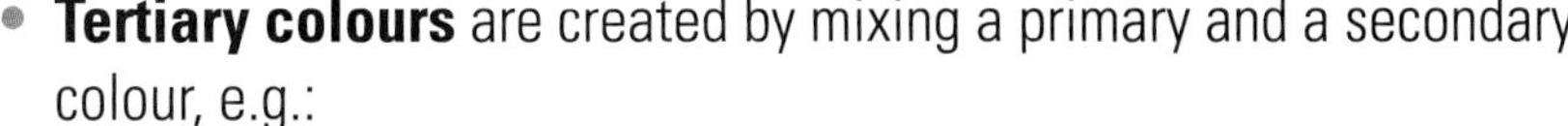

yellow + green = olive

blue + green = turquoise

red + purple = mauve

Don't Forget!

The colour wheel is a useful device for understanding how colours relate to one another and how to combine them in a colour scheme.

Did You Know?

A tint is a colour lightened by adding white. A shade is a colour darkened by adding black.

Colour can be described as:

- **Warm**: Create a warm, cosy atmosphere. They are best used in small amounts, e.g. red, orange, pink.
- **Neutral**: Often used as a background for other colours, e.g. black, white and shades of these. Shades of cream and beige are also used as neutral colours.

- **Cool**: Create a cool, relaxing atmosphere. They are best used in warm, sunny rooms, e.g. blues and greens.
- **Pastel**: These are pale, soft shades of blue, green, yellow and pink. They are usually used in bedrooms and nurseries.

Further Investigation

To watch an informative video that explains colour, go to YouTube and watch 'Interior Decorating Tips Using the Color Wheel' (2:29).

Did You Know?

Dulux has a visualiser app that lets you see your room in any colour before you paint it, making it easy to create your own colour schemes. Visit the app store on your smartphone or go to ***www.dulux.ie***.

When we choose and combine colours in clothing and rooms, we express our individuality and personality. When strong colours are used together they attract attention. There are no right or wrong colour combinations – it is simply a matter of personal taste.

Texture

Texture is how an object feels: smooth, rough, hard, soft or silky.

- **Smooth surfaces**, e.g. ceramic tiles, are generally hygienic, easy to clean and cold to touch.
- **Rough surfaces**, e.g. carpets, are usually warmer, comfortable, cosy and help absorb sound.

Pattern

A pattern is a decorative design that adds variety and contrast to an object. A pattern is usually found either all over an object, e.g. a cushion or a dress, or on part of it. The following should be noted about patterns when decorating a room:

- They need to be used carefully
- A room without pattern can be boring
- Overuse of patterns can make a room fussy and crowded

Design principles

When designing anything, e.g. a room, a piece of furniture or clothing, there are certain principles or rules that should be followed to get good results. These include:

- Balance
- Emphasis
- Proportion
- Rhythm

Balance happens when there is harmony between each part of the design of a room. This means that the colours, patterns and textures all work together. A well-balanced room is attractive.

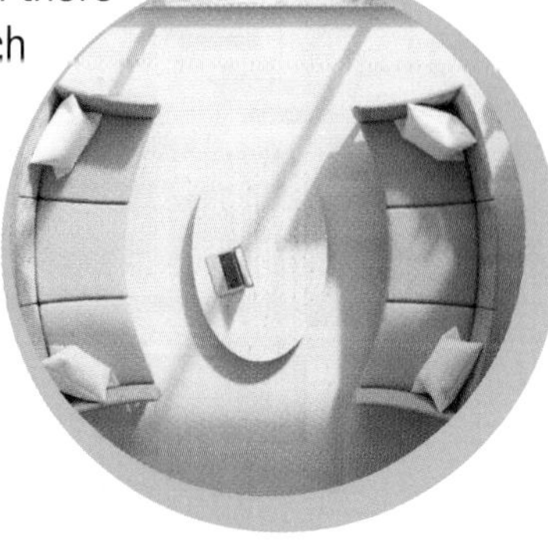

Emphasis involves drawing attention to a particular feature of a room. This can be done by using colour, lighting, strong shapes or patterns. Emphasis adds interest and variety to a room.

Proportion is when all the pieces of furniture in a room relate to each other, and to the size of the room, e.g. a large antique wardrobe would look out of place in a small, modern bedroom with low ceilings.

Rhythm is the repeated use of colour, pattern or texture, which brings harmony and unity to a room.

Room planning

To create a home that is comfortable and attractive, it is important to design and plan each room carefully. This is so that the occupants can carry out all their day-to-day activities in an efficient and safe way.

What to consider when planning a room

1. The function of the room and the amount of use it will get.
2. The budget – think about how you could save money by repurposing and upcycling.
3. The likes and dislikes of the occupants of the room.
4. The position of fixtures, windows, furniture, the fireplace and the radiators.
5. Heating and lighting must be decided early on, as rewiring, etc. may need to be done.
6. The size and shape of the room – make full use of space.
7. Ensure there is enough storage and furniture space for the functions of the room without being cluttered.
8. The aspect of the room (the direction the window faces) affects the amount of natural light and warmth that enters the room, which in turn should affect the colour choice, e.g. a naturally dark room should be decorated in bright colours.
9. Traffic flow – the movement of people around the room. Be careful with furniture placement and ensure people can move about easily and comfortably.

A well-planned room is:

- Comfortable
- Functional
- Attractive
- Well lit
- Well heated
- Properly ventilated
- Safe
- Easy to clean

Revision Toolkit

Can you come up with a mnemonic to help you remember the features of a well-planned room?

Don't Forget!
Room design priorities will vary depending on the function of the room, e.g. a bathroom will require privacy and must be hygienic and easy to clean.

Don't Forget!
When decorating a room it is a good idea to repurpose or upcycle objects or pieces of furniture. Existing items can be redesigned to fit in with the new colour scheme. It saves money and protects the environment.

Revision Questions

Use your workbook to revise this chapter

1. Outline the features of a good design.
2. Explain each of the following terms in relation to room planning: (a) proportion, (b) emphasis, (c) balance.
3. How does colour influence our home?
4. Suggest ways we can be environmentally aware when designing our homes.

Floor plans

A **floor plan** is a sketch of a room drawn to scale on graph paper, showing the position of fixtures like doors and windows. Furniture can be drawn to scale, cut out and moved around the plan to find the best fit.

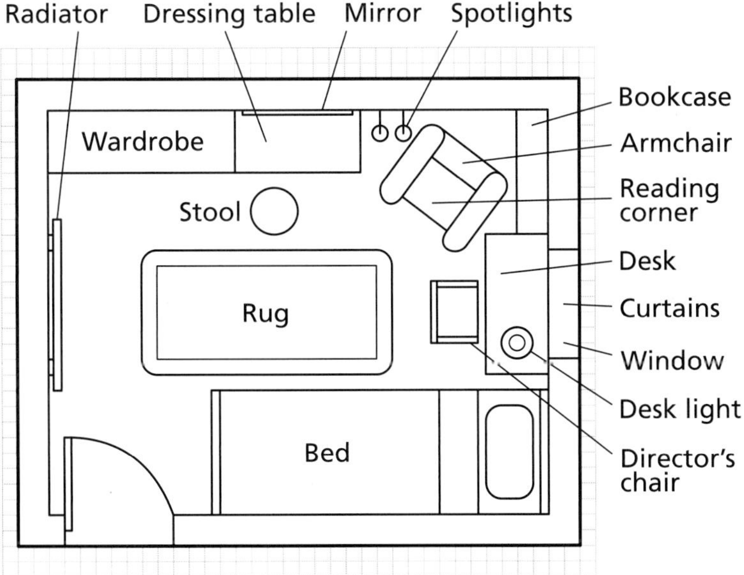

Discovery Learning

There are a number of free room design software apps for iPads, tablets and PCs to help you design rooms. Find out what is available and share your discoveries with the class.

Steps to decorating a room

1. Decide on a colour scheme.
2. Choose a floor covering.
3. Remove all the furniture and fittings from the room.
4. Carry out any structural changes or repairs.
5. Sand down and fill in any cracks or holes, wash all surfaces and allow to dry.
6. Cover any surfaces that need protection.
7. Decorate in the following order: ceiling, woodwork then walls.
8. Lay the floor covering and arrange the furniture in the room.

When designing a room, you must consider the following:

Colour scheme	Consider the aspect of the room and the amount of light it receives, as well as personal preferences.
Wall finish	Wallpaper (consider type, pattern and colour), paint (colour and type of finish, e.g. matt or satin) or tiles (size and type).
Furniture/ storage	Consider the function of the room and choose furniture to suit, e.g. in a bedroom – bed, wardrobe, dressing table, shelves/storage units, locker, desk, chair, stool, armchair. Furniture can be free-standing or built in.
Floor	Consider the function of the room and choose appropriate floor coverings: carpets, vinyl, cork, laminates, sanded and sealed floors or tiles, e.g. in a bathroom, tiles should be easy to clean; in a bedroom, carpet should be warm underfoot.
Soft furnishings	Chosen to complement the colour scheme and furniture, and include curtains, blinds, duvet covers, throws, rugs, cushions and lampshades.
Lighting	Consider activities that will be carried out in this room and choose lighting for each, e.g. central light, desk lights, reading lights, spotlights, bedside lights and recess lighting.
Ventilation	Windows, ventilation grills and extractor fans for kitchens and bathrooms.
Heating	Central heating, radiators, portable heaters, underfloor heating, open fires or stoves.

Recess lighting is a light fixture that is installed into a hollow opening in a ceiling.

(Resource management, see p. 289, and hygiene and safety in the kitchen, see p. 84)

Kitchens

Ergonomics is used in kitchen planning to make a room efficient, safer and easier to use during food preparation, cooking and clean-up.

Considerations when planning kitchens

- The size and shape of the room.
- The layout – taking into account the work sequence and the work triangle.
- Ensuring the following:
  - It is hygienic and easy to clean
  - It is safe to work
  - It has enough storage and work surfaces
  - It has adequate ventilation, lighting and heating

Ergonomics is the study of how efficiently people work in an environment, e.g. how comfortable is your desk in school? How efficient is your working space in the kitchen?

The kitchen work sequence

The work involved in the preparation of food follows a logical order or sequence.

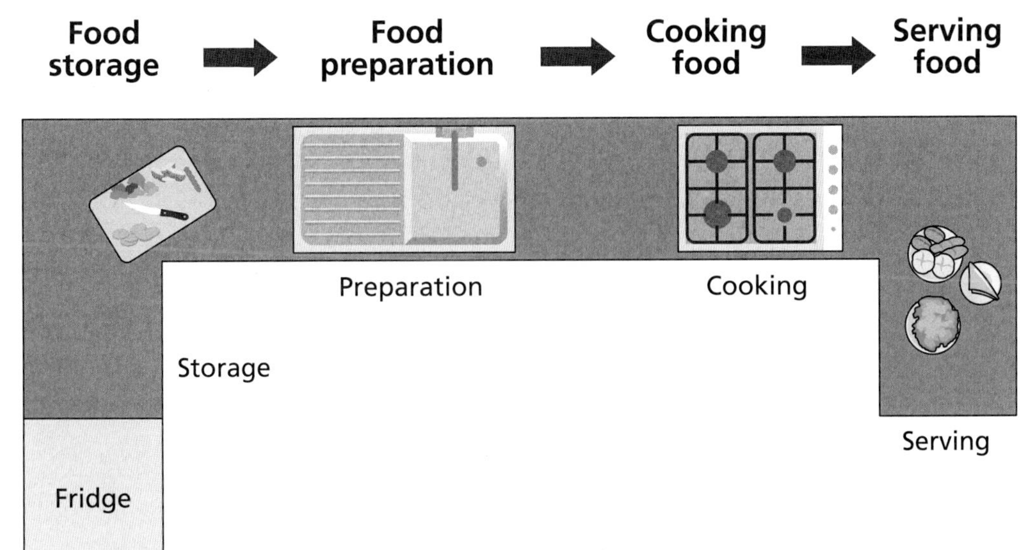

The work triangle

When planning a kitchen, the sink, fridge and cooker are placed at three points of an imaginary triangle to reduce the amount of walking involved in food preparation (**kitchen hygiene and safety, see p. 84**).

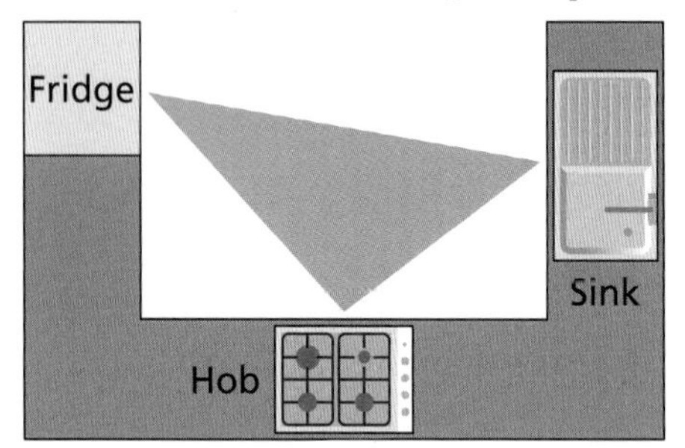

U-shaped

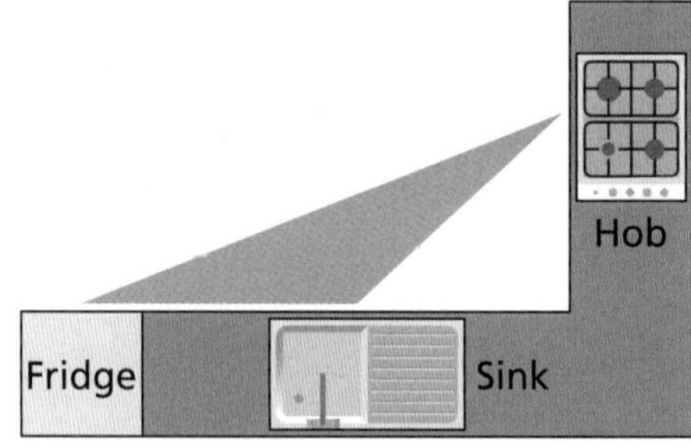

L-shaped

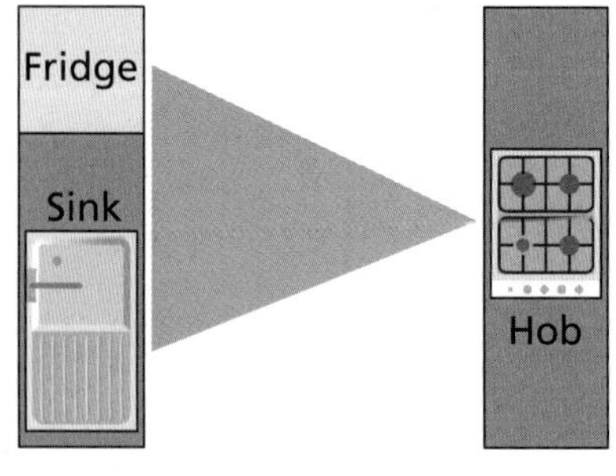

Galley

Don't Forget!

Good ventilation is very important in a kitchen, as a lot of heat and steam are created from cooking and washing, providing ideal conditions for bacteria to thrive. An extractor fan or cooker hood is necessary to remove steam, stale air, cooking fumes, bacteria, and to lower the temperature, which prevents condensation.

Revision Questions

1. Draw a room plan for a family living room, indicating the position of: (i) the windows and doors, (ii) the furniture and (iii) suitable lighting. Suggest a suitable colour scheme, wall covering, floor covering and heating system and justify your choices.
2. What are the most important considerations when designing a kitchen?

Services to the home

An efficient, safe and sustainable home is dependent on a variety of services. These include gas, electricity and water.

Gas

- Natural gas is found under the sea bed. It is a fuel formed over millions of years beneath the surface of the earth from decaying plants and animals.
- Service pipes lead into individual homes. Bottled gas or gas tanks containing liquified petroleum gas (LPG) can be used in areas where piped gas is not available.

Uses of gas in the home

- Cooking
- Central heating
- Heating water
- Portable heaters
- Gas fires
- Underfloor heating

Gas safety

- Natural gas is odourless, so an odour is added to it for safety reasons. Gas needs to be used carefully.
- All gas appliances should be installed and serviced by a qualified person.
- Gas appliances should be used in well-ventilated rooms.
- Carefully follow all the manufacturer's instructions on all gas appliances.
- Buy appliances that have a safety mark.

If you suspect a gas leak

- Do not ignore the smell.
- Turn off the gas at the mains.
- Open all doors and windows.
- Telephone the gas emergency line from outside.
- Do not use a naked flame, e.g. matches or a lighter.
- Do not smoke.
- Do not turn on a light or use any electrical appliances.

Further Investigation

Watch the following gas safety videos on YouTube:

- 'If You Smell Gas - Gas Networks Ireland' Public Gas Safety Advertising Campaign' (0:30)
- 'Even if it's Daniel - Registered Gas Installers 30 second TVC' (0:30)

How do these advertisements differ in their approach?

Did You Know?

Gas is a non-renewable source of energy so gas reserves are limited. If consumption continues to rise, natural gas reserves may be depleted by 2050 (unless new fields are discovered). Can you suggest any alternative sources of energy that are more sustainable?

Don't Forget!

If you suspect a gas leak, do not turn lights or electrical equipment on or off. Call Gas Networks Ireland's 24-hour emergency line on 1850 20 50 50.

Electricity

- Electricity is not a fuel – it is a clean and efficient form of energy. Some electricity is generated from fossil fuels, i.e. coal, gas and oil, and renewable energy sources, e.g. water and wind.
- Electricity enters the house through a service cable. It passes through a sealed fuse box with a meter to record the amount used. Some houses have a second meter to record the use of off-peak (night rate) electricity, which can reduce costs.
- It then passes into a consumer unit which contains the main switch. This can be turned off if an electrical fault occurs or if any repairs are being made.
- The consumer unit has a safety device called a miniature circuit breaker (MCB) or trip switches which turn off if a fault develops.

Discovery Learning

Nightsaver meters can save money and help reduce fuel consumption at peak times. Find out the rates from each supplier and see which offers the best value to the consumer.

Uses of electricity

- Cooking
- Central heating
- Heating water
- Portable heaters
- Electric fires
- Lighting
- Powering appliances
- Underfloor heating
- Washing and drying clothes

Further Investigation

To learn how to wire a plug, watch the video 'How to Wire a Plug on Woodies TV' (6:07) on YouTube.

Did You Know?

A doubly insulated electrical appliance has been designed in such a way that it does not require a safety connection to an earth wire, e.g. a hairdryer.

Guidelines for the safe use of electricity

- ✓ Be careful when using electricity and electrical appliances to prevent accidents.
- ✓ Repair and maintain appliances as required.
- ✓ Be careful not to mix electricity and water.
- ✓ Take extra care with children – keep all appliances out of reach and use socket covers.

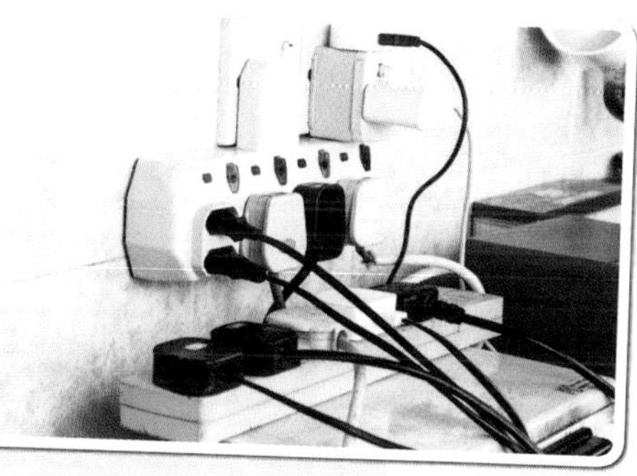

Appliance safety

- Buy appliances with recognised safety symbols.
- Always read and follow the manufacturer's instructions.
- Ensure plugs are correctly wired and have the correct fuses to prevent overheating.
- Replace broken plugs, sockets and frayed and damaged flexes.
- Never overload a socket with plugs or use multiple adaptors – instead, use fused multi-socket boards with a **surge protector**.
- Unplug all electrical appliances at night, except the fridge and freezer, and do not leave TVs on standby.
- Take extra care when using electrical appliances outdoors – ensure they do not get wet.

Electrical safety in the bathroom

Special precautions apply to wiring in a bathroom due to high moisture content.

- Never use portable electrical appliances in bathrooms, e.g. hairdryers or heaters.
- Ensure electric showers are wired separately.
- There should be no socket outlets, except recommended lights and shaver units.
- Only use pull-cords for operating wall heaters and shavers.

A **surge protector** is an appliance or device designed to protect electrical devices from voltage spikes.

Electrical safety in the kitchen

Electricity, water, hot surfaces and trailing flexes make the kitchen a dangerous part of the home.

- Switch off and unplug all appliances before cleaning them.
- Do not use or attempt to repair faulty appliances.
- Never handle appliances, plugs or sockets with wet hands, so always dry hands before touching any electric appliance.
- Never trail flexes across cooker hobs or sinks.
- Do not overload sockets by using adaptors or extensions.
- Do not use a knife to remove toast from a toaster.

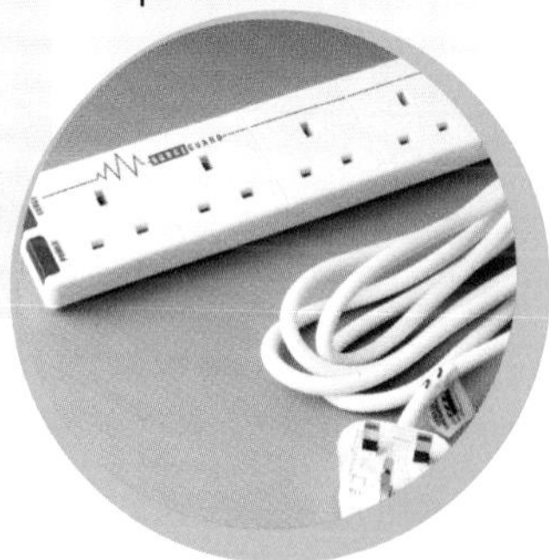

Electrical safety in the bedroom

- Read and follow the manufacturer's instructions on electric blankets and check regularly for wear and tear. Never repair an electric blanket – replace as necessary.
- Never warm clothes near or on electric heaters.
- Unplug all appliances at night and when not in use.

Fuses

- A fuse is a deliberate weak link in an electrical circuit; today we find fuses in plugs. In older houses fuses were placed in a fuse panel.
- It acts as a safety device: if a fault develops the fuse will blow, cutting off the electricity before any more damage can be done.

Don't Forget!
If there is an electrical fault, the fuse within the plug will also blow and will have to be replaced with a fuse of the same strength.

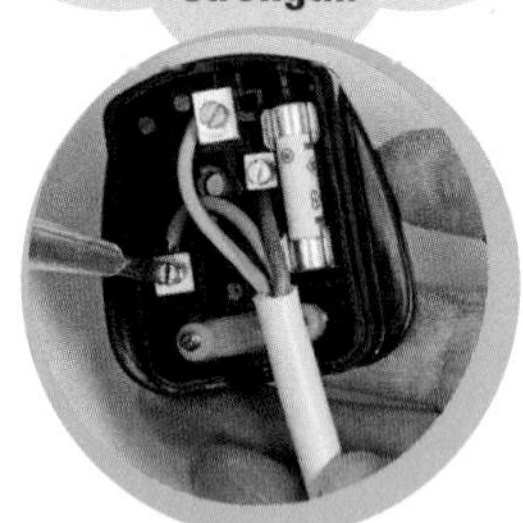

- In modern homes, we use MCBs are used instead of fuse panels. An MCB will trip because of a faulty appliance, e.g. an overheated iron, faulty wiring of a plug, or overloading of the circuit, which is caused by too many appliances running at the same time.
- The MCB must be reset after the fault has been fixed.

Did You Know?
Electricity itself will not run out, but non-renewable fuel sources used to make electricity will, so we have move our dependence to renewable sources, e.g. on-shore wind farms, hydropower and solar power. The government has set a target of 40% electricity consumption from renewable sources by 2020 under the National Renewable Energy Action Plan.

Lighting

Good lighting is important in a home to:
- Prevent accidents
- Ensure good hygiene
- Prevent eyestrain
- Provide adequate lighting for activities like reading
- Create an atmosphere in each room

Further Investigation
Find out more about Bord na Monas's 'Naturally Driven' sustainable energy programme: visit www.bordnamona.ie and watch the 'Naturally Driven' video on the home page (5:09).

There are two types of light: natural and artificial.

Natural light (sunlight)	Enters the house through glass windows, doors, skylights, sun tunnels and glass bricks.
Artificial light (usually electric)	• Filament bulbs • Fluorescent bulbs • Compact fluorescent lights (CFLs) • Halogen bulbs • A light-emitting diode (LED) bulb

Energy-efficient lighting

All bulbs are given a rating to indicate their energy efficiency. CFLs and LED bulbs are the most efficient bulbs available with an A rating. They use less electricity, last longer and are more environmentally friendly, but they are expensive to buy.

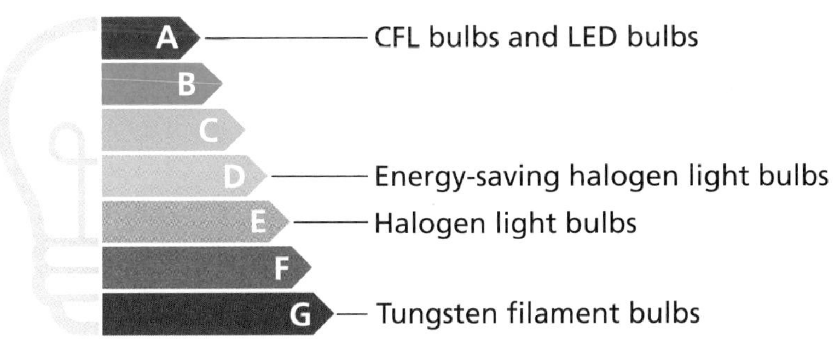

Further Investigation

If you want to find out more about the science behind LED lighting, go to **www.eslightbulbs.com**, scroll down to the bottom of the home page, and click on 'How Do LED Light Bulbs Work', or go to YouTube and watch the video 'How LEDs work' (2:15).

Lighting safety

- Good lighting does not flicker or cause a glare as this may lead to headaches and eye strain.
- Dangerous areas such as stairs should be well lit.
- Lights in a bathroom should operate on a pull-cord switch or an outside switch.
- Ensure all light fittings and shades are safe and use the correct strength of bulb for the fitting.
- The shade should not be too close to the bulb.

Water

Water is one of our most important resources.

- The water we use in our houses begins as rain. The rain falls, seeps into the ground and forms springs that flow into rivers and lakes.
- It is held in lakes (natural) or man-made reservoirs, before it is treated and piped to our houses.
- Water flows from the reservoir to the water treatment plant, where it is treated to make it suitable for use.
- First the water is left to **settle**, then is **filtered** to remove impurities (grit and plant materials).
- To **soften** the water, chloride of lime is added.
- Chlorine is added to **kill bacteria**.
- Fluoride is added to reduce tooth decay (**🔗 tooth decay, see p. 77**).

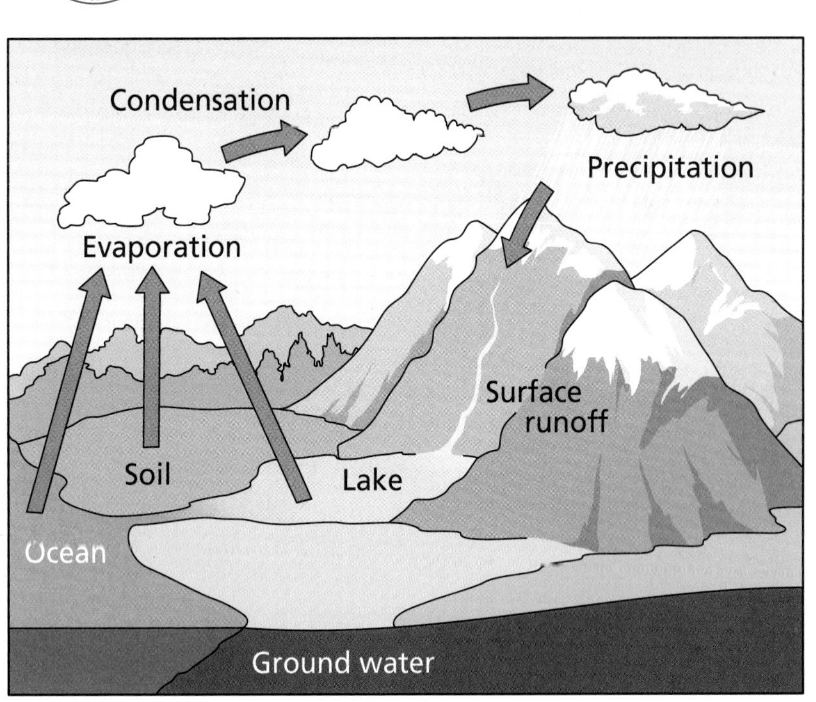

Did You Know?
A person can live for weeks without food, but only a few days without water. Every living thing on earth depends on water for survival.

- Water leaves the treatment plant in large pipes called **mains**.
- A branch of the mains pipe, called a **service pipe**, goes into each house.
- There is a **stop valve** on the service pipe that can be used to turn off the water for repairs.
- The service pipe supplies cold water directly to the kitchen sink tap. This is the freshest water in the house and should be used for drinking and cooking. The service pipe also fills the storage tank in the attic.
- The attic tank supplies the water to toilets, other cold taps and to the cylinder in the hot press, where it is heated.

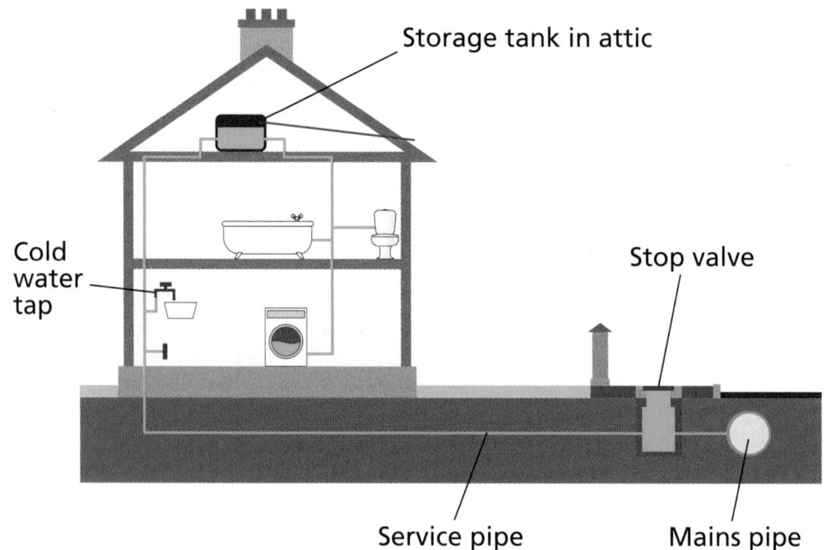

Did You Know?
Sea water makes up 97% of the water on our planet, so the remaining 3% is fresh water. Less than half of fresh water (1.3%) can be used for human consumption.

The kitchen sink

This is usually located under a window on an outside wall, as it makes plumbing easier and it provides good lighting and ventilation. Most kitchen sinks are made from stainless steel because they are durable, stain- and heat-resistant, easy to clean and hygienic.

Underneath the sink there is an 'S' trap or U-bend, which is designed so that it always contains water. This prevents smells and bacteria coming back into the kitchen from drains or sewers.

After a sink is emptied, the 'S' trap should be flushed with clean water from the cold tap.

Sinks and drains need to be disinfected regularly to kill bacteria.

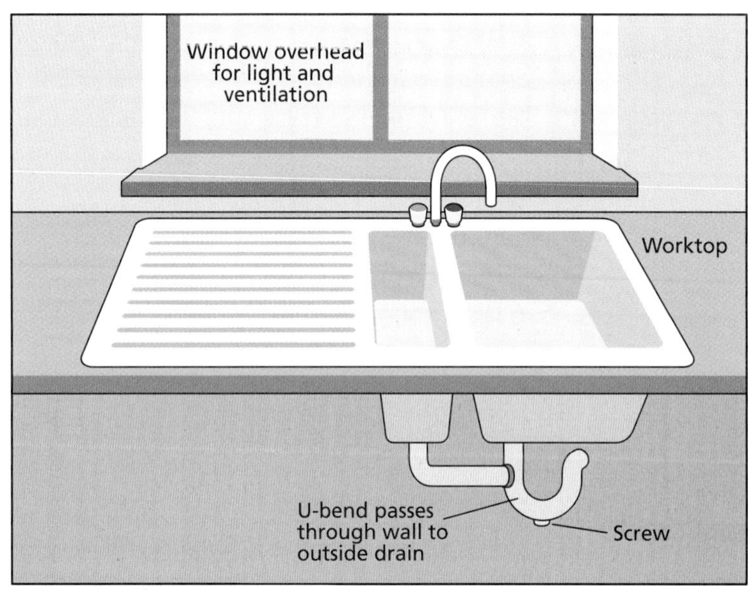

Discovery Learning

Find out what to do if your kitchen sink becomes blocked. Provide this information to the rest of the class.

Discovery Learning

Can you find out what other materials kitchen sinks are made from? What type of sink would you choose for your home? Explain why.

Don't waste water!

- Never brush teeth or wash hands under a running tap.
- Take shorter showers and install water-saving showerheads.
- Install a dual-flush toilet.
- Fill up dishwashers and washing machines before using them, and use the economy load setting.
- Collect rainwater for using in the garden and for washing cars.
- Use a spray head on a hose.
- Make sure that there are no leaks in the system.
- Can you add anything else to this list?

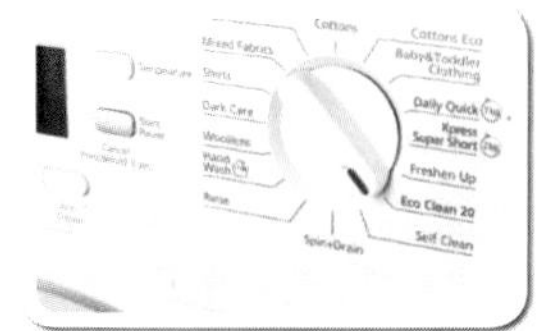

Did You Know?

Showers can use anything between 6 and 45 litres of water per minute.

Don't Forget!

Always fix a dripping tap. A dripping tap can waste 15 litres of water a day, or 5,500 litres of water a year!

Burst pipes

Sometimes water pipes freeze in very cold weather. When water freezes, it expands. This might cause the pipe to crack, and then a leak could occur when the water thaws.

What to do if a pipe bursts:

- Turn off water at the stop valve (**see p. 320**) on the service pipe
- Run all cold taps to drain the system
- Do not turn on central heating or use a back boiler
- Call a plumber

Heating

A home can be heated in a variety of ways, but all methods involve heat transfer (conduction, convection or radiation) (**heat transfer in cooking, see p. 119**). A home can be heated by central heating, background heating or by individual heaters.

Central heating	• Central heating means that the whole house is heated from a boiler. • The boiler heats the water, which passes around the house through radiators or in pipes under the floor. • Boilers are fuelled by electricity, gas, oil and solid fuel such as coal, turf and smokeless fuels. They can also be partially fuelled by solar panels. • Central heating systems generally also heat the domestic hot water.
Background heating	• Background heating such as electric storage heaters give off gentle background heat. • They often need to be supplemented by another form of heating. • Storage heaters use off-peak electricity.
Individual heaters	• Individual heaters can be gas, electric or solid fuel. • Some gas and electric heaters such as fan, radiant or infrared heaters can be portable. • Solid fuel heaters include open fires and stoves.

Discovery Learning

There are various types of heating solutions for a home. Find out more about one type of heating and present a factsheet to the rest of the class, which:

- **must** contain a description and picture/diagram/photograph of the solution.
- **should** include the advantages and disadvantages of this solution.
- **could** include prices and additional information.

Be creative!

Insulation

Heat is lost through the roof, walls, windows, doors and floors of a house. Good insulation can reduce this loss by 75%. Insulation works on the principle that the materials used are poor conductors of heat, e.g. air, fibreglass and polystyrene, thereby reducing heat loss from the house. Good insulation makes a house comfortable and warm, helps to soundproof a house and saves money on fuel bills.

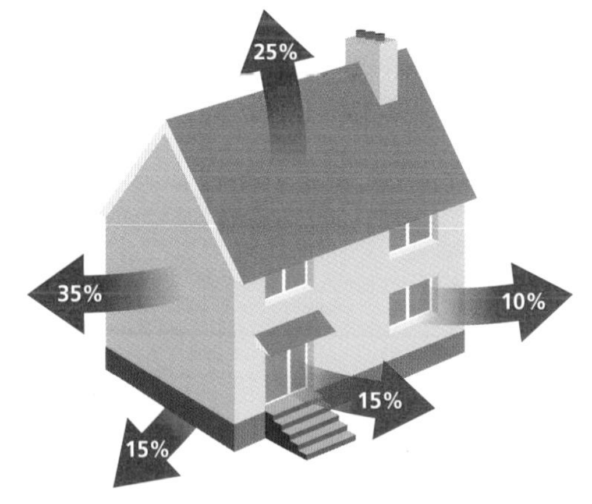

Discovery Learning

In pairs, find out what types of insulation can be used in the home. Then look at which are the most energy-efficient and sustainable. Present your findings to the class.

Ventilation

Ventilation is the removal of stale air from and the introduction of fresh air into the home. It is needed to control temperature and humidity and to prevent **condensation**.

Condensation is the process by which water vapour in warm air is changed into liquid when it comes into contact with cold surfaces.

Discovery Learning

Find out why ventilation is important in our homes and how it is provided. Find out what condensation is, the problems it causes and how to prevent it. Share your findings with the class.

Did You Know?

Houses are rated on a scale from A to G, depending on their efficiency. This rating is calculated using details of house construction, insulation, heating, lighting and ventilation. All houses for sale or rent must have a Building Energy Rating (BER) certificate. Now watch 'Building Energy Ratings (ber) ratings explained' (0:56) on YouTube.

Further Investigation

To find out more about BER ratings, go to **www.seai.ie**, click on 'Energy Ratings' on the home page, and then click on 'Building Energy Rating (BER)'.

Discovery Learning

Make a list of what you do to save energy in your home at the moment. Suggest four other ways of saving energy in your home.

Revision Questions

1. What should you do in the event of a gas leak in the home?
2. List four guidelines for the safe use of gas in the home.
3. Why is it important to conserve water?
4. Outline the benefits of using a central heating system in the home.
5. Give two benefits of insulation in the home and suggest three areas within a home where good insulation is important.
6. Explain why ventilation is important in the kitchen.
7. What are some advantages of having an energy-efficient home?

Summary

- Houses provide **shelter**, while homes cater for our physical, emotional and social needs.
- Housing types include houses, flats or apartments, bedsits, sheltered, residential housing and mobile homes.
- Our **choice of housing** is influenced by location, cost, size, style, special needs, availability and energy efficiency.
- A **community** is all the people who live in the local area. Each community has its own services and amenities. Some community services are statutory and some are voluntary.
- The **features of good design** include function, form (shape and line), colour, texture and pattern.
- **Design principles** include balance, emphasis, proportion and rhythm.
- When **planning a room**, consider the function of the room, the amount of use it will get, the budget, the likes and dislikes of the occupants, the position of fixtures and furniture, storage, heating and lighting, and the size and shape of the room. Make full use of space, aspect and traffic flow.
- A **floor plan** is a sketch of a room drawn to scale on graph paper, showing the position of fixtures like doors and windows.
- **When decorating**, decide on a colour scheme, choose a floor covering, remove all the furniture and fittings from the room, carry out any structural changes or repairs, sand down and fill in any cracks or holes, wash all surfaces and allow to dry, and cover any surfaces that need protection. Then decorate in the following order: ceiling, woodwork and walls. Finally, lay the floor covering and arrange the furniture in the room.
- **The work sequence** is the work involved in the preparation of food. It follows a logical order or sequence.

- **Services to the home** include the following:
  - **Gas** is a fuel that is available piped or bottled. It is used for cooking, central heating, heating water, portable heaters, gas fires and underfloor heating. Gas can be dangerous, so use a qualified person to install it and ensure you have good ventilation.
  - **Electricity** is not a fuel; it is a clean and efficient form of energy that is generated from fuels, i.e. coal, gas and oil, and some from water and wind. It is used for cooking, central and underfloor heating, portable fires, lighting and powering appliances. Be careful when using electricity – never mix with water.
  - **Lighting** is natural (sunlight) or artificial (light bulbs). Good lighting is important for preventing accidents and eyestrain, ensuring good hygiene and creating an atmosphere. It is provided naturally through windows, glass doors and bricks, skylights or sun tunnels, or artificially with filament, fluorescent, CFL, LED and halogen bulbs.
  - **Water** is one of our most important resources. It begins as rain which falls, seeps into the ground and forms springs that flow into rivers and lakes. It is held in reservoirs before it is treated. It is then filtered, softened and chlorine and fluoride are added. Then it is piped to our houses. We must not waste water!
- A home can be **heated** in a variety of ways, but all methods involve heat transfer (conduction, convection or radiation). A home can be heated by central heating, background heating or by individual heaters.
- Heat is lost through the roof, walls, windows, doors and floors of a house. Good **insulation** can reduce this loss by 75% and saves resources. Insulation uses materials that are poor conductors of heat, e.g. air, fibreglass and polystyrene. Good insulation makes a house comfortable and warm, helps to soundproof a house and saves money on fuel bills.
- **Ventilation** is the removal of stale air from and the introduction of fresh air into the home. It is needed to control temperature and humidity and to prevent **condensation**.
- **The Building Energy Rating (BER)** is a way of grading houses on their energy efficiency.

23 DESIGNING A SAFER HOME

Learning Outcomes 1.5, 1.16, 2.4, 2.5, 2.6, 2.7, 2.8, 2.9, 2.10, 2.12, 3.6, 3.7. 3.8, 3.9

What I Will Learn

- to identify the main causes of accidents in the home
- to consider how to prevent accidents in the home
- to understand the importance of learning basic first aid
- to describe how to stock and use a first aid kit
- to demonstrate how to safely store and use medicines, chemicals and cleaning agents
- to identify common safety symbols
- to discuss how to prevent burns, scalds, strains, sprains, choking, fainting and poisoning
- to devise an appropriate response to a fire in your home
- to understand the importance of proper waste management
- to distinguish between organic and inorganic waste
- to identify the causes and effects of air, water and noise pollution
- to investigate ways that the consumer can protect the environment

Key Words

✓ Accidents
✓ Safety hazard
✓ Fatal
✓ First aid
✓ Preserve
✓ Patient
✓ Danger
✓ Sprain
✓ Strain
✓ Smoke detector
✓ Fire extinguisher
✓ Fire blanket
✓ Carbon monoxide
✓ Burn
✓ Scald
✓ Corrosive
✓ Explosive
✓ Toxic
✓ Flammable
✓ Irritant
✓ Organic
✓ Inorganic
✓ Biodegradable
✓ Pollution
✓ Acid rain
✓ Halons
✓ Chlorofluorocarbons
✓ Compost
✓ Ozone

Creating a safer home

Many of the accidents that happen in and around the home can be avoided. By identifying and understanding potential accident risks in the home, parents can take some basic safety steps that will keep children safe and give them peace of mind.

Did You Know?

Accidental injury is one of the biggest single causes of death in Ireland for children over the age of one. More children die each year as a result of accidents than from illnesses. Accidents are also to blame for almost half of all deaths among 10–15-year-olds, according to the Health Service Executive (HSE).

Accidents in the home happen for a variety of reasons. They can be caused by:

- Poor lighting and bad design features in rooms or stairs.
- Badly maintained houses, furniture and floor coverings.
- Incorrect use of services or faulty equipment.
- Careless storage of dangerous equipment or chemicals.
- Careless behaviour by people: inattentive adults and teenagers, active and curious children or forgetful older people.
- Bad luck or by chance, for no apparent reason.

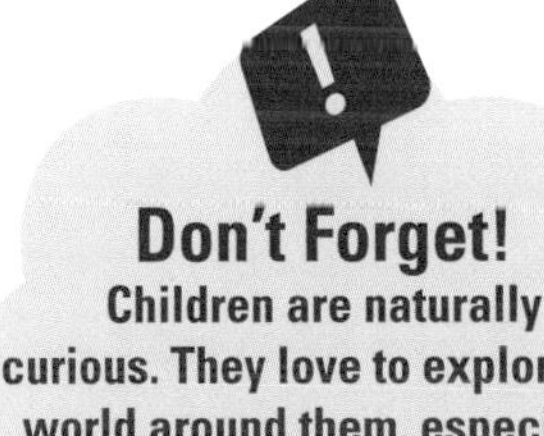

Don't Forget!
Children are naturally curious. They love to explore the world around them, especially in the comfort of their own home, but there are dangers – both obvious and hidden.

Many accidents occur due to a combination of the above factors, so the cause is not always easy to identify. However, with a little care and attention, many accidents could be prevented.

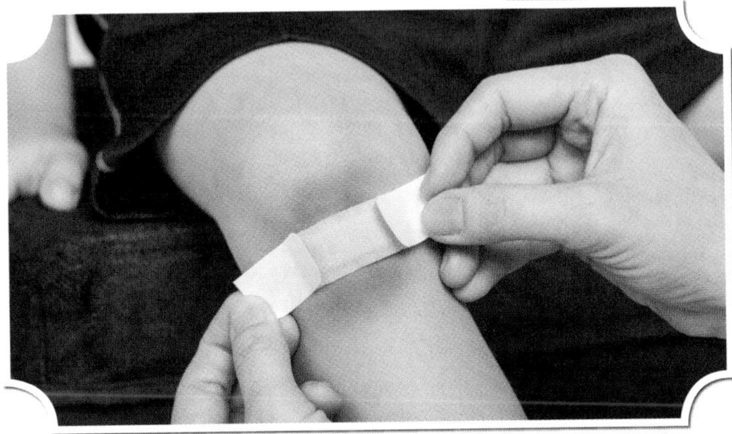

A **safety hazard** is anything that has the potential to cause an accident.

Making your home safe for everyone is so important to prevent the risk of accidents. It is would also be useful to learn basic first aid to deal with any minor accidents that may occur.

Basic first aid

As a parent it is important learn basic **first aid** in order to deal with small accidents quickly and calmly in the home. The aim of first aid is to **preserve** life. It is important to:

- Keep a well-stocked first-aid box in a clearly visible place, e.g. in the kitchen.
- Keep it out of reach of small children.
- Keep it very clean and tidy.
- Keep items in wrappings or use small plastic bags to keep them clean.
- Medicines and drugs should be kept in a separate, locked medicine cupboard.

Discovery Learning
Find out what items should be included in a well-stocked first aid kit. Present your findings in a creative way.

Serious accidents

In the case of serious accidents stay calm, act quickly and make the patient comfortable and reassure them without worsening the condition until the arrival of a doctor or ambulance. A **fatal** accident results in the death of the patient.

Further Investigation
To prevent choking and keep the airways open, it is important to place an unconscious person in the **recovery position.** Watch the video 'First aid - How to put someone in the recovery position' (1:33) on YouTube, then practise the techniques with a partner.

Did You Know?
CPR stands for **cardiopulmonary resuscitation**. It is a method of reviving (resuscitating) the heart (cardio) and lungs (pulmonary). If done correctly, it can save a life. To find out more about CPR training and its benefits, visit ***www.croi.ie/croi-cpr-courses***.

Types of accidents

Slips, trips and falls

Falls by slipping and tripping are by far the most common type of accident in the home. They account for 44% of all children's accidents. Young children are likely to fall over and get knocks and bruises as they learn to walk, but serious accidents can be avoided.

Did You Know?

The biggest danger for babies is rolling off the edge of something like a table, bed or sofa. Toddlers quickly learn how to climb and explore, and it is very easy for a child to fall off a piece of furniture, down the stairs or out of a window or balcony.

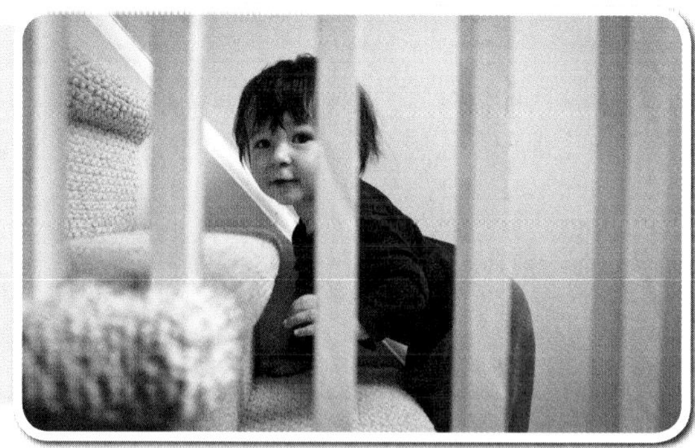

How to avoid slips, trips and falls

- Have stairs and awkward corners lit well; use dual light switches at the top and bottom of stairs.
- Install a safety gate at top and bottom of the stairs if small children are about.
- Objects such as toys should never be left on the stairs or floors.
- Avoid frayed rugs and over-polishing floors. Non-slip backing is available for rugs that are prone to slipping around.
- Have hand grips on the bath and shower, especially when used by older people.
- Use strong household steps to reach to high places rather than a stool or chair.
- Do not leave a child unsupervised on a changing unit, or put them on a table or worktop. They can easily bounce off the edge. Keep small babies strapped into baby chairs out of harm's way while working in the kitchen.
- Fit restrictor locks to upstairs windows so they cannot be opened more than 10 cm.
- Do not put chairs or anything a child might climb on near windows.
- Wipe up spills immediately.

Did You Know?

A **strain** is a pulled muscle, and a **sprain** may have torn or damaged ligaments.

Discovery Learning

Find out what to do if a person suffers from a strain or sprain. Present your findings in a creative way.

Cuts, grazes and scratches

Glass and sharp objects can cause serious cuts. Many people are injured when glasses and bottles break. Sharp objects should always be stored in a secure place, out of reach of small children.

How to avoid cuts, grazes and scratches

- Use safety glass at a low level, such as in doors and windows.
- When buying furniture that includes glass, make sure it is safety approved.
- Always dispose of broken glass quickly and safely, wrapping it in newspaper before throwing it in the bin.
- Do not let a toddler walk around holding anything made of glass or anything sharp, such as scissors and sharp pencils.

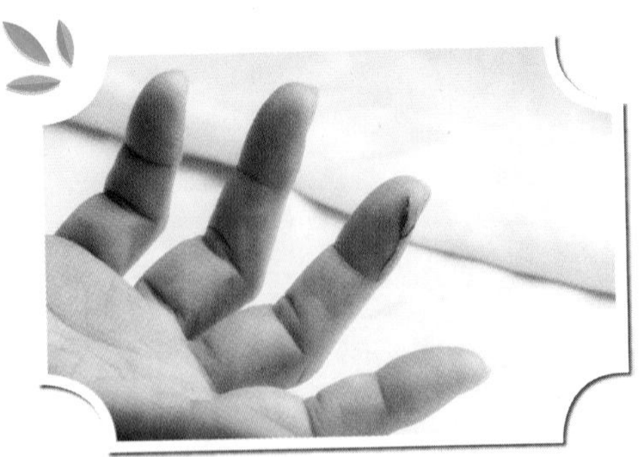

Discovery Learning

Find out what a tetanus shot is and why it is important to get one after getting cut with metal. Do you know how to deal with a nose bleed? Or a cut? If not, find out and share the information with the class.

Did You Know?

The Department of Health recommends that you don't use pillows for babies and that you ensure they can't snuggle down too far inside a quilted sleeping bag.

Suffocating and choking

Another big risk to babies is choking or suffocating, which occurs when the airways are blocked and the victim cannot breathe. They can easily swallow, inhale or choke on small items such as buttons, peanuts and small toys so keep small objects out of the reach of small children and babies.

How to avoid suffocation and choking

- Choose toys that are designed for the age of the baby or child. Encourage older children to be careful with their toys around younger children (**safety symbols, see p. 331**).
- Lay a baby on its back in a cot to sleep. Do not put babies to sleep in an adult bed or on the sofa, and do not use pillows, as they can cause suffocation.
- Be careful with plastic bags, as young children can put these over their heads and suffocate.
- Curtain and blind pull cords should be kept short and out of reach of children.
- Remove bones from fish as they are a choking hazard for people of all ages.

Poisoning

Many household cleaning products and medicines contain poisonous substances that can cause serious injury if swallowed or spilled onto the skin.

Safety with medicines	Safety with chemicals and cleaning agents
• Store all medicines in their original containers. • Use according to the directions on the label. • Keep them locked in a press out of the reach of children. • Dispose of all out-of-date medication safely. • Never use medicines prescribed by a doctor for one person on another person in the family.	• Store in the original containers and follow the directions for use. • If you must remove a substance from the original container, transfer it to a glass or plastic container. Label it clearly with the name of the chemical and store in a cupboard that is out of reach of children and can be locked. • Store in a cool, dry place. Aerosols are dangerous if overheated, and dampness will rust many containers.

Safety symbols

Cleaning agents and household chemicals carry hazard symbols and safety warnings to protect users. Always follow instructions carefully.

Did You Know?

Since 1 June 2017, all safety symbols appear in the shape of a red diamond with a white background. These have replaced the old orange square symbols that may still be on older products stored in some homes.

Corrosive

Toxic

Explosive

Highly flammable

Environmentally damaging

Irritant

Discovery Learning

There are some new safety symbols to be found. See how many you can find.

- If a poisonous substance is swallowed, bring the patient to hospital immediately. Bring the container of poison along with you.
- If the victim is unconscious, place him/her in the recovery position and call an ambulance.
- If the poison is **corrosive** (eats into and damages body tissue) **do not** induce vomiting. Instead, give the victim sips of milk to neutralise the poison.

Drowning

Children can drown in just a few centimetres of water and should be supervised at all times when near any water.

- Never leave babies or children in the bath unsupervised, not even for a minute.
- Do not leave uncovered containers of liquid around the house.
- Store away paddling pools when not being used.
- Preferably, fill in garden ponds while children are small. If this is not possible, cover ponds with a rigid grille or fence them off securely.

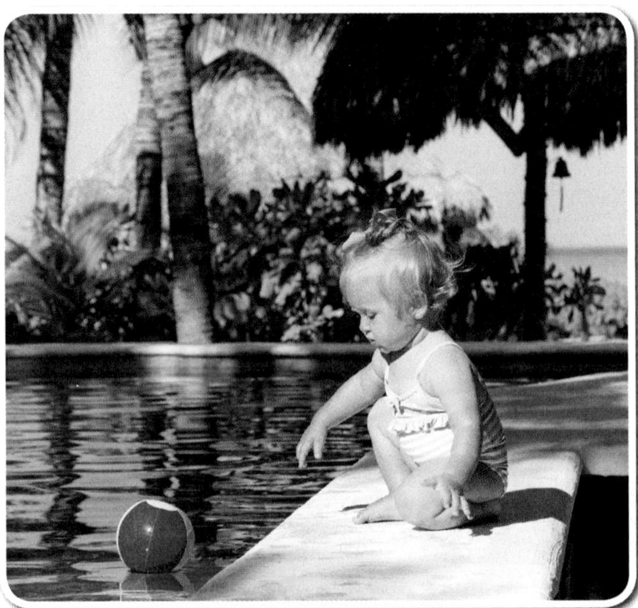

Fire safety

To protect a home and reduce the risk of fire:

- Install smoke alarms (**smoke detectors**) and test batteries weekly to check that they are working.
- Keep a **fire extinguisher** in the centre of the house.
- Keep a **fire blanket** near the cooker in the kitchen.
- Place a **fireguard** around fires. Never hang a mirror over a fireplace.

- Wear flameproof nightwear (particularly children).
- Keep matches and lighters out of children's reach and extinguish and dispose of cigarettes carefully. Never smoke in bed.
- Never leave a frying pan unattended.
- Before going to bed, unplug the TV and other appliances and close all doors to prevent the spread of fires.

Further Investigation

To find out more about fire safety visit **firesafetyweek.ie** and learn how to STOP fire.

Did You Know?

A total of 366 deaths connected to 326 fires were recorded across Ireland from 2005 to 2014, according to statistics provided by fire services across the country and published by the Department of the Environment (now the Department of Housing, Planning and Local Government). Cigarettes were the suspected cause of a quarter of the fatal fires according to these records.

Fire Escape Plan

Every public building, e.g. school, hospital or work place, must have a Fire Escape Plan. This is an outline of how to behave in the event of a fire; it details the actions to be taken by all staff in the event of fire and the arrangements for calling the fire brigade. A fire drill is a practice of what to do in advance, so that you can identify any likely problems that could occur and adapt the plan. It is advisable to have an escape plan for your home too.

Don't Forget!

It is important to have an escape plan worked out for your family home and to tell everyone in the house what to do in case of a fire. Practise the plan regularly. The fire brigade offer a consultancy service to home owners and workplaces.

Discovery Learning

Find out what you should do in the event of a fire in the school. Prepare an information leaflet for students telling them what to do in case a fire breaks out in your school.

Small fires

- Use fire extinguisher or blanket to put out fire.
- Water may be used on solid-fuel fires, but never on electricity or burning fat.
- If the fire cannot be extinguished, call the fire brigade.

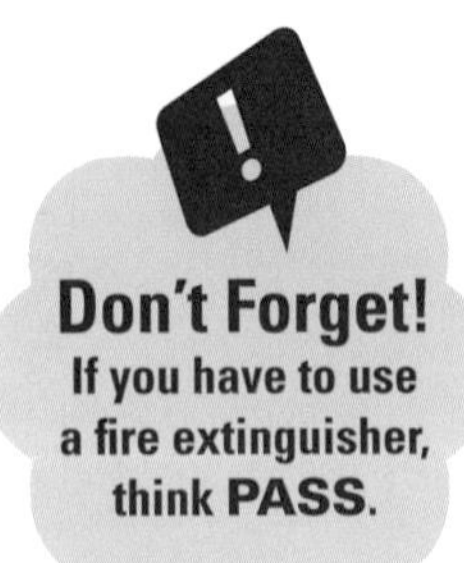

Don't Forget!
If you have to use a fire extinguisher, think **PASS**.

To operate an extinguisher:

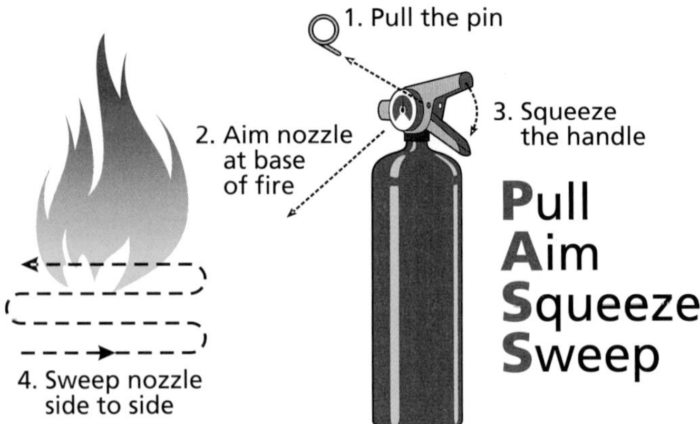

Large fires

- Keep calm and raise the alarm.
- Get out of house and ring the fire brigade.
- Remember there is more oxygen near the floor; cover the face with damp cloth and crawl towards nearest exit.
- Make sure everyone leaves the house, closing all doors to prevent fire spreading.
- Never re-enter a burning house.

Did You Know?

It can take as little as three minutes for permanent damage to be caused by smoke inhalation. So it is essential to insert smoke detectors in the home. It is suggested that at least four should be installed in a standard two-storey house: one on each landing and in the living room, and a heat detector in the kitchen.

A carbon monoxide detector is a piece of safety equipment that detects carbon monoxide (CO), which is an odourless but harmful gas produced by open fires, boilers and some heaters. It can cause fatal accidents if there's a leak. To find out more, watch the video 'Tommy McAnairy Lethal as Hell Music Video' (2:24) on YouTube.

Electrical and gas safety

(🔗 Electrical, see p. 317; gas, see p. 315)

Treating burns and scalds

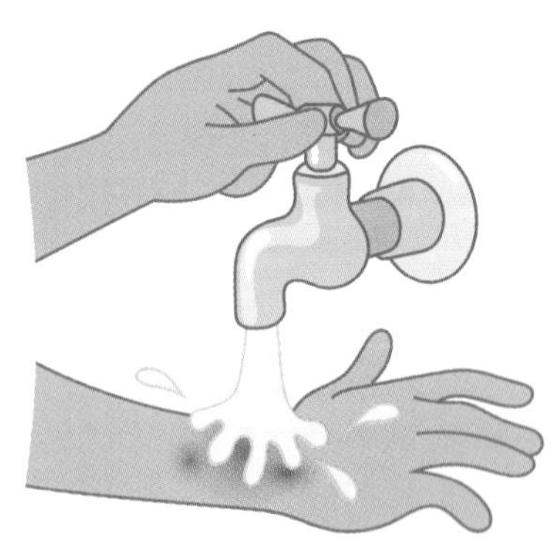

Burns are caused by dry heat, e.g. a fire, cooker or iron, while **scalds** are caused by moist heat, e.g. steam or boiling liquid. They should be treated in the same way.

- The heat sterilises the wound, so avoid handling it too much or you will re-introduce bacteria.
- Submerge the burnt area in cold water until the pain eases.

- Spray with burn spray or apply burn gel, then cover with gauze or a sterile dressing to exclude air.
- Do not remove any clothing that is stuck to wound – leave this to a doctor, who can take it off without causing extra damage.

Revision Questions

1. Identify the main causes of accidents in the home.
2. Choose three types of accidents that occur in the home and explain how to prevent them happening.
3. Why is it important for parents to learn basic first aid?
4. Discuss how to safely store and use medicines, chemicals and cleaning agents.
5. Explain how to treat one of the following: burns, scalds, strains, sprains and bleeding.
6. Outline the procedure you would follow if you discovered a fire in your home.

Protecting the environment from our homes

(Resource management, see p. 289)

A hygienic home has a major impact on our general health and wellbeing, making it a pleasant and safe place to be. Where bacteria are allowed to thrive in damp and dirty conditions **(see p. 86)** the risk of infection and disease is higher.

The kitchen and bathroom are two areas that require a high standard of hygiene. Good standards of personal hygiene are also required.

In order to prevent waste of our natural resources and protect our environment we must become aware of how our behaviour in our homes can affect the world outside.

Household waste

Each year we throw away millions of tonnes of household waste, which is disposed of by local authorities or private companies. How we deal with disposal of waste is very important.

Waste produced in the home falls into two categories:

Organic waste	Inorganic waste
Is biodegradable which means it breaks down naturally over time and does no harm to the environment, e.g. sewage, paper and food waste.	Is not biodegradable which means it does not break down but can be recycled, e.g. glass, plastic and metal.

Local authorities also ensure that sewage is disposed of hygienically. Private companies run bin collection services. A lot of waste is sent to be disposed of in landfill, which is the least favoured option in the EU waste hierarchy. New pricing systems for bins were implemented at the beginning of July 2017 to encourage proper waste disposal, e.g. charging by weight for refuse should encourage people to recycle and compost.

Did You Know?

The amount of waste sent to landfill rose by more than 110,000 tonnes last year – a 40% increase – according to the Environmental Protection Agency (EPA).
Many local authorities have produced an informative PDF called 'Waste Prevention and Recycling: Tricks and Tips', which can be downloaded from their individual websites and is a useful guide towards better waste management.

Composting

Roughly one-third of your household wheelie bin is made up of organic kitchen and garden waste, which is easily biodegradable. Organic waste materials are divided into greens and browns.

Green organic waste is usually wet or moist, is often green in colour and has a high nitrogen content, which activates the decomposition process.

Brown organic waste is very often brown in colour, is generally dry and has a high carbon content. In contrast to its green counterpart, this type of waste is slower to break down.

A compost recipe
Green (nitrogen rich) waste + brown (carbon rich) waste + oxygen + moisture + time = Compost!

Discovery Learning

Find out how to compost and why it is important for the environment.

The EU Waste Hierarchy

These are the guidelines issued by the EU that describe how to make your waste more environmentally friendly.

PREVENTION
PREPARING FOR RE-USE
RECYCLING
(ENERGY) RECOVERY
DISPOSAL

Prevention

- Refuse products that are not environmentally friendly.
- Buy only what you need, and preferably products that can be re-used, e.g. rechargeable batteries and refillable ink cartridges.
- Maintain and repair goods rather than replacing them.
- Avoid over-packaged products, use refills, and do not buy pre-packed fresh fruit and vegetables.
- Buy one all-purpose household cleaner instead of different ones for each cleaning job.

Preparing for re-use

- Walk or cycle to work/school if possible, or car pool instead of driving.
- Some materials like plastic, cardboard and glass can be re-used, e.g. glass jars for preservation.
- Sell or give away unwanted items to charities. You could even sell your possessions in a car-boot sale and earn some extra cash.
- Choose re-usable shopping bags over disposable ones.
- Catch water run-off from the roof into a bin to water the garden with.

Recycling

- A lot of household waste can be recycled into useful products thereby conserving resources (**see p. 223**).
- Compost kitchen waste for garden fertiliser.
- Purchase goods made from recycled products.

Classroom-Based Assessment

This section can be linked to CBA1: Creative Textiles.

Energy recovery

- Energy can be recovered, e.g. by using gases emitted from landfill sites to produce heat.

Disposal

- This is the least favoured option as it is the most wasteful of resources and causes environmental problems, e.g. landfill, polluting oceans, etc.

Further Investigation

Find out how to manage our waste efficiently at **www.askaboutireland.ie**. Search for 'Irish Waste Hierarchy', and click on levels of the pyramid for more information.

Further Investigation

Consumers can play an active role in waste management by refusing, reducing, re-using and recycling. Find out more at **www.recycling.ie**.

Did You Know?

Your school can sign up to ***www.weeepledge.ie*** to participate in a free battery recycling programme and access free educational assets for schools.

WEEE Directive (Waste Electrical and Electronic Equipment)

Under this EU directive, producers must organise for the collection and treatment of waste electrical and electronic equipment. This includes anything with a plug or battery, and large and small appliances can be recycled for free.

Advantages of recycling

- Lowers waste disposal costs and the amount of waste going to landfill
- Creates jobs
- Reduces litter and pollution problems
- Reduces our use of raw materials, like trees and metals
- Saves energy

Recycling symbols

Discovery Learning

Did you know that many recycle bins become contaminated very easily? Visit the Repak website to find out how to protect our environment by disposing of waste correctly: **www.repak.ie/for-home**.

Recycling symbol

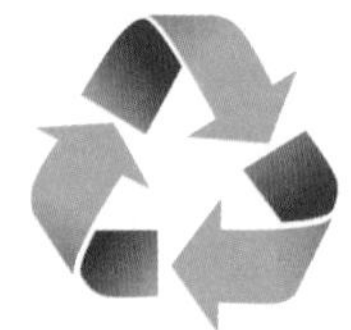

The recycling symbol is used by manufacturers to indicate that goods and packaging are recyclable.

Green dot

The green dot indicates that the suppliers of the packaging bearing the green dot have contributed financially to the cost of recycling. In Ireland the green dot symbol is only used by members of Repak.

EU Ecolabel

Recognised across Europe and worldwide, the EU Ecolabel helps identify products and services that have a reduced environmental impact throughout their life cycles.

Pollution

We all contribute to the pollution of our environment. We **use up** resources like water and fuels, **produce waste** like carbon dioxide (CO_2) and sewage and **pollute** the air and water with smoke, fumes and litter. If everyone made an effort to reduce pollution, the whole planet would benefit in the long term. There are different types of pollution.

Pollution is any harmful addition to the environment.

Water pollution

Causes	• Toxic factory waste including chemicals • Farm waste like leaching or seepage of fertilisers, insecticides and slurry • Domestic waste like seepage from sewage and waste water • Oil spills and illegally dumped rubbish • Vegetation, dirt and bacteria from the natural environment
Effects	• Causes algal bloom, which uses up oxygen in water and destroys aquatic life • Looks and smells horrible • Kills fish and marine life • Harms our tourist and fishing industries • Leaves water unsafe to drink
Steps towards change	• Use green/organic cleaning products and detergents • Safely dispose of all household chemicals • Limit our use of artificial fertilisers and pesticides • Be more aware of how we dispose of waste and **do not** litter The **government** need to: • Monitor factory and farm waste • Construct more efficient sewage treatment systems • Have heavy penalties for illegal disposal

To **leech** means to drain away.

Air pollution

Causes	• Smoke from industrial and domestic burning of fossil fuels produces gases like nitrogen, carbon dioxide and sulphur dioxide • Carbon monoxide from exhausts of cars • Sulphur dioxide from traffic and incomplete burning of fuel • CFCs (**chlorofluorocarbons**) used in old fridges and aerosols • Overuse of chemical sprays and cleaning agents
Effects	• Global warming affects the earth's climate • Ozone layer is damaged which leads to skin cancer and eye damage • Increase in respiratory conditions like asthma and bronchitis and allergies • Acid rain lowers pH of soil so damages plants and wildlife; it also damages metals and stone
Steps towards change	• Use renewable energy resources • Avoid products with CFCs, choose pump-action and ozone-friendly products • Use smokeless fuels and unleaded petrol • Use cars less, so car-pool, use public transport, or walk or cycle more • Buy energy-efficient appliances • Use green/organic cleaning products and detergents

Acid rain is the term to describe polluted rainfall. The moisture in the atmosphere mixes with gases like sulphur dioxide and carbon dioxide, forming a weak acid. Acid rain affects the plant and animal life of rivers and lakes by reducing the numbers of some species.

Noise pollution

Causes	• Aircraft, rail and road traffic • Loud music, TV, radio • Industrial noise – factories, construction work and lawnmowers • Burglar and car alarms and dogs barking • Night clubs, pubs and discos • Electrical appliances – food mixers, washing machines and lawnmowers
Effects	• Can have difficulty selling property • Poor image of an area • Upset residents and tension • Headaches, irritation and insomnia
Steps towards change	• Choose vehicles with lower noise emissions, e.g. hybrid or electric cars • Have consideration for neighbours • Insulate your home well • Choose housing away from transport systems and discos

The ozone layer

Ozone (O_3) is a form of oxygen located 20–30 km above the earth's surface. It protects the earth by absorbing the sun's harmful ultraviolet rays. When the ozone layer is damaged, ultraviolet radiation can reach the earth and have harmful effects including:

- Increase in skin cancer
- Increase in eye cataracts
- Damage to plant and animal life

The ozone is destroyed by:

- **Chlorofluorocarbons** (CFCs) found in aerosols, old refrigerators, air conditioning systems, foams used in furniture packaging and insulation
- **Halons** found in fire extinguishers

We can reduce damage to the ozone layer by:

- Using ozone-friendly pump action sprays and products
- Using non-aerosol alternatives, e.g. roll-on deodorants
- Disposing of old fridges in an environmentally safe way through the WEEE scheme

Did You Know?

A hole in the ozone layer has already developed over Antarctica. Bans on the use of CFCs in aerosols and refrigerators in most countries have halted this depletion and the ozone layer is already showing signs of recovery.

Did You Know?

Greenhouse gases including carbon dioxide and ozone help to keep the earth warm. However, if too many greenhouse gases such as CFCs build up in the atmosphere, too much heat is trapped, causing global warming which raises sea levels and causes damaging climate change, such as storms and flooding.

Discovery Learning

It is important to be environmentally aware, to help protect our planet and preserve it for future generations. There are a lot of Irish and international organisations that have relevant and up-to-date information on environmental issues. Visit their websites, and if you find out anything interesting, share this information with the class.

Environmental Protection Agency (EPA)
Visit ***www.epa.ie*** to find out more

seai SUSTAINABLE ENERGY AUTHORITY OF IRELAND

Sustainable Energy Authority Ireland (SEAI)
Visit ***www.seai.ie*** to find out more

An Taisce
Visit ***www.antaisce.org*** to find out more

GREENPEACE

Greenpeace
Visit ***www.greenpeace.org*** to find out more

Green-Schools

Many Irish schools are participating in the Green-Schools programme. Green-Schools is Ireland's leading environmental management and award programme, working with primary and secondary schools across the country. Schools apply online to participate and then work through eight themes:

- Litter and Waste
- Energy
- Water
- Travel
- Biodiversity
- Global Citizenship – Litter and Waste
- Global Citizenship – Energy
- Global Citizenship – Marine Environment

An internationally recognised award, the Green Flag, is awarded to the school when each theme is completed.

This programme reduces waste, litter, energy and water consumption, promotes sustainable and active travel to and from school. It develops the decision making skills of the students, builds their confidence and gives a sense of pride in their improved school environment.

Further Investigation

To find out how to get your school involved in the Green-Schools programme, visit **www.greenschoolsireland.org** to explore the themes and start your journey towards getting your first Green Flag.

Revision Questions

1. Explain why it is important to manage household waste appropriately.
2. Distinguish between organic and inorganic waste.
3. Identify the causes and effects of air, water and noise pollution.
4. Discuss ways that consumers can protect the environment.

Summary

- Many of the **accidents** that happen in and around the home can be avoided. By identifying and understanding potential accident risks in the home, parents can take some basic safety steps that make their house safer.
- Accidents can be caused by badly designed and maintained houses, incorrect use of services or faulty equipment, careless people, careless storage of dangerous items and bad luck.
- It is important that parents learn how to do basic first aid. This helps them to deal with the problem calmly, and prevent the condition from becoming worse.
- In case of a **serious accident**, stay calm, check for breathing, stop any bleeding by using pressure, reassure the victim and call an ambulance. An unconscious victim can be placed in the recovery position to keep their airways clear.
- **Slips, trips and falls** can be prevented by keeping areas well-lit and clutter-free, wiping up spills, not over-polishing floors, supervising children and using safety equipment.
- To prevent **cuts**, be careful when handling glass, especially if broken. Wrap it in newspaper and dispose of it safely. Store sharp objects securely out of reach of small children. When cuts occur, apply pressure to the wound to stop the bleeding and then wash cuts with water, clean them with antiseptic and cover with a plaster or dressing.
- Watch **young children** carefully as they put all sorts of items into their mouth, which could make them choke.

- If a **poisonous substance** is swallowed, take the patient and the container of poison straight to the hospital.
- Store **medicines** safely in a locked cabinet, away from children. Cleaning agents and chemicals have warnings and safety symbols and should be kept out of reach of children too.
- Children can **drown** in just a few centimetres of water and should be supervised at all times when near any water. If they are drowning, call an ambulance and do CPR.
- **Fire safety** includes having fire safety equipment at home, e.g. smoke detectors, extinguishers, blankets and guards. Be careful with electricity, matches and cigarettes, and during cooking.
- In the case of a fire, raise the **alarm**, get everyone out of the house, do not re-enter the house and call the fire brigade. Be prepared by having an escape plan in place.
- Treat **minor burns or scalds** with cold water or burn gel/spray. If a burn is **major**, pour water onto it or wrap in a wet sheet – do not remove any clothing stuck to it. Treat the victim for shock and get medical help.
- A **hygienic** home has a major impact on our general health and wellbeing, making it a pleasant and safe place to be. In order to prevent waste of natural resources and protect our environment we must become aware of how our behaviour in our homes can affect the world outside.
- **Organic waste**, e.g. food waste, breaks down naturally over time (biodegradable). Inorganic waste, e.g. metal and glass, does not, but it can be recycled.
- The **EU waste hierarchy** consists of the following options: prevention, preparing for re-use, recycle, energy recovery and disposal.
- **Recycling** lowers waste disposal costs and the need for landfill, creates jobs, reduces litter and pollution problems and saves the planet's resources.
- **Pollution** is any harmful change to the environment.
- **Water pollution** is caused by factory, farm and domestic waste, oil spills, illegally dumped rubbish and vegetation, and dirt and bacteria from the natural environment. It causes algal bloom, kills fish and marine life, harms the fishing and tourist industries, looks and smells bad and leaves water unsafe to drink.
- **Air pollution** is caused by smoke from burning fuels, emissions from cars, CFCs and overuse of chemicals. It causes global warming and acid rain, damages the ozone and affects people's health (e.g. causing respiratory conditions).
- **Noise pollution** is caused by traffic, industry, electrical appliances and dogs barking. It causes tension, irritation, insomnia, headaches and hearing damage.
- The **ozone layer** protects the earth from the sun's UV rays. Damage to the ozone layer causes an increase in skin cancer and damage to plant and animal life.
- **Greenhouse gases** can build up in the atmosphere, causing global warming and climate change.

Section 3: Competent Consumers

24 CONSUMER AWARENESS

Learning Outcomes 1.6, 1.7, 1.15, 1.16, 1.17, 1.18, 1.19, 2.2, 2.8, 2.9, 2.10, 2.11, 2.12, 2.13, 3.8, 3.9

What I Will Learn

- to appreciate the importance of consumer education
- to understand why consumers need to be informed
- to define consumer terms and give examples
- to categorise and give examples of consumer services
- to discuss consumer resources
- to identify the factors that influence consumers' choices
- to apply the decision-making process
- to examine the rights and responsibilities of a consumer
- to identify high quality goods and services

Key Words

✓ Consumer	✓ Knowledge
✓ Resource	✓ Creativity
✓ Redress	✓ Ideas
✓ Goods	✓ Need
✓ Service	✓ Want
✓ Direct	✓ Luxury
✓ Indirect	✓ Priority
✓ Money	✓ Quality
✓ Information	✓ Rights
✓ Skill	✓ Responsibilities
✓ Time	

Consumer education

Consumer **information** is any knowledge that helps the consumer to shop wisely. Consumer **education** is using this **knowledge** to make informed decisions when buying goods and services.

Redress means to set right, make amends.

Consumers need to be educated so they can become more aware, in order to:

- Make wise buying decisions;
- Get value for money;
- Understand consumer law, so they know how to get **redress**.

What is a consumer?

A **consumer** is anyone who **buys** or uses **goods** or **services**.

Everyone is a consumer – we all buy and use food, clothes, cars, phones, computers and many other goods. A consumer is not just a shopper, as we also consume energy in the form of electricity, oil and gas, and use roads, schools and public amenities. We also use services for payment.

Goods are products that are consumed, used or worn, e.g. food, mobile phones and clothes. They can be bought or sold.

A **service** is work done done by another person or by a business usually for payment, e.g. hairdressing, car repair, waste collection.

Years ago people were much more self-sufficient – they grew their own food, made their own clothes and built their own homes. In the modern world, we depend on others to provide us with the goods and services we need. We pay for these with money either **directly** with cash or credit or **indirectly** through paying taxes.

Did You Know?

Cattle are probably the oldest of all forms of money. Livestock as money dates back to 9000 BC, and in some parts of the world cattle are still used for trading. The first coins, pieces of bronze shaped like cattle, appeared around 2000 BC.

Discovery Learning

Get into small groups and write a list of six services that you pay for **directly** and six that are paid for **indirectly**. Share your list with the rest of the class.

Some consumer services are provided locally, e.g. shops, cinemas, doctors, taxis, dry cleaning and mechanics. Others are provided by the state, e.g. health services, schools, Gardaí, public lighting and postal services. Some services are provided by voluntary groups, e.g. sports clubs and St Vincent de Paul (**sustainable home and amenities, see p. 302**).

Don't Forget!

If consumers complain every time a service is unsatisfactory, they will eventually force suppliers to improve the service.

Characteristics of a good service:

- ✓ Clean, well-organised and ergonomic premises
- ✓ A friendly atmosphere, helpful, friendly and efficient staff
- ✓ Immediate attention paid to the consumer
- ✓ Short queues
- ✓ Good access and facilities for people with disabilities
- ✓ Family friendly
- ✓ Aware of its environmental impact

Further Investigation

Many retailers are trying to make their businesses more ethical, environmentally friendly and sustainable. Find out how they are doing this by going to **www.shelflife.ie**, searching for 'sustainable practices' and clicking on the article: 'Snapshot of sustainable practices being carried out by Irish retailers'. Focus on one Irish retailer and present your findings to the class.

Consumer resources

(Resources, see p. 289)

A **resource** is something you need to achieve a goal or complete a task. Consumers use the resources available to them to achieve their **goals**. These include:

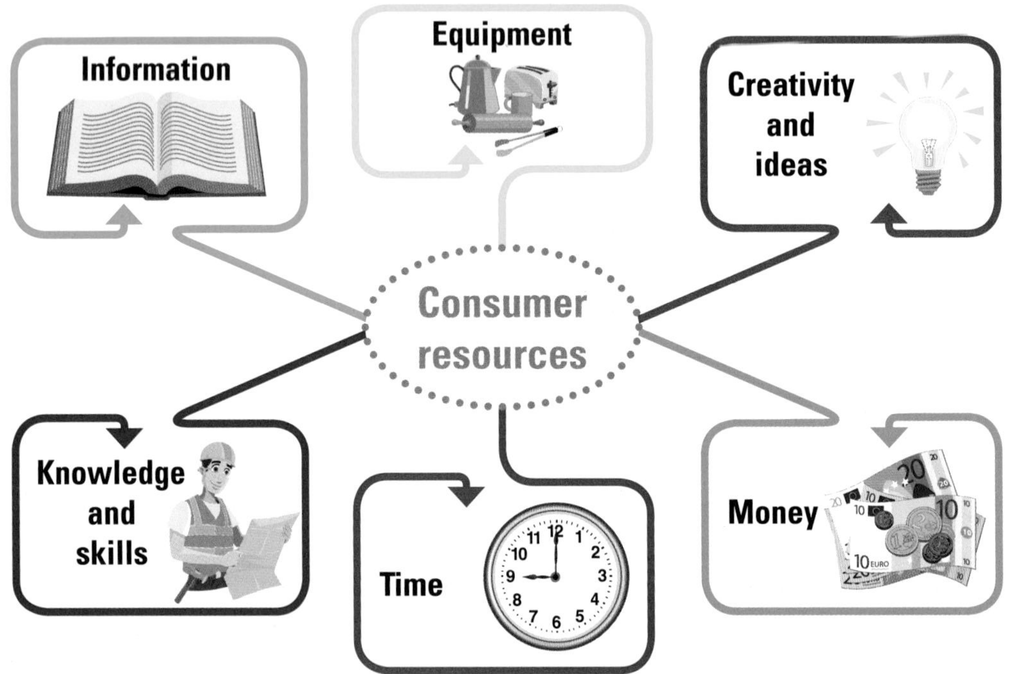

The wise consumer

We must be able to distinguish between the things we **want** and those we actually **need**.

Needs are things we cannot do without, something you must have to survive and live, e.g. food, water, clothing, shelter and warmth.

Wants are things we would like to have but do not need to survive, e.g. holidays, expensive cars and smart phones.

A **priority** is something that is very important to you.

A **luxury** is something inessential that's difficult to get – either due to expense or rarity – that is extravagant and brings great pleasure to the owner.

Needs and wants

Today it can be difficult to decide what is a **need** and what is a **want**. People consider consumer goods like washing machines, freezers or televisions a need, though our grandparents survived without them. In modern society, it often comes down to money. A family on a low

income may only be able to satisfy basic needs, while those on a higher income can satisfy more of their wants. Many wants are considered to be **luxuries**.

Factors that influence choice

(Resource management, see p. 289)

We use our decision-making skills to make the best choices when selecting goods and services. The decisions we make daily as consumers are influenced by many factors, both internal (personal) factors and external (outside) influences.

Internal factors include:

- **Age**: A child's needs differ from those of a teenager; a young parent's needs and wants will differ greatly from those of an older person.
- **Culture**: Some of our needs as Irish people could be considered luxuries in a third world country.
- **Circumstances**: Lifestyle, occupation and location influence our needs and wants.
- **Personal values**: Our own values and preferences will influence our choices, but needs should always have priority over wants.

External factors include:

- **Money**: Lack of money can limit choice, while having lots of it can widen choice.
- **Needs** and **wants**: Whether or not we actually need an item should have a large bearing on what we buy. However, we often buy what we want or desire rather than what is absolutely necessary.
- **Emotions**: Feelings can affect our buying habits and shops do what they can to play to consumers emotions, e.g. playing music in background. Our emotions often lead to impulse buying.
- **Family** and **peers**: Young children are influenced by their parents' ideas, tastes and values. Teenagers are more influenced by their peers and friends.
- **Trends** and **fashion**: Many people especially young people are influenced by what is popular or in fashion at a particular time, e.g. clothes and music.
- **Advertising** and **marketing** have major influence on the choices we make. We are influenced by radio, TV and internet advertising, free samples, celebrity sponsorship and in-store promotions. Attractive presentation and packaging also have a bearing on what we buy.

Decision making is an important consumer skill. Every day we are faced with a wide range of goods and services from which to choose, so it is necessary to make wise choices and decisions, as very few people have money to waste. Making a decision means choosing from several alternatives. A decision can be made on impulse or using the decision-making process, which involves eight logical steps **(resource management, see p. 289)**.

Impulse buying means buying an item on the spur of the moment without considering the consequences.

Decision-making process	
Step	**Example**
1. Defining the problem or task Identify the problem and look at the decision to be made, and why it must be made.	Cora's favourite band announce a concert date in her local town and the tickets go on sale on Friday morning. She has some money saved but wants to buy a new guitar.
2. Doing your investigation and research Gather information and find out more about the situation by asking others, using the internet, checking prices – this reduces risk.	Cora checks out ticket prices on line, talks to her friends to see who is going to the concert, checks music shops and newspaper advertisements, then discusses her options with her parents.
3. Generating ideas Consider various ways of dealing with the problem, the options and alternatives.	Cora considers her priority: guitar or ticket? Should she buy the ticket because this opportunity to see the band locally may not happen again? She needs a guitar for lessons she is taking in September. Is there any way to get both?
4. Developing possible solutions Think about each option or decision and look at the pros and cons of each.	If she does not buy the ticket, she may never get the chance to see the band with her friends. She could borrow money to pay for the ticket from her parents, but it could take a lot of time to pay it back. She really wants to learn to play the guitar and her parents have paid for lessons – could she get a second-hand guitar to save money and be able to go to the concert, too?
5. Presenting ideas to others for feedback Get another person's perspective on your problem or idea.	Cora talks through her ideas with her parents and friends and gets their feedback. This helps her make her decision.
6. Refining your ideas or choices Having weighed up all the options and consequences, make your choice.	Cora decides to buy a second-hand guitar to learn to play, as it is much cheaper, and buy a ticket for the concert.
7. Take action	Cora buys her ticket and gets a second-hand guitar.
8. Evaluate the outcome Think back on the decision and assess whether it was the right choice.	Cora is delighted she has a chance to see her favourite band live in concert, and she can still learn to play the guitar without going into debt. Cora can save up for a new guitar and resell her old one when she has enough money saved.

Overall assessment:

- Do you think Cora is a wise consumer?
- What factors influenced her choice?
- Has her decision had any impact on the environment?

Classroom-Based Assessment

This section can be linked to CBA1, CBA2 and the Practical Food Skills examination. Apply the Design Brief Process and the principles of design and sustainability to your textile CBA1. When you get your cookery brief, you will use the decision-making process to help you complete CBA2 and prepare for the Practical Food Skills examination.

When you actually come to buy a product, it is important to make wise decisions, so take your time and consider the following:

- **Money**: Think about how much you can afford to spend.
- **Value**: Is it good value for money? It is important to shop around to compare prices, products, brands, features and sizes.
- **Quality**: Is it made from good quality ingredients or materials?
- **Design** and **purpose**: Is it well finished? Does it look good? Is it effective? Is it designed to do its job properly?
- **Durability**: Think about how long it will last.
- **Safety**: Is it safe? This is very important in electrical goods and children's toys. Health concerns are also important, e.g. additives in food, chemicals in household products like cleaning agents. It is important to look at labels and safety symbols (**see p. 331**).
- **Environmental considerations**: Does the product use limited resources? Does it pollute? Can it be recycled? Is it biodegradable? (**see p. 223**)
- **Maintenance** and **aftercare** are important especially with electrical items and technology.
- **Comfort**, **fit** and **size** are important to consider when shopping for clothing and shoes.
- **Reliable shop**: Find a shop with a good reputation for quality, value and aftersales service.

Further Investigation

It is important to be an informed consumer – a person who knows their rights and responsibilities when they buy goods and services. An informed consumer should know about things like consumer laws, product labelling and quality. To learn more, visit the Competition and Consumer Protection Commission website at **www.ccpc.ie**.

Rights and responsibilities

- Every person has **rights**, like the right to be free and the right to vote. As consumers we also have certain rights, which protect us from manufacturers and sellers who might try to take advantage of us.
- Many of our rights are protected by law (**see p. 360**) so it is important to be aware of what we are entitled to.
- As consumers, we have choices and decisions to make when we buy goods or use services; therefore, we have **responsibilities** as well as rights.
- The first and most important consumer responsibility is to **know your rights**, as the law cannot always protect us from making foolish decisions.

A **right** is something to which you are entitled.

A **responsibility** is something for which you are accountable.

Further Investigation

To find out more about your rights and responsibilities as a consumer, visit YouTube and watch 'Consumer Rights & Responsibilities' (5:04).

Consumer rights

1. **The right to honest and accurate information**
   - Information provided to the consumer must be honest, truthful, accurate and clear.
   - Information must not be misleading or false.
   - It is the consumer's responsibility to gather the necessary information before buying a product or service.
   - It is illegal for manufacturers to give false information about a product or service.
   - Food must be labelled accurately so we know what we are eating. Inaccurate food labelling could lead to serious health problems for people with allergies or intolerances.

Don't Forget!

The consumer has a right to information from the seller and manufacturer, but also has a responsibility to look for information before buying. Gathering as much information as possible ensures that we are less likely to make costly mistakes.

2. **The right to choice**
   - Being able to choose from a variety of products and services is important, as it means we have lots of choice. There is a lot of competition between shops and manufacturers, which means better value for the consumer, and it forces those shops and manufacturers to raise their standards.
   - It is important to learn to complain (**see p. 366**).

A **monopoly** is when there is only one provider of a product or service. There are no other options available: no choice, e.g. Iarnród Éireann is the only train provider in the country.

3. **The right to value for money**
   - The consumer pays the appropriate price for goods and services based on the true quality of the product.
   - A sale item is only a bargain when good quality items are reduced and you need them.
   - Goods must be fit for purpose, e.g. food must be edible, a dishwasher must clean dishes.
   - If you buy cheap products, you cannot expect the same high standards or quality that you would expect from a more expensive one.

Don't Forget!
A bargain is only a bargain when you need the item and it is usable, otherwise it is a bad buy.

4. **The right to quality**
   - The law states that goods should be of merchantable quality, i.e. they must be of a certain standard and fit for use. So goods must be able to do what they are meant to do and be of good quality, e.g. a waterproof jacket should keep out the rain.
   - Manufacturers usually test goods for quality before they leave the factory; this is called 'quality control'.
   - Many products have quality marks and guarantees as an indication of quality (**quality and safety symbols, see p. 356**).

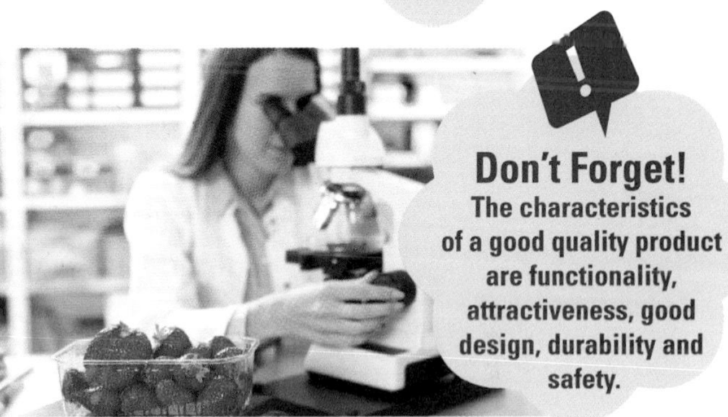

Don't Forget!
The characteristics of a good quality product are functionality, attractiveness, good design, durability and safety.

5. **The right to safety**
   - Consumers are entitled to products and services that will not put their health or lives at risk, so goods and services must be safe for consumers to use.
   - Electrical items, children's clothes and toys must follow strict safety rules protected by law.
   - Dangerous goods, e.g. bleach, must carry warning symbols.
   - Manufacturers of certain goods must carry out safety tests and provide warning labels and safety instructions.

6. **The right to redress**
   - If you are sold a product that is faulty or a service that does not provide what it is supposed to, you have a right to complain and get some form of compensation. Depending on the situation, you may be entitled to one of the 'three Rs':
     - **Repair** – the item is fixed free of charge.
     - **Replacement** – e.g. a new pair of shoes.
     - **Refund** – your money back.
   - Most retailers, manufacturers and service providers deal with complaints efficiently and quickly since a satisfied customer will return, while a dissatisfied customer will go elsewhere.

24.6

Biased information means to have an unfair preference or dislike for something. For example, if a sales person is on commission, they will promote the product that makes them the most money.

Consumer responsibilities

1. **The responsibility to inform yourself about goods and services so you can choose wisely**
   - Consumers need to be able to make wise decisions about goods and services to ensure they get value for money. They must understand the laws which protect the consumer to enable them to take the correct action if they feel they have a cause for complaint (**see p. 366**).
   - Sources of consumer information:
     - **Product packaging**, e.g. date stamps, ingredient lists.
     - **Care labels** on garments.
     - **Manufacturers' leaflets** often give detailed specifications of products, e.g. dimensions and features.
     - **Other consumers**: The experiences of other consumers who have used the product before can be invaluable.
     - **Magazines** and **newspapers**, particularly consumer magazines like Consumer Choice. These are available in your local library or online.
     - **Telephone directory** and Golden Pages.
     - **Community information services**, e.g. Citizens' Information Centres.
     - **Advertising**: Advertisements give information but it is often biased.
     - **Showrooms and exhibitions**: Looking around showrooms helps identify what products and services are available, e.g. Ideal Home Show. Exhibitions provide demonstrations.
     - **Salespeople**: Well-trained staff have a good knowledge of what they are selling. However some can put pressure on the consumer.
     - **Examination of products**: Handle and examine product with a critical eye, look at labels and symbols, date stamps and instructions for use. Check sizes and look for any faults.

- **TV/radio**: Consumer programmes like RTE's The Consumer Show look at some of the issues facing Irish consumers as well as getting to grips with individual viewers' complaints: visit *www.rte.ie/tv/theconsumershow* or email *consumers@rte.ie*.
- **Internet consumer sites** and advice agencies like the Consumer Association of Ireland and Competition and Consumer Protection Commission. These can be accessed quickly on smart phones, too.

2. **The responsibility to understand the balance between cost and quality**
   - Consumers need to be discerning (show good judgement). They should ensure that they get value for money – does the quality match the price being paid? A high price does not necessarily mean better quality goods or services.

3. **The responsibility to read labels and follow manufacturers' instructions**
   - It is the consumer's responsibility to read and follow any specific instructions supplied with a product regarding its use, safety, care etc. Quality and safety marks can help consumers with their rights and responsibilities.

Further Investigation

The Consumers' Association of Ireland is an independent voluntary organisation working on behalf of Irish consumers. It also produces the monthly *Consumer Choice* magazine. To find out more, visit **www.thecai.ie**.

Quality marks

Quality marks are symbols used on products and services to show that they are of a high standard. They can be withdrawn if standards are not maintained.

Symbol	Meaning	Found on
	Guaranteed Irish is the national symbol of provenance and trust. The GI symbol is awarded to homegrown and international businesses which have chosen to invest in Ireland. These businesses create jobs, contribute to the community and promote pride of Irish provenance.	• Zip firelighters • Brennans Bread • SMA
Quality Certified	**Q Mark**: Products and services are produced, provided and sold in Ireland to the highest standards.	• Avonmore • Odlums • Fyffes • Shamrock
FOOD SAFETY I.S. EN ISO 22000:2005 NSAI Certified	**Irish Standard Mark**: The symbol assures customers that the item meets certain basic standards and has been produced under a system of quality control supervised by National Standards Authority of Ireland (NSAI).	• Glanbia Foods Ireland Ltd
	Kitemark (British Standards Institute): Products and services of high standards of quality and safety.	• Electrical goods • Yale locks • Car industry

Safety symbols

Safety Symbol	Meaning	Found on
CE	**Communanité Européenne**: Goods comply with European standards of safety	• Toys • Electrical goods
	Double Insulated: The outside metal/plastic case of the appliance is securely insulated from any electrical wiring inside the tool. If a wire should come loose inside the tool, it cannot contact the outside metal case of the device, no matter what.	• Small electrical appliances/ products, e.g. DVD players and hairdryers

(Safety symbols, see p. 331)

Revision Toolkit

To revise symbols, go to **quizlet.com** and search for 'Home Economics Consumer Symbols'.

4. **The responsibility to complain about faulty goods and services**
   - Consumers should complain if a product or service is faulty or not as expected. Complaining and reporting faults will help ensure a better standard of product or service in the future (**see p. 366**).

5. **The responsibility to know your rights** (**see p. 352**)

6. **The responsibility to know consumer law** (**see p. 360**)

7. **The responsibility to avoid wasting resources and protect the environment** (**see p. 335**)

Revision Questions

1. Explain the importance of consumer education.
2. Explain the difference between a need and a want.
3. List four consumer resources.
4. Explain the difference between a direct and indirect service, and give four examples of each.
5. Identify the factors that influence consumers' choices.
6. You are looking for a new pair of jeans. What are the six most important considerations when you go out to buy them?
7. List the main steps in the decision-making process.
8. Discuss three consumer rights.
9. List five consumer responsibilities.

Use your workbook to revise this chapter •

Summary

- Consumer **information** is any knowledge that helps a consumer to buy wisely and consumer **education** is using this knowledge to make informed decisions when purchasing goods and services.
- A **consumer** is anyone who buys or uses goods or services. **Goods** are products that are consumed, used or worn, e.g. food, mobile phones and clothes. They can be bought or sold.
- A **service** is work done, usually for payment, e.g. hairdressing, car repair, waste collection.
- **Characteristics of a good service** are: a clean, well-organised and ergonomic premises, a friendly atmosphere with helpful, friendly and efficient staff who give immediate attention, short queues, good access and facilities for people with disabilities, family friendly, awareness of the environmental impact of the business or service.

- A **resource** is something you need to achieve a goal or complete a task. Consumers use the resources available to them to achieve their goals. These include information, knowledge, creativity and ideas, skills, equipment, time and money.
- The decisions we make daily as consumers are influenced by many factors, both **internal** factors and **external** influences. Internal factors include: age, culture, circumstances, personal values and likes. External factors include: money, needs and wants, emotions, family and peers, trends and fashion, advertising and marketing. We can also be influenced by radio, TV and internet advertising, free samples, celebrity sponsorship, in-store promotions, and attractive presentation and packaging.
- **Decision making** involves the following steps:
  - Defining the problem or task
  - Doing your investigation and research
  - Generating ideas
  - Developing possible solutions
  - Presenting ideas to others for feedback
  - Refining your ideas or choices
  - Taking action
  - Evaluating the outcome
- Consider the following when making decisions: money, value, quality, design and purpose, durability, safety, environmental considerations, maintenance and aftercare, comfort, fit and size and reliability of shop.
- **Consumer rights** are things you are entitled to. They include rights to honest information, to choice, to value for money, to quality, to safety and to redress.
- **Consumer responsibilities** include becoming informed about goods and services so you can choose wisely; understanding the balance between cost and quality; reading labels and following manufacturers' instructions; knowing your rights; being aware of consumer law; being able to complain about faulty goods and services; and avoiding wasting resources and protecting environment.
- **Quality goods** are attractive, functional, well designed, hardwearing and safe. A **quality service** is reliable, friendly, helpful, hygienic and safe. Quality symbols include Guaranteed Irish, Q Mark, Irish Standard Mark and the Kitemark. **Safety marks** include the CE mark, the double insulated mark and safety and health warnings.

25 CONSUMER PROTECTION

Learning Outcomes 1.6, 1.18, 1.19, 2.3, 2.8, 2.9, 2.10, 2.11, 2.12, 3.7, 3.8, 3.9

What I Will Learn

- to explain how consumers are protected in Ireland
- to discuss the laws that protect Irish consumers
- to understand why consumers need to be protected
- to explain how to get redress
- to discuss the role of statutory and voluntary organisations in consumer protection
- to state the guidelines for making consumer complaints
- to write a letter of complaint
- to discuss the value of using the Small Claims Court

Key Words

✓ Protection
✓ Unscrupulous
✓ Law
✓ Courts
✓ Claims
✓ Contract
✓ Statutory
✓ Voluntary
✓ Misleading
✓ Redress
✓ Replace
✓ Repair
✓ Refund
✓ Merchantable
✓ Guarantee
✓ Warranty
✓ Ombudsman
✓ Complaint
✓ Credit note
✓ Receipt

Consumer protection is necessary to:
- Stop unscrupulous manufacturers or retailers taking advantage of consumers
- Protect the rights of consumers
- Make sure consumers can get redress if their rights are abused (see p. 362)

Consumers are protected by:
- The law and the courts
- Government (statutory) agencies, e.g. the Competition and Consumer Protection Commission and the Ombudsman
- Voluntary organisations, e.g. the Consumers' Association of Ireland

Unfortunately, the law cannot protect us from ourselves. If we buy on impulse, don't check prices, or examine the goods, or don't bother to read labels or instructions, we are likely to make many mistakes or bad buys.

Unscrupulous means having or showing no moral principles; not honest or fair.

Did You Know?

The Latin phrase '**caveat emptor**' means '**let the buyer beware**'. This means that the person who buys something is responsible for making sure it is in good condition and works properly.

Consumer laws and the courts

Consumer rights are protected by legislation. These laws are necessary to prevent unscrupulous manufacturers and suppliers taking advantage of consumers, e.g. by misleading consumers about goods, services or price. They also ensure that if consumer rights are infringed people have a means of redress.

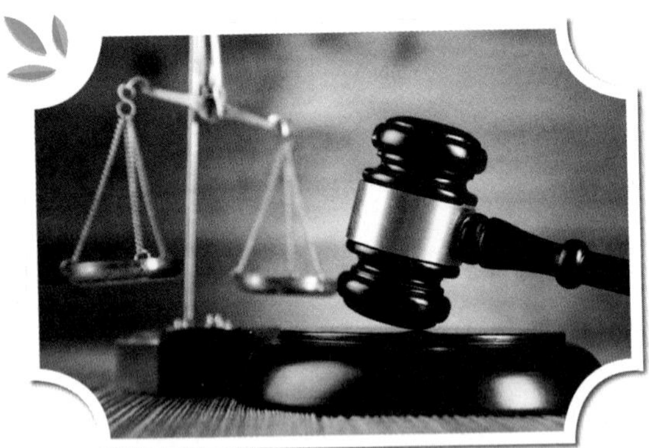

Many laws are passed by the state and the EU which protect the consumer. As many new situations arise when new products and services come on stream like credit cards and online shopping, new laws have to provide for these.

The courts enforce consumer law, and claims up to €2,000 may be dealt with by the small claims procedure (**see p. 367**) in the district courts.

Higher claims are dealt with in the circuit court and high court, both of which are very expensive and time consuming.

To **infringe** is to actively break the terms of an agreement or a law.

Further Investigation

To find out more about how the Irish court system operates, visit **www.citizensinformation.ie**, click on 'Justice' then on 'Courts system'.

Sale of Goods and Supply of Services Act 1980

The Sale of Goods and Supply of Services Act 1980 states the basic rights of the consumer.

- When you buy a product or use a service, you are making **a contract** with the **retailer or supplier**. It does not have to be in writing; if you pay for a product and it is faulty, it is the **seller**, not the manufacturer, who has the legal obligation to put it right.
- Goods must be of **merchantable quality**. This means that they should be of reasonable quality (in good order and undamaged). It is important to consider what the product is meant to do, its durability and its price. When you buy goods in a sale you have the same rights as when you pay full price for the goods.

- Goods must be **fit for the purpose** intended, suitable for use and function as expected, e.g. electrical products must work safely and efficiently, a dishwasher should wash dishes and food must be edible.
- Goods should be **as described** by the salesperson, on a label, in a brochure or in an advertisement, e.g. waterproof, genuine leather.
- If goods are sold on the basis of seeing a sample, they must **correspond to the sample** on display, e.g. the paint in tin should correspond to colour shown on tin or duvet set to its picture.
- Services should be provided by a skilled person, with due care and diligence, using quality materials.

Did You Know?

If goods are clearly marked as seconds or have defects pointed out at time of sale, then you do not have any redress under the act. This also applies if you change your mind about a product.

If goods do not comply with these conditions, the seller has broken the contract. Remember, once the product is of 'merchantable quality', fit for purpose and as described, you have no right to go looking for a refund or an exchange.

This act also deals with the following:

- **Notices in shops**: It is an offence for notices such as the following to be displayed:

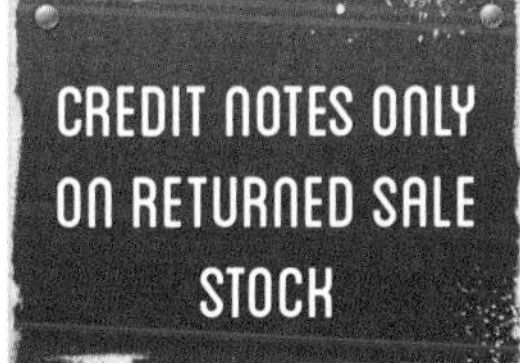

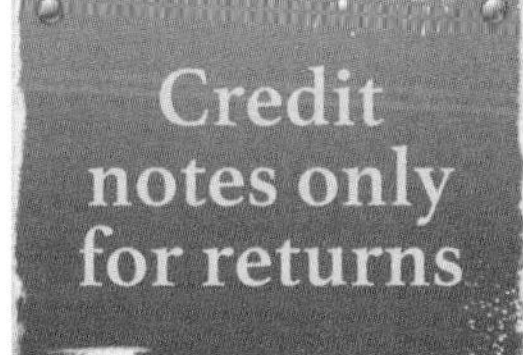

- **Guarantees**: A guarantee or warranty on a product gives additional protection. It is a contract between the manufacturer and the consumer that indicates that the manufacturer will repair or replace an item within a set amount of time after it has been purchased. Guarantees are legally binding. The guarantee must:
  - Be legible;
  - Refer to a specific product;
  - Name the product, and give the name and contact details of person/company offering the guarantee;
  - Show the length of the guarantee from the date of purchase;
  - Outline how to make a claim;
  - Explain what the manufacturer will do – what the customer should expect to receive in the event of a fault;
  - Identify any extra charges the claimant might pay for getting the product repaired (such as postage and packaging).

  Products like household goods, e.g. pots/pans, furniture and electrical goods, typically come with a guarantee. Some services may also be guaranteed, e.g. work undertaken in a house (such as double glazed windows) may be guaranteed for a specific period of time.

Redress

A consumer is entitled to redress or compensation for faulty goods or poor services. Under the act, consumers are entitled to complain. The type and amount of compensation depends on

- How serious the fault is;
- How soon after purchase the fault occurred;
- How soon you complain (see p. 366).

One of the following must be offered, provided that the product is returned with a receipt and has not been tampered with:

- Repair
- Replacement
- Refund or partial refund
- Compensation
- Credit note
- In the case of service, repeated without charge

Don't Forget!
The sooner you return the goods, the stronger the case you will have. Do not use the product once you discover the fault, and do not attempt to repair it, or you may lose your rights under this act.

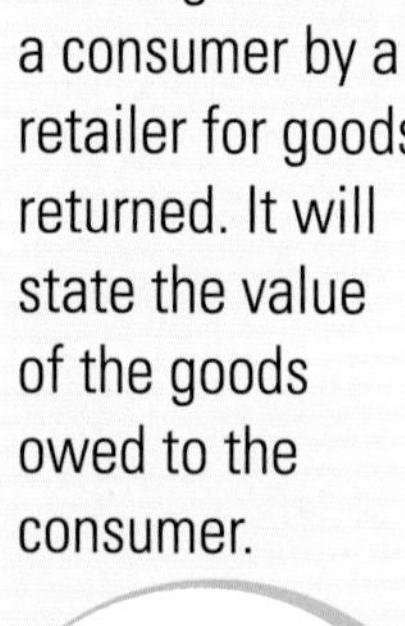

A **credit note** is a note given to a consumer by a retailer for goods returned. It will state the value of the goods owed to the consumer.

CREDIT NOTE
[Customer Name]
[Customer Address 1]
[Customer Address 2]
[Customer Town]
[Customer City]
[Customer Postcode]
Description
Faulty Widgets on Invoice INV-0001

A consumer might be entitled to a **full refund** (money back) or **replacement** if goods are incapable from the start of doing what they are supposed to do, or if the goods are not as described (i.e. the consumer has been **misled**).

If you are not entitled to a full refund, you may still get a **partial refund** if goods worked for a short time after purchase. The retailer might offer to **repair** the goods. Any repairs should be permanent and carried out quickly.

A retailer can offer credit notes as a matter of goodwill if they feel you do not have a valid complaint, e.g. if you have changed your mind.

Consumer Protection Act 2007

The Consumer Protection Act 2007 protects the consumer against false or misleading claims about goods or services. It also forbids false or misleading information about the price, previous price or recommended retail price of goods or services.

Any extra costs should be stated on the price tag, i.e. if the price of a food mixer does not include all the attachments displayed, the extra cost must be clearly stated. If an item is priced now 'half price' from €30 to €15, it must have been on sale at the original price for 28 consecutive days in the previous three months.

The act also protects the consumer from **false or misleading claims** about **goods** or **services**, either orally, e.g. from a sales assistant, or in advertising or catalogue descriptions, e.g. if a product is said to be guaranteed Irish, it must be produced in Ireland, or if a shop claims to open '24 hours a day', it must do so.

Examples of claims made include:

- 'Pure wool'
- '100% cotton'
- 'Made in Ireland'
- 'Waterproof'
- 'Free from artificial colours'
- 'Bone china'
- '18-carat gold'
- 'Low fat'
- 'High fibre'
- 'Lowers cholesterol'
- 'Genuine leather'
- '24-hour service'
- '1-hour photos'
- 'Delivery to all areas'
- 'Ireland's most punctual airline'

Did You Know?

If a shop incorrectly labels something with the wrong price and it is lower than the price charged at the till, you do not have an automatic right to buy the goods at the marked price. As long as the seller tells you before your money is taken, you can decide not to buy it.

Don't Forget!

It is not an offence for a shop or service provider to increase their prices to take advantage of seasonal demand or a particular occasion as long as the prices quoted are accurate.

Electronic Commerce Act 2000

The Electronic Commerce Act 2000 was established under the EU and protects consumers when shopping online. It states that e- bookings and agreements have the same status as written documents.

The following transactions are exempt:

- Sale of land
- Concert tickets
- Home delivery of food and drinks
- Flight tickets
- Holiday bookings
- Auctions

When you buy online you have the right to:

- Clear and accurate information before you buy
- A refund, if your goods are not delivered
- Return something because you change your mind
- Cancel a service
- Return something that is faulty
- Cancel digital purchases

Further Investigation

To find out more about your rights online, visit **www.ccpc.ie/consumers** and search for 'Your rights online'.

Don't Forget!
When buying goods always examine the goods carefully before you buy and store all receipts (a proof of purchase) and guarantees safely.

Consumer protection organisations

There are a number of statutory (established by the government) and voluntary organisations and agencies that protect the consumer.

Statutory organisations

The Competition and Consumer Protection Commission

www.consumerhelp.ie

The CCPC's role is:

- To **promote** and **protect** the consumer through high advertising standards.
- To **enforce** consumer law and to **investigate** any breaches, i.e. unfair and illegal trading practices.
- To **inform** consumers of their rights – leaflets, website and newsletters.
- To guarantee that products sold in Ireland **conform** to Irish safety standards by carrying out surveillance activities, alerting consumers about unsafe products, and advising manufacturers, suppliers, retailers and their representative bodies about their responsibilities.
- To ensure that **food labels** supply all the legally required information.
- To **protect** and **strengthen competition**, to ensure good value for consumers, to stimulate business and enhance the economy as a whole.
- To **advise** government on consumer issues and legislation.

The Office of the Ombudsman

www.ombudsman.gov.ie

The Ombudsman service is free, and their role is:

- To **investigate unresolved complaints** made against **public service providers**: government departments, local authorities, the HSE, private nursing homes and publicly-funded third-level education bodies.
- As a last resort, if no resolution can be made between the consumer and department or agency in question.
- To **examine the case** and make a **recommendation**. It is not legally binding, but it is usually complied with.

National Standards Authority of Ireland

www.nsai.ie

The NSAI's role is:

- To set, monitor and develop standards of safety and quality in Ireland.
- To ensure Irish Products meet EU and international standards.

Citizens Information Board

www.citizensinformation.ie

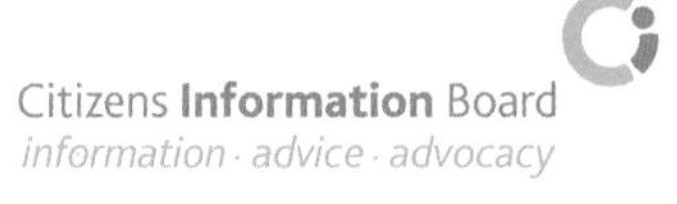

This board provides the public with accurate information and advice on a range of public and social services areas including consumer rights. This information is provided through:

- A website
- A phone service
- Citizens Information Centres countrywide

It advises on personal debt and money management through the Money Advice and Budgeting Service (MABS) (see p. 297).

European Consumer Centre Ireland

www.eccireland.ie

Cabhair agus comhairle do thomhaltóirí san Eoraip ECC-Net

European Consumer Centre Ireland

The European Consumer Centre provides free and confidential information, advice and support on your consumer rights when buying goods and using services in other EU countries. It is part of the European Consumers Centre Network (ECC-Net), which covers 30 countries (all EU countries, plus Norway and Iceland), and:

- Participates in research, and in the ECC Network of 30 countries.
- Co-operates with national consumer organisations and enforcement agencies.
- Assists in solving **cross-border** consumer disputes.
- Provides **education** and **outreach** programmes for schools, universities, community groups and others.

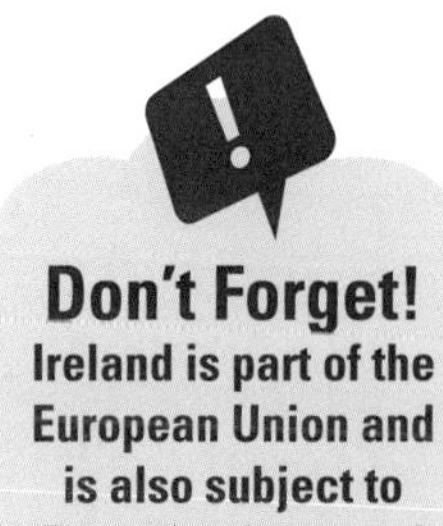

Don't Forget!
Ireland is part of the European Union and is also subject to European laws and standards.

Voluntary organisations

Consumer Association of Ireland

thecai.ie

Consumers' Association of Ireland

The Consumer Association of Ireland is a not-for-profit independent organisation that:

- **Informs** and advises consumers of their rights.
- **Publishes** leaflets and *Consumer Choice* magazine.
- **Lobbies the government** to improve consumer laws.
- Represents consumers' interest in **media**.
- Carries out **surveys and reports** on consumer products and services.
- **Encourages high standards** of quality in Irish products/services.
- **Represents the public** on various bodies such as the Food Safety Authority.

Don't Forget!
Complain promptly to the supplier if there is a problem with a service.

The Advertising Standards Authority of Ireland

www.asai.ie

The ASAI is an independent, self-regulatory body set up by the advertising industry in Ireland. Its role is:

- To ensure advertising are legal, decent, honest and truthful. It may recommend that an advertisement is altered or removed.
- To investigate consumer complaints.

Consumer complaints procedure

How to seek redress:

- Return to the shop as soon as possible with the faulty goods and your receipt as proof of purchase.
- Ask to speak to manager, and politely explain your problem. State what you expect the shop to do about the faulty goods or service. Consumers must be realistic about compensation – not every complaint merits a full refund. Sometimes the best you can expect is a repair or a credit note.
- If the shop refuses to accept responsibility, the complaint should be made in writing by letter or email to the retailer or head office.
- If the response is still unsatisfactory, help may be sought from consumer agencies such as Consumer Association of Ireland or the Competition and Consumer Protection Commission.
- The final step is to take legal action through the Small Claims Court.

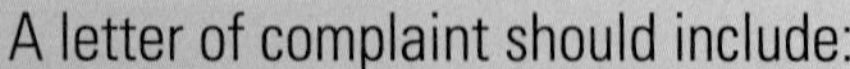

A letter of complaint should include:

- Your address and the date (not needed if sending by email)
- The name and address of the business (not needed if sending by email)
- When and where product was bought
- Description of the goods – model, brand, price
- Clear details of the complaint
- Action you would like taken
- Copies of receipts and guarantee

Discovery Learning

Learn to write a letter of complaint: go to ***www.ccpc.ie/consumers***, click on 'How to complain' and then 'complaint letter templates'. Now go ahead and write one letter or email for faulty goods and one for poor service.

Small Claims Court

The aim of the Small Claims Court procedure is to provide an inexpensive, fast and easy way for consumers to resolve disputes without the need to hire a solicitor. The Small Claims service is provided by the local District Court office.

Claims include faulty goods and bad workmanship for any dispute up to €2,000 for a fee of €25.

- An application form is completed in writing or online by the consumer and sent to local District Court office. This outlines the details of the claim.
- The Small Claims Registrar contacts the retailer or service provider, who can accept the claim, challenge the claim, counterclaim or ignore it.
- If it is disputed, the Registrar attempts to resolve the issue. Otherwise, the case will be resolved in court.
- If they then do not reply or challenge the claim within 15 days, it is settled in favour of the consumer. The retailer or service provider has 28 days to comply with the judgement.

Further Investigation

To find out how the small claims court works, visit **www.citizensinformation.ie**, click on 'Justice', then 'Courts System', then 'Small Claims Court'.

Did You Know?

Some people get consumer complaints resolved by using the media – newspapers, TV, radio and social media like Facebook.

Revision Questions

1. Explain why consumers need to be protected.
2. Name two consumer laws and explain how each protects the consumer.
3. Name one statutory organisation and explain how it helps consumer.
4. Name one voluntary organisation and explain how it helps consumer.
5. Discuss why it is important to complain when goods are faulty or service is poor.
6. Outline the guidelines for making consumer complaints.

Use your workbook to revise this chapter •

Summary

- **Consumer protection** is necessary to stop unscrupulous manufacturers or retailers taking advantage of consumers, to protect consumers' rights and to make sure they can get redress if their rights are abused.
- Consumers are protected by the **law** and the **courts**, **statutory** organisations, e.g. the Competition and Consumer Protection Commission and the Ombudsman, and **voluntary organisations**, e.g. the Consumers' Association of Ireland
- The **Sale of Goods and Supply of Services Act 1980** states that when you buy a product or use a service, you are making a **contract** with the retailer or supplier. Goods must be of **merchantable quality, fit for the purpose and as described**. Services should be provided by a **skilled person, with due care and diligence using quality materials**.
- If goods are **faulty**, you might be entitled to **redress** in the form of a **refund**, **repair** or a **replacement**. A **guarantee** gives additional protection; it is a contract between the manufacturer and the consumer that says the manufacturer will repair or replace an item within a set amount of time.
- The **Consumer Protection Act 2007** protects the consumer against **false** or **misleading claims** about goods or services either orally, e.g. sales assistant, or in advertising or catalogue descriptions.
- **Electronic Commerce Act 2000** provides cover when you buy online. You have the right to: clear and accurate information before you buy; a refund if your goods are not delivered; return something because you change your mind; cancel a service; return something that is faulty; and cancel digital purchases.
- Learning **how to complain** is important to get a better service. Initially, complain **in person**. If you do not get satisfaction, write a **letter of complaint**. Be polite and describe the problem, and outline the redress you require – but be realistic. As a final resort, you can go to the Small Claims Court.

26 SHOPPING WISELY

Learning Outcomes 1.1, 1.2, 1.3, 1.6, 1.7, 1.15, 1.16, 1.17, 1.18, 1.19, 2.1, 2.3, 2.6, 2.8, 2.9, 2.10, 2.11, 2.12, 2.13, 3.7, 3.8, 3.9

What I Will Learn

- to describe and evaluate the different types of shopping outlets
- to differentiate between self-service and counter service shops
- to discuss the changes in shopping in recent years
- to discuss the different methods of paying for goods
- to evaluate the techniques used by shops to encourage consumers to spend
- to state the functions of advertising
- to state the characteristics of effective advertising
- to explain the controls on advertising
- to list the advantages and disadvantages of advertising
- to evaluate the value of consumer information to a shopper
- to discuss how to become a responsible shopper

Key Words

✓ Shopping outlets
✓ Retail
✓ Advertising
✓ Marketing
✓ Techniques
✓ Cash
✓ Credit card
✓ Debit card
✓ Cheque
✓ Direct debit
✓ Sponsorship
✓ Loyalty cards
✓ Barcode
✓ Biodegradable
✓ Loss leader
✓ Bulk buying
✓ Unit price

Shopping is part of everyday life. The way we shop has changed over the years and there is greater choice now. However, there is a temptation to overspend and waste resources, so we need to become responsible and ethical shoppers (**see p. 348**).

Shopping outlets

Small independent shops

Independent stores are traditional small shops, often family-run and sometimes open long hours. They may offer less choice and can be more expensive, but they provide a more personal service, and often offer a line of credit.

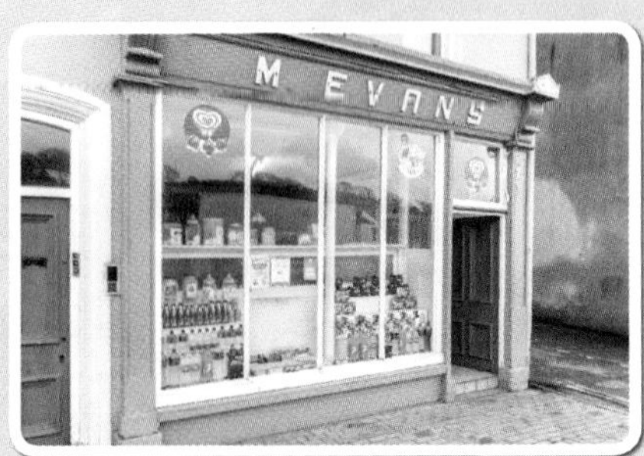

Specialist shops

Some stores specialise in one type of stock, e.g. shoes, books or jewellery.

Supermarket

Supermarkets are large, open-plan grocery shops. They are self-service and usually easy to move around in. They have a wide variety of goods, from food and cleaning products to clothing and electricals, and offer their own brands alongside other brands. Some offer internet shopping with home delivery, loyalty cards and special offers for regular customers. Supermarkets are often cheaper than independent stores, as, because of the bigger turnover of stock, they can buy products in bulk, reducing unit cost.

Did You Know?

Hypermarkets are similar to supermarkets and department stores combined. They are on a much larger scale than regular supermarkets and combine a huge range of stock, usually at cheaper prices. An example of a hypermarket is Carrefour, in France.

Department stores

Department stores are large, open-plan shops that are easy to move around and predominantly self-service, though many offer a personal shopping service too. They offer a wide variety of products, laid out in separate departments, e.g. make-up, shoes, household, clothing etc. They offer good value for money with competitive pricing.

Multiple chain stores

When there is one company with many branches, each with the same layout and style, selling the same products, these are known as chain stores. They are competitive and good value due to bulk buying and shared advertising, and are usually self-service. They are located in large towns. Examples include Penneys, Topshop, and Dunnes Stores.

Discount stores

Discount stores can be part of a chain or independent. Some are based on catalogue orders while others offer counter service. They sell cheaper items, pre-packed goods that cannot be examined before purchase and goods that many need to be assembled. They have limited stock in stores, good returns policies and can offer online ordering for instore pickup. Others focus on a wide array of low-cost items to encourage impulse buying, and these have a high turnover and are self-service.

Discovery Learning

There are a wide variety of ways to shop online. Research one online shop and present the information to the rest of the class in a creative way.

Don't Forget!
Your rights and responsibilities are the same when you shop online as they are when you shop instore.

Online shopping	
Advantages	**Disadvantages**
• Easy to use, and a wide variety of websites can be accessed quickly • Easy to compare brands, prices and styles • Goods can be bought from home, day or night, making it more convenient • May be cheaper, as it's easy to compare prices • Next day delivery and order tracking are offered by some companies	• Increased risk of impulse buying and overspending, which can lead to debt • The product may not be as expected, as you cannot examine the product or try it on • You need to have a credit card: there is a higher risk of credit card fraud online • Delivery can take a long time • Postage charges can add to the cost of products

Other shopping outlets include:
- Street markets
- Farmers' markets
- Auctions
- Shopping centres
- Party selling
- Teleshopping
- Vending machines
- Mail order
- Door-to-door selling
- Outlet shops

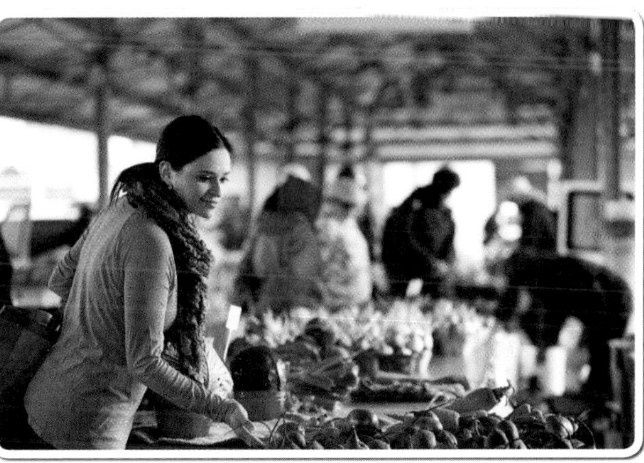

In recent times, many shops have moved from counter service to self-service. In the past, supermarkets were just large outlets where you could buy groceries more cheaply. They were impersonal and provided little choice of fresh foods. Today, competition between them has improved variety and service greatly.

Counter service	
Advantages	**Disadvantages**
• Personal service • Easier especially for older people • Usually local, handy if you run out of something • May offer credit and free delivery	• May be slow and inefficient • More expensive • Smaller choice • Prices not always visible

Self-service	
Advantages	**Disadvantages**
• Quick and convenient • Goods are displayed well and clearly priced • You can take your time to browse and select • Less expensive because they buy in bulk and have lower overheads • Own brands are particularly cheap • A quick turnover means fresher produce • Greater choice – wide range of products available • It is easy to examine and compare products • Trolleys make it easier to shop in bulk • Credit cards or cash can be used	• Greater temptation to impulse buy • Less personal • Queues at checkouts especially at peak times • You may have to pack your own groceries • Can be difficult to buy small amounts • May need a car for out-of-town shopping • Can be difficult for older people to find what they need

How shopping has changed

Shopping has changed significantly over the past 50 years.

- Many **small local** shops have **closed down**.
- There are more **large shopping centres** that offer a '**one stop shopping**' experience with many retail outlets. **Parking** is usually available and free with other facilities such as crèches and restaurants.
- Checkouts use barcodes and scanners (**see p. 378**) and some shops have **self-service** checkouts.
- We make less frequent trips to the shops, because we **buy in bulk**, which is more economical.
- **Opening hours** have changed: some shops have online stores, some offer late and early opening times, some even have a 24-hour service.
- **Payment methods** have changed: online and phone buying has increased due to the availability of credit and debit cards. This has also decreased the need for consumers to carry cash, which encourages impulse buying.
- **Environmental awareness** has increased among consumers. The introduction of the plastic bag levy and electrical recycling charge has forced retailers to become more environmentally aware, choosing fair trade and organic products that appeal to consumers (**see p. 102**).
- A higher **awareness of nutrition** has led to more detailed labels and increased availability of 'healthy' meal options in take-away outlets.

- Consumers demand a **higher standard of hygiene** in retail and food outlets, as they are now aware of the link between poor hygiene and illness.
- The increase in the number and variety of retail outlets has led to pricing competition, and more discount shops lead to **price wars**, e.g. Lidl and Aldi vs. Dunnes and SuperValu.
- Consumers are much more **aware of their rights** and the need to shop around for value for money.
- The retail and food industry have adapted products to cater for the **variety of cultures** living in Ireland.

Discovery Learning

Find out why debit and credit cards have gained in popularity over cash and cheques when compared to the past.

Paying for goods and services

You can pay for goods and services in a variety of ways.

Method	Advantages	Disadvantages
Cash	• Quick and easy to use	• Not convenient for very expensive items • May be lost or stolen
Cheque	• Safe and convenient • Filled-in stub acts as proof of purchase • Useful for postal payment	• You need a bank account • Can be easy to overspend • Bank charges apply
Debit card 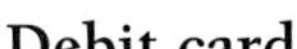 	• Quick and easy to use • Flexible • Cash back available in some shops • PIN or contactless payment methods • Payment taken directly from your account within 1–3 days	• You have to pay bank and government charges

Discovery Learning

Can you find out what the letters PIN and ATM stand for when using a debit or credit card?

Method	Advantages	Disadvantages
Credit card 	• Quick and easy to use • Flexible • PIN or contactless payment methods • Interest-free if paid within 28 days	• Cash back available in some shops is expensive • Easy to overspend • Bank and government charges apply
Direct debit	• Automatic transfer from your bank account • Bills always paid on time	• Cash back available in some shops is expensive • Easy to overspend • Bank and government charges apply

Loss leaders are a small range of goods sold at cost price to bring people into the store. Once they are in, they usually buy more.

Techniques to encourage spending

Consumers are continually being encouraged to buy. Shops study consumers' buying habits and use a variety of techniques to increase spending and impulse buying:

- Background music, nice lighting, warmth and pleasant smells create a relaxing atmosphere
- Attractive displays of tempting items
- Special offers and free samples
- Loyalty cards and money-off vouchers
- Products at checkout, e.g. sweets, health and beauty products and magazines, to tempt and encourage impulse buying
- Luxuries at eye level, essentials lower down.
- Essentials scattered around shop and far away from checkout
- Heavy goods, e.g. vegetables, placed at entrance to get customers to take a trolley
- Associated items placed together, e.g. tea and biscuits
- Own brand items are often the same size and colour as branded products, so you may pick them up instead
- Changing store layout can cause consumers to search for their desired products, again increasing impulse buying

Further Investigation

Watch 'Top 10 Grocery Store Tricks to Get You to Buy More' (9:19) on YouTube to find out more about how shops encourage us to buy.

An **advertisement** is a way to provide consumers with information in order to persuade them to buy a particular product or use a particular service.

Did You Know?

Even though advertising adds to the cost of products, it reduces the cost to the public of TV, radio, concerts, festivals, sporting events, newspapers and magazines.

Functions of advertising

- To provide information about a product or service
- To promote a brand name
- To persuade consumers to buy a product or use a service
- To introduce new products to the market
- To increase sales of the product

Mailshots: the sending of advertisements or brochures to a large number of people at one time through An Post.

Places to advertise

- Television and radio
- Newspapers and magazines
- Cinema, videos and DVDs
- Billboards and bus shelters
- Buses and trains
- Shop windows and packets
- Mailshots and leaflets
- Classified ads
- Email
- Text and online advertising
- Sponsorship of sporting, cultural and musical events

Characteristics of effective advertising:

✓ Captures your attention
✓ Keeps your interest
✓ Creates a desire for the product
✓ Persuades you to buy the product

Did You Know?

Important public information advertisements are usually placed in newspapers and public buildings, e.g. hospitals, on matters like health and social welfare issues.

Techniques used in advertising

Advertising is about persuasion, so, to convince consumers, advertisers use many clever techniques.

- **Attractive images**: beautiful scenes, sunlit countryside, snow-capped mountains or golden sand.
- **Glamour, love and romance**: used to sell luxury items like cars, jewellery and perfumes.
- **Play on emotions**: e.g. guilt ('All good mothers use …'), fear ('Is your family safe?') and other insecurities.
- **Envy and social acceptance**: keeping up with the neighbours, moving up the social ladder.
- **Humour, popular music and bold colours**: e.g. red and gold for luxury.
- **Celebrities**: well-known actors and sportspeople promote products.
- **Clever language**: words that often have no clear meaning, e.g. 'almost',' probably', 'whiter than white'.
- **Patriotism**: the suggestion that purchasing a certain product shows your love for your country, e.g. 'Buy Irish' and 'Think Irish'.
- **No faults pointed out**: no soft drinks manufacturer will point out that drinking too much soft drink will rot your teeth!

Further Investigation

To find out how advertising has evolved, watch 'Psychological Advertising' (9:02) on YouTube.

Discovery Learning

Pick out a TV, radio and magazine advertisement, and look at what persuasive techniques are being used in each. Which do you think is most effective and why?

Further Investigation

To find out more about the Misleading Advertising Directive, visit **ec.europa.eu**, click on 'Consumers', then 'Consumer rights and law', then 'Unfair commercial practices', and finally 'Misleading advertising'.

Controls on advertising

Advertising is controlled by legal and voluntary methods to protect the consumer.

Legal controls	Voluntary controls
Consumer Protection Act 2007 makes it an offence to make a false or misleading claim about goods or services (see p. 362). **The EU Misleading Advertising Directive** can prevent the publication of misleading advertisements, in relation to price and comparison to similar products. **The Employment Equality Act 1998–2015** makes it an offence for job advertisements to discriminate on the grounds of gender, marital status, sexual orientation, religion, age, disability or race.	The Advertising Standards Authority for Ireland (ASAI) is an independent self-regulatory body which was set up and is financed by the advertising industry (see p. 366).

What is a 'good' advertisement?

A good advertisement for the consumer is one that tells us as much as possible about the product – its price, effectiveness, durability, care and use. For the manufacturer, it is one that will sell the product.

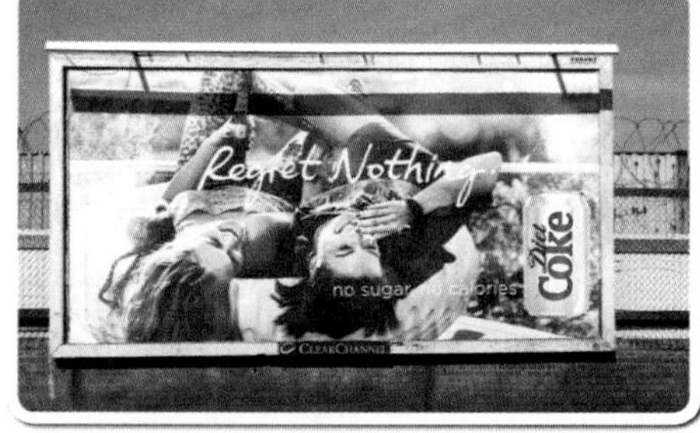

Advantages of advertising

- Provides information on products, events and services
- Provides important information on our rights and entitlements, e.g. health and social welfare
- Creates jobs and employs many people
- Increases sales
- Keeps down the costs of newspapers, magazines and TV programming
- Useful if a consumer wishes to buy or sell products, e.g. car, house

Disadvantages of advertising

- Increases the price of goods and services
- May mislead the consumer
- Can persuade people to buy things they can't afford, leading to debt
- Portrays an unrealistic lifestyle with many products out of the financial reach of many families, causing dissatisfaction
- Reinforces stereotypes, e.g. a mother cleaning the home, a father washing the car
- Can have a negative effect on our environment, with big billboards with loud colourful advertisements

Marketing

Marketing encompasses a wide range of activities used by companies to make sure their products meet the needs of the consumer and ultimately sell more. It includes:

- **Market research**: Companies do market research to identify consumers' likes and dislikes. Information is gathered by questionnaires, surveys, interviews, loyalty cards and phone calls. This data is then used to target potential consumers by improving the product to meet their needs. It is also used in advertising so advertisements will appeal to more people.
- **Advertising** (see above).
- **Packaging and presentation** can attract consumers to a product or service.
- **Sales promotions** like free gifts, 'buy one get one free' offers, competitions and unsolicited mail, e.g. leaflets.
- **Product placement** in shops, in public places or on TV programmes influences consumers unconsciously.
- **Sponsorship of large events**, e.g. Guinness Pro 14 Rugby.
- **Logos** that are easy to recognise, e.g. the Nike 'tick'.
- **Website** and email marketing.
- **Merchandising** at music events, spin offs from films and sports teams

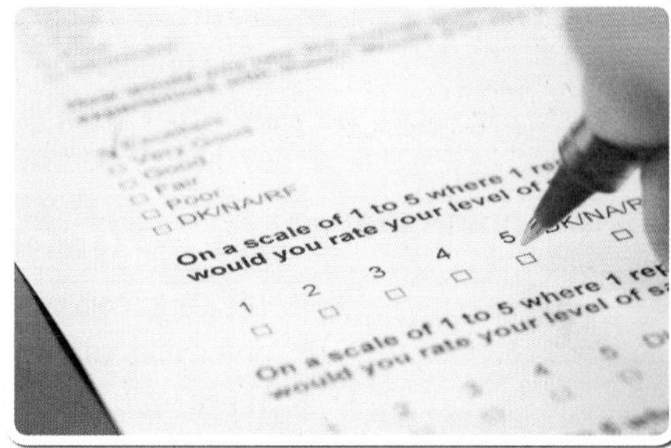

(**Food processing and preservation, see p. 214; environmental protection, see p. 226**)

Packaging

Packaging and **labelling** are very important sources of consumer information, especially when shopping (**see p. 104, 227**).

1. They display date stamps:
   - **'Use by'** is used on foods with a shelf life of less than six weeks. It is the deadline for using a product.
   - **'Sell by'** is the same as 'use by', but it allows for two or three days' storage at home.
   - **'Best before'** is used on foods with a longer shelf life, from 3 to 18 months, e.g. dried or canned foods. This is a guideline for use.

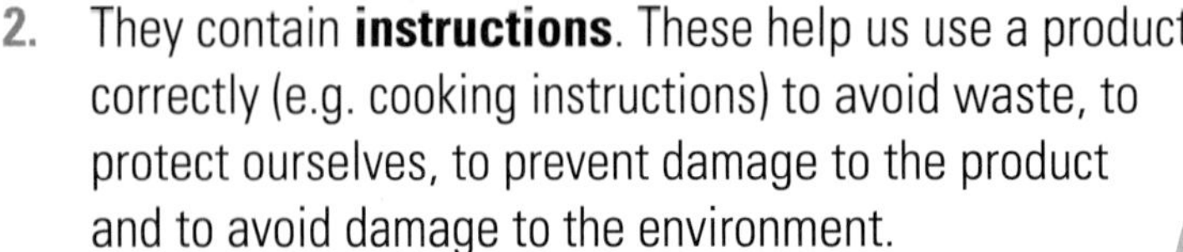

2. They contain **instructions**. These help us use a product correctly (e.g. cooking instructions) to avoid waste, to protect ourselves, to prevent damage to the product and to avoid damage to the environment.
3. They display **unit pricing**. This is the price per unit, per item, per gram, kilogram, millilitre or litre, e.g. per bar or per 100g.
   - Foods that are sold loose and weighed when bought, e.g. fruit and vegetables, must display a unit price.
   - Some prepacked foods, e.g. cheese, meat, that are priced by weight also have the unit price on the label.
   - By law, unit prices must be clearly visible in shops, either on the label, on the shelf edge or on a notice close to the food. This makes it easier to compare products sold in packages of varying weights.

4. They display **barcodes**. Bar codes are sets of blacklines and spaces printed on packaged products.
   - Each product has its own bar code.
   - They are read by passing them over a laser scanner at the checkout.
   - These let the retailer keep an accurate record of sales and how much stock they have.
   - They save work, as products do not need to be individually priced and are quicker at the checkout, and even allow for self-service in some shops.
   - They provide more detailed receipts with names and prices of products.

9 394026 214938

5. They contain environmental information, including the origin and type of product, e.g. organic, fairtrade (see p. 102), and how to disposal of the product/its packaging (see p. 104).

Revision Questions

Use your workbook to revise this chapter •

1. Describe four types of shopping outlets.
2. Discuss four changes in shopping in recent years.
3. Outline the different methods of paying for goods.
4. Evaluate the techniques used by shops to encourage consumers to spend.
5. State the functions of advertising and the characteristics of effective advertising.
6. Evaluate the value of consumer information to a shopper.
7. Discuss four ways to become a more responsible shopper.

Summary

- **Shopping** is part of everyday life. The way we shop has changed over the years and there is greater choice, but there is more temptation to **overspend** and **waste resources**. Therefore, we need to become **responsible** and **ethical shoppers**.
- Shopping **outlets** include small independent shops, specialist shops, supermarkets, department stores, multiple chain stores, discount stores and other shopping outlets e.g. online shopping.
- Many shops have moved from **counter service** to **self-service**. Many small shops have closed down, while more **large shopping centres** are opening. **Opening hours** are longer – some shops have a 24-hour service, 7 days a week. There is a **wider choice** available to consumers.
- Goods can be **paid for** with cash, credit and debit cards, cheques or by direct debit.
- Consumers are continually being **encouraged to buy** using the following techniques: background music, lighting, warmth, pleasant smells, attractive displays, special offers, loyalty cards and money-off vouchers and strategic product placement.
- **Advertising** introduces new products, provides information, promotes a brand name, persuades consumers to buy and increases sales of a product. Advertising outlets include TV, radio, newspapers and magazines, sponsorship, billboards, carrier bags and websites.
- **Marketing** includes advertising, packaging, presentation, product placement, sales promotion, competitions, logos, online and sponsorship of events.
- Becoming a **wise shopper** involves making a list, shopping around for value, availing of special offers, buying in bulk, using own brands, choosing less packaging, checking date stamps and keeping receipts.
- **Environmental awareness** has increased among consumers. The introduction of the plastic bag levy and electrical recycling charge has forced retailers to become more environmentally aware, choosing biodegradable or recyclable packaging, and fair trade and organic products that appeal to consumers.

Strand 3
Textiles and Craft

Section 1: Focus on Fabrics

27 TEXTILES ALL AROUND US

Learning Outcomes 1.8, 2.4, 2.5, 2.10, 2.11, 2.12, 3.6, 3.7, 3.8, 3.9

What I Will Learn

- to appreciate the importance of textiles in our lives
- to identify the functions of clothing
- to discuss the factors that influence our clothing choices
- to explain what is meant by 'fashion'
- to describe the different effects that can be created by the use of colour, texture, form, shape and pattern
- to design an outfit and accessorise it
- to identify the uses of textiles in our homes
- to identify the characteristics and properties of textiles
- to discuss the factors that influence our textile choices in the home
- to design a textile-based household item

Key Words

✓ Textiles	✓ Absorbent
✓ Accessories	✓ Crease-resistant
✓ Fashion	✓ Blend
✓ Trends	✓ Durable
✓ Fads	✓ Resilient
✓ Couturiers	✓ Upholstery
✓ Haute couture	✓ Blend
✓ Prêt-à-porter	✓ Pile
✓ Off the peg	✓ Tog
✓ Characteristics	✓ Upcycling

Textiles

A **textile** is a fabric or cloth.

Textiles are all around us. We wear them and use them in many other different ways, inside and outside our homes.

Clothing

Clothing is one of our basic human needs, but we wear it for a variety of reasons:

- **Protection from the weather**: In Ireland, we can experience extremes of weather, so we need a variety of clothing to keep us warm and protect us from the cold. In winter, some of our clothes need to be windproof and waterproof, and in summer we need protection from the sun while still keeping cool.

- **Identification**: Uniforms are used to identify people, e.g. Gardaí. Uniforms are used in schools, workplaces and sport. Many cultures have national costumes that are associated with their culture, e.g. the sari in India.
- **Safety**: Certain items of clothing are used to protect people. Protective gear can be important for work, e.g. fire fighters wear clothes that protect them from the fire and smoke inhalation. Sportswear also offers protection, e.g. helmets, shin guards and gloves. Clothes protect the wearer when doing dirty jobs or handling harmful substances, e.g. a mechanic, while others wear clothes for hygiene reasons, e.g. food handlers and doctors.

Accessories are the extra items worn to complete a look, or to change the look of what we wear. They express our own personal taste and style or create an interesting look.

- **Self-expression**: A person's personality is represented through their clothing. Some people are casual; some are more formal in their style of dressing. Moods can be expressed through clothing, e.g. at a funeral people wear black. Clothes should be attractive, functional and comfortable. If they flatter us, we feel more confident. Some people wear designer brands as a status symbol.
- **Modesty**: The idea of modesty varies across different cultures, religions and times. Our culture expects us to wear clothes and cover our bodies, but not to the same degree as in the past. On the beach, we are still expected to be reasonably covered up.

Choosing clothes

As competent consumers we must be aware that sustainability comes into play at each stage of a garment's life, from the initial design to the recycling when it's worn out. Sustainable processes are a better way of producing the clothes that we buy and wear, it is kinder to the environment and safer for the people involved in the production process. Many other factors influence our choice of clothing:

Clothes **fit** properly when they are the correct size, flatter the figure and are comfortable to wear.

- Age
- Cost
- Personal taste
- Peers and friends
- Lifestyle and occupation
- Suitability for the purpose or for an occasion
- Care and cleaning
- Colour, style and design
- Quality
- Comfort
- Fit and size
- Origin
- Fashion trends
- Culture
- Where they are made
- The clothes you already have

Did You Know?

Over a million tonnes of textiles are thrown away every year, mostly from domestic sources, of which only 25% are recycled. Can you suggest some ways to improve this situation?

Fashion

Fashion is about any trend that is accepted and followed by lots of people. Many people want to be fashionable. This could mean wearing the latest styles of clothes, using the latest colours and styles in the home or listening to a popular style of music.

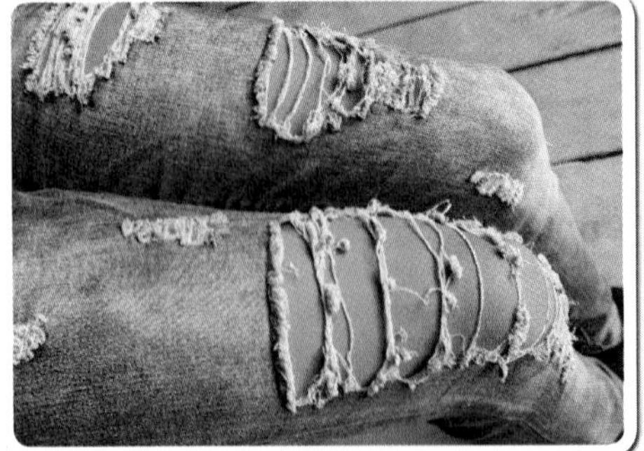

Fashion in clothes can change very quickly or it can last for years, e.g. jeans have been popular for decades because they are durable and comfortable, but the style has changed. Dress lengths and shapes change, too. Some fashions come and go very quickly. These are called fashion fads, e.g. ponchos, ripped jeans, platform shoes.

Fashion is changing constantly, and these changes are referred to as fashion trends. They are influenced by:

- The fashion industry
- Famous people
- Technology
- World events

Discovery Learning

Philip Treacy is a famous Irish hat designer. Ireland has produced some very famous fashion designers, so choose one, let the class know about them and their designs and present to the class in a creative way.

The fashion industry

Fashion designers are called **couturiers**. Twice a year, they show their collections of new designs at fashion shows in London, New York, Paris and Milan. These set fashion trends for the next season, dictating things like how long skirts are, whether clothes are fitted or flowing and what colours are most worn. To create turnover, the industry promotes new colours and styles each season, making last year's fashion out of date, so they sell more clothes.

The clothes modelled at these shows are called '**haute couture**' (high fashion). This means that each design is original, handmade, exclusive and very expensive. '**Prêt-à-porter**' (ready to wear) clothes are the less expensive, machine-made ranges from the top designers. Manufacturers buy or copy these designs using cheaper fabrics and mass production methods to make '**off the peg**' clothes, which are sold much more cheaply.

Street fashion is when everyday clothes rather than designers influence fashion, e.g. grunge, jeans, baseball caps.

Further Investigation

Designers are becoming more aware of how the design, process and consumption of their products impact on the world around them. Can you find a designer or company that are producing sustainable clothing and feed back to your class how they are achieving this?

Famous people

Famous people often set trends with what they wear. 'Influencers' include royalty – like Kate Middleton in the UK – as well as singers, actors, sport stars and people in the media. If they wear a particular garment or accessory, sales of similar items increase.

Some famous people design their own brand of clothes. The rugby player Tommy Bowe and the actress Amy Huberman are examples of Irish people designing their own ranges of clothes and shoes. Other fashion brands use high-profile celebrities to front their campaigns, e.g. Lady Gaga for Versace or Kristen Stewart for Chanel.

Technology

Advances in technology have greatly influenced the production and marketing of fashion. Automation has led to mass production, which has cut the costs and increased production of designer clothes and accessories.

Discovery Learning

Research one eco-friendly fabric. Find out what makes it sustainable and present your findings to the class in a creative way.

The Industrial Revolution saw the beginning of major changes in the production of textiles and clothing. Advances in technology have brought down the costs of manufacturing, making a wide range of textiles and clothing available, through mass production.

- The invention of high speed **spinning machines** replaced hand spinning on a spinning wheel.
- **Automatic weaving and knitting machines** replaced handlooms and knitting needles.
- The **invention of man-made fibres and fabric finishes** gave us a wider range of fabrics, and new fabrics with more desirable properties are constantly being developed (e.g. Tencel).
- Then came the **sewing machine**, which sped up the production of clothes and household items.
- **Computer-aided design (CAD)** programmes allow designers to design textiles and garments on a computer screen. The designs are then easily transferred to the machines that manufacture the products, e.g. laser machines that cut out the fabric.

The internet has had a major impact on the fashion industry. Many brands use social media to promote their products and get consumer feedback. Fashion bloggers such as Pippa O'Conner (***www.pippa.ie***) write about current fashion trends and can have a big influence on consumers. A single post on social media can create a new trend and create huge demand.

Online shopping means that people can access the latest trends online, via apps or on internet-enabled devices, e.g. laptops, tablets or desktop computers.

World events

Today and in the past, world events have influenced fashion trends. World War I changed women's fashions to a more practical style: full skirts disappeared and trousers emerged because women began to work on farms and in factories. Shorter hairstyles became more widespread. During World War II, skirts became shorter, straighter and more fitted, due to fabric shortages.

New technologies that were developed during times of war to help feed and clothe the soldiers have helped develop new mass production methods and new textiles like nylon and polyester.

Textiles and the environment

We live in a very consumer-driven society. This has led to a lot of textile waste and environmental damage (**pollution, see p. 339**):

- Farmers use pesticides to protect textiles as they grow. This can harm wildlife, contaminate other products and get into the food we eat.
- The chemicals that are used to bleach and colour textiles can damage the environment and people's health.
- Most of the machinery used in textile production cause noise a nd air pollution.
- Old clothes that we throw away take up precious space in landfill sites, which fill up rapidly.
- Over-usage of natural resources like plants and water depletes or disturbs the ecological balance.
- The working conditions of many people in the textile and clothing industry are sub-standard and exploitative.

Did You Know?

It has been estimated that an item of clothing still has 70% of its useful life left after it has been discarded. Charity shops sell donated garments to raise funds – this is a great way of recycling unwanted clothing and footwear. Can you find out if there are any charity shops in your local area, and what charities they support?

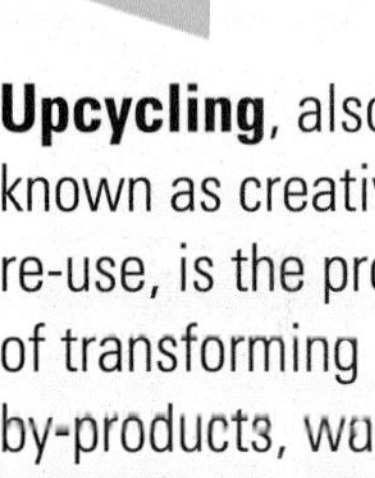

Upcycling, also known as creative re-use, is the process of transforming by-products, waste materials, useless and/or unwanted products into new materials or products of better quality or for better environmental value.

Ways of recycling fashion

1. **Using fabrics made from recycled fibres or products**, e.g. recycled polyester made from used drinking bottles or fabrics made from recycled yarns.
2. **Recycling textile fabrics**, e.g. using unwanted factory surpluses, offcuts or materials which would otherwise be thrown away.
3. **Upcycling or repurposing clothing**, taking second-hand clothing and re-fashioning or repairing it so it is given a second life.

Don't Forget!

By re-using existing fibres and textiles, there is no need to make these textiles from raw materials. This saves on the energy used and pollution caused during manufacturing processes like dying, washing, and scouring.

Further Investigation

Look at how creative Irish students are with junk: visit **www.junkkouture.com**. Does this inspire you?

Design features

It is necessary to be aware of the following design features when designing and upcycling garments.

- **Colour**: The colours we wear should suit our skin tone and the colour of our hair and eyes. Most people choose colours that they like, and which express their personality. Primary colours attract the eye and make a person stand out while neutral colours are classic and safe and do not date.
- **Pattern**: Pattern adds interest and variety to a garment, but is often a matter of fashion and taste. It should be used carefully in household textiles and clothing as too much can appear fussy.
- **Shape**: Shape refers to outline of an object. Colour, pattern and line in fabrics can visually alter the body shape. Well-shaped garments draw attention to our best features and away from our less flattering ones. Line in textiles can create an optical illusion by appearing to change the shape of something.

- **Texture**: Texture refers to the feel or touch of the textile. The texture of household textiles is important. Texture is also significant in clothing, as bulky or very textured fabrics can alter body shape.

Design principles

- **Balance**: All parts of an outfit should work well together
- **Emphasis**: Using colour or pattern to draw attention to a particular feature
- **Proportion**: The parts of an outfit are in proportion to each other and to the figure

The same design features and principles apply to textile design as they do to interior design (**see p. 306**).

Designing an outfit

Factors you need to consider when designing an outfit are:

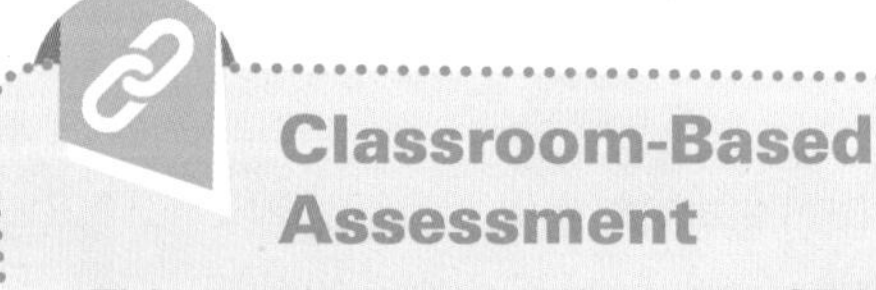

Classroom-Based Assessment

This section can be linked to CBA1: Creative Textiles.

- The occasion
- The function of the garment and its suitability for purpose
- Style and design features
- Current fashion trends
- What complements your body shape and size, and your skin tone
- Resources such as money, equipment, knowledge, skills and time
- Washing and care (**see p. 412**)

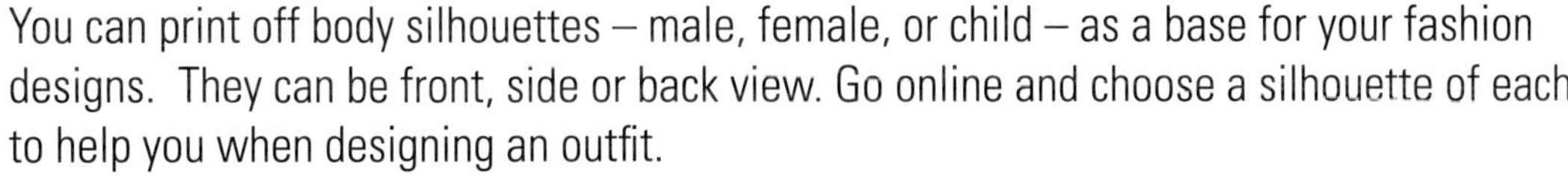

Discovery Learning

You can print off body silhouettes – male, female, or child – as a base for your fashion designs. They can be front, side or back view. Go online and choose a silhouette of each to help you when designing an outfit.
There are a variety of fashion design apps available free for your PC, phone or tablet. Research them, choose one that you find easy to use and explain how it works to your classmates.

Revision Questions

Use your workbook to revise this chapter

1. Explain what a textile is and why they are important in the modern world.
2. Identify the functions of clothing.
3. List the factors that would influence you when buying clothes.
4. Name, sketch and describe a fashionable item of clothing that is popular with teenagers.
5. (a) Design, sketch and describe an outfit you could make for your friend's birthday party. Bearing in mind the costs involved, one part of your outfit **must** be upcycled.
   (b) Justify your fabric, colour and design choices.
   (c) Suggest suitable accessories to make this outfit more attractive.

Household textiles

Upholstery refers to the outer covering of fabric on chairs, sofas and mattresses and the filling inside the padding, springs and webbing. This makes the item more attractive and comfortable.

Textiles have many uses around the house. They add colour, pattern, texture, warmth, comfort and style to the home (**interior design, see p. 306**).

Textiles are used for:

- Soft furnishings, e.g. upholstered furniture, cushions, carpets, rugs, curtains and blinds
- Bed linen, e.g. blankets, duvets, pillows and throws
- Hand, bath and poncho towels
- Kitchen cloths, e.g. tea towels, sponges and oven gloves
- Table linen, e.g. tablecloths, napkins
- Draught excluders

Characteristics and properties of textiles

The characteristics or properties of a fabric refer to how it looks, feels, reacts to heat or water and how it wears.

When choosing a household textile it is important that it has the right properties for its function. The properties and characteristics of textiles include:

cool STRONG WASHABLE absorbent RESILIENT
hardwearing soft light textured DRAPES WELL
rough insulating waterproof DELICATE WARM
STRETCHY heavy SMOOTH closely woven

Finishes can be added to textiles to improve their properties also.

FLAME RESISTANT PRE-SHRUNK stain resistant
crease resistant MOTH-PROOFED colourfast
FADE RESISTANT

Choosing household textiles

When choosing household textiles you need to consider:

1. **Properties**: choose those that are fit for purpose, e.g. towels must be absorbent and soft.
2. **Cost**: the amount of money you have to spend will influence the type and quality of soft furnishings.
3. **Durability**: the fabric must be able to withstand a reasonable amount of wear and tear.
4. **Ease of cleaning**: household textiles should be easy to clean e.g. machine washable.
5. **Colour, pattern, texture and style**: textiles should complement the décor and colour scheme of the room (🔗 **design features, see p. 306**).

Soft furnishings

The function of soft furnishings is to:

- Influence the style and character of a room
- Express our personal tastes
- Make a room attractive by adding colour, texture and pattern to a room
- Add interest, warmth and comfort to the home (🔗 **interior design, see p. 301**)

Upholstery

Upholstery means the outer covering fabric of sofas, armchairs, stools, mattresses and the filling inside it. The outer covering can be made from many fabrics including leather, wool (tweeds), Dralon®, cotton, linen, corduroy and velvet.

In the past, the foam used as padding gave off toxic fumes if it went on fire, so all upholstered furniture must contain Combustion Modified Highly Resilient (CMHR) foam for safety. Now, all upholstered furniture must have one of the following labels:

- **Green swing label**: **Cigarette and match resistant**
  Filling material(s) and covering fabric(s) meet the requirements for resistance to cigarette and match ignition in the 1988 safety regulations (as amended in 1989, 1993 and 2010).

- **Red swing label**: **Not match resistant**
  A triangular label stating that the cover fabric is not match resistant but that the item is lined with the appropriate 'barrier' cloth (**fire safety, see p. 332**).

Did You Know?

All natural, synthetic and regenerated (**see p. 397**) fabrics tend to be flammable. Therefore, non-toxic and durable treatments are applied to fabrics to alter their reaction to flames, e.g. PROBAN®. Fabrics with flame-retardant finishes will self-extinguish when the flames are removed. They do not multiply the flames. Back-coatings are used on upholstery and carpets.

Curtains

When choosing curtains it is important to remember the following:

- Suitable fabrics include cottons, wool, linen, Dralon®, polyester, velvet, voile or cotton net (**textile care, see p. 397**).
- Curtains should hang and drape well, must be pre-shrunk, fade and fire resistant, easy to clean, durable and closely woven to keep out light.
- Curtains should add to the décor of the room, keep out light, give privacy, prevent draughts and insulate the room to keep it warm.
- The amount of money available – if you have a low budget think about upcycling or embellishing older curtains, e.g. dyeing or beading.
- The type of window and style of the room will influence the length (full length or short) and width (they should be 2–2½ times the width of the window).
- Lined curtains hang better, are less likely to fade and provide better insulation for a home (**why is that important?**).
- Blinds are an alternative to curtains or can be used with curtains to add to the décor of the room.

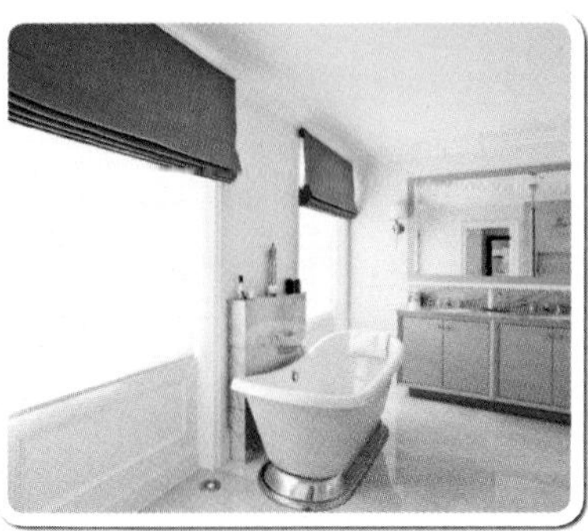

Bed clothes

- **Bed linen**: sheets, pillowcases and duvet covers are made from cotton, polyester cotton, linen or silk. Polyester cotton is the cheapest, easiest to wash, dry and iron. Bed linen is available in a wide range of colours and patterns which can add to the attractiveness of a room. Complete sets are available to suit all styles and tastes.
- **Blankets and throws** are made from wool, acrylic, cotton or a blend of these. Acrylic is cheaper and easier to clean but not as warm or durable as wool. Fleece blankets are popular now.
- **Duvets** are made of insulating material like down or feathers or a polyester wadding sandwiched between two layers of fabric. The warmth of a duvet is described in its 'tog rating', from 4.5 tog (relatively cool) up to 15 tog (very warm).
- **Cushions** made from cotton, polyester cotton, linen, wool or silk are used to decorate sofas, chairs and beds.

A **blend** is a mixture of fabrics that gives better properties and costs less.

Pile is the upper surface of a carpet.

Resilient fibres are strong, tough and keep their shape.

Carpets

- Modern carpets can be made from a variety of fabrics, including wool, acrylic, nylon, cotton or a blend of these. Carpet blends that consist of 80% wool and 20% nylon are generally very good quality and hard wearing.
- Some carpets are woven (**see p. 407**): the pile is woven into a canvas backing, making them stronger and more durable. In others, the pile is fixed into a backing using an adhesive.
- The pile can be long, short, looped or embossed (where piles of different lengths are combined to form a pattern).

Carpets should be:

✓ Resilient
✓ Warm
✓ Sound absorbing
✓ Moth proof
✓ Fire resistant
✓ Durable
✓ Easy to clean
✓ Easy to maintain

- Carpets are graded by how hardwearing they are:
  - **Light domestic**: suitable for bedrooms where there would be light use
  - **Medium domestic**: for living rooms where there would be more use
  - **Heavy domestic**: used in rooms with a lot of foot traffic like the living rooms, halls and stairs

Designing a household item

Textiles have a wide variety of uses in the home and many household items can be easily made providing a great way to use recycled materials or upcycle older items.

What you need to consider:

- The function of the item and its suitability for purpose
- Style and design features
- Current interior design trends
- What complements the décor of the room
- Resources such as money, equipment, knowledge, skills and time
- Washing and care (see p. 412)

Classroom-Based Assessment

This section can be linked to CBA1: Creative Textiles.

What you could make:

cushion cover PILLOWCASE tissue box cover TOILET BAG
oven gloves tea cosy DRAUGHT EXCLUDER
laundry bag storage unit picture wall hanging NAPKIN AND NAPKIN HOLDER

Can you think of anything else?

Discovery Learning

To get inspiration and ideas for upcycling or repurposing textile items, look on craft websites such as ***www.pinterest.ie*** and ***www.craftsy.com***.

Revision Questions

1. List some uses of textiles in our homes.
2. Discuss the properties that should be considered when choosing fabric for household textiles.
3. Name, sketch and describe a textile-based household item that you could make using cotton fabric.

Summary

- Textiles are used in **clothing** and in our **homes**.
- Clothing is one of our basic human **needs**. We need clothing for a variety of reasons: **protection** from the weather, **identification**, **safety**, **self-expression** and **modesty**.
- Many factors influence our **choice** of clothing including age, cost, personal tastes, peers and friends, lifestyle and occupation, suitability for the purpose or for an occasion, care and cleaning, colour, style and design, quality, comfort, fit and size, origin, fashion trends, culture, where it is made and the clothes you already have.
- **Accessories** are the extra items worn to complete a look, or to change the look of what we wear. They express our own personal taste and style or create an interesting look.
- Fashion is about any **trend** that is accepted and followed by lots of people. Fashion is changing constantly. These changes are referred to as fashion trends. They are influenced by the **fashion industry**, **famous people**, **technology** and **world events**.
- **Technology** has had a major impact on the textile industry. Machines took over jobs that were previously very labour-intensive. Advances in technology have brought down the costs of manufacturing, making a wide range of textiles and clothing available through mass production.
- We live in very **consumer-driven** society and this has led to a lot of textile **waste** and **environmental damage** because pesticides, chemicals, and the machinery used in textile production can kill wildlife, damage the environment and cause noise, sound and air pollution. They disturb the ecological balance and many textile workers work in sub-standard conditions.
- The **design features** that apply to textiles are colour, pattern, shape and texture, and the design principles of balance, emphasis and proportion apply also.
- When **designing** an **outfit** consider the occasion, function of the garment, its suitability for purpose, the style and design features and current fashion trends. Look at what complements your body, shape, size and your skin tone; resources such as money, equipment, knowledge, skills and time; and how to wash and care for it.
- **Textiles** have many uses in our homes. They add colour, pattern, texture, warmth, comfort and style to the home.

- **Soft furnishings** include upholstered furniture, cushions, carpets, rugs, curtains and blinds, bed and table linen, towels, kitchen cloths and draught excluders.
- The **characteristics** or **properties** of a fabric refer to how it looks, feels, reacts to heat or water and how it wears. When choosing a household textile it is important that it has the right properties for its function.
- When choosing household textiles you need to consider the **properties**, **cost**, **durability**, ease of **cleaning**, **colour**, **pattern**, **texture** and **style**.
- The **function of soft furnishings** is to influence the style and character of a room, express our personal tastes, make a room attractive by adding colour, texture and pattern to a room and add interest, warmth and comfort to the home.
- **Upholstery** means the outer covering fabric of sofas, armchairs, stools, mattresses and the filling inside it. Upholstered furniture must contain Combustion Modified Highly Resilient (CMHR) foam for safety and must have a green or red fire safety label.
- **When choosing curtains** they should hang and drape well, be pre-shrunk, fade and fire resistant, easy to clean, durable and be closely woven to keep out light. Lined curtains hang better, are less likely to fade and provide better insulation for a home. Blinds are an alternative to curtains or can be used with curtains to add to the décor of the room.
- **Bed linen** made from a blend of polyester cotton is the cheapest, easiest to wash, dry and iron. Bed linen is available in a wide range of colours and patterns, which can add to the attractiveness of a room.
- **Carpet** blends that consist of 80% wool and 20% nylon are generally very good quality and hard wearing. Some carpets are woven: the pile is woven into a canvas backing, making them stronger and more durable. In others, the pile is fixed into a backing using an adhesive. The pile can be long, short, looped or embossed. Carpets should be resilient, warm, absorb sound, and be moth-proofed, fire resistant, durable, easy to clean and easy to maintain. Carpets are graded by how hardwearing they are; **light**, **medium** or **heavy domestic**.
- Many textile-based household items can be easily made providing a great way to use recycled materials or **upcycle** older items.
- You must consider the **function** of the item and its suitability for purpose, the style and design features, current interior design trends and what complements the décor of the room. Resources such as money, equipment, knowledge, skills and time and how to wash and care for it must be considered, too.

28 FABRIC CARE

Learning Outcomes 1.8, 2.4, 2.5, 2.7, 2.8, 2.9, 2.10, 2.11, 2.12, 3.6, 3.7, 3.8, 3.9

What I Will Learn

- to classify fabrics into natural and man-made
- to describe how each fabric is produced
- to discuss the properties of each fabric
- to identify some uses of each fabric
- to explain what a blended fabric is
- to discuss the advantages of using blended fabrics
- to explain how to convert fibres into fabrics
- to investigate finishes that are applied to fabrics and discuss why they are used
- to identify fabric finishes that can be applied to fabrics to embellish them
- to discuss how to care for clothing and household textiles
- to understand care labelling
- to prepare clothes and household textiles for laundering
- to use a washing machine
- to explain how to remove stains
- to choose detergents and conditioners
- to use a dryer and an iron correctly
- to apply this knowledge in a practical way

Key Words

✓ Fibres
✓ Labels
✓ Yarn
✓ Weaving
✓ Natural
✓ Knitting
✓ Bonding
✓ Finishes
✓ Polishing
✓ Brushing
✓ Man-made
✓ Embellish
✓ Synthetic
✓ Dyeing
✓ Printing
✓ Washing
✓ Stain removal
✓ Regenerated
✓ Detergent
✓ Conditioner
✓ Drying
✓ Bleaching
✓ Blend
✓ Ironing

Textile care

Textiles get dirty and stain easily. It is important to clean them before the dirt and stains become ingrained into the fabric, because then they are more difficult to remove. Clean clothes that are well cared for look better and last much longer, so it is important to look at fabrics and how to care for them.

Fibres are tiny hair-like threads. They are twisted together into **yarn** and the yarn is then made into **fabric**.

Fibres can be divided or classified into two groups: **natural** fibres and **man-made** fibres. Each group can be divided again.

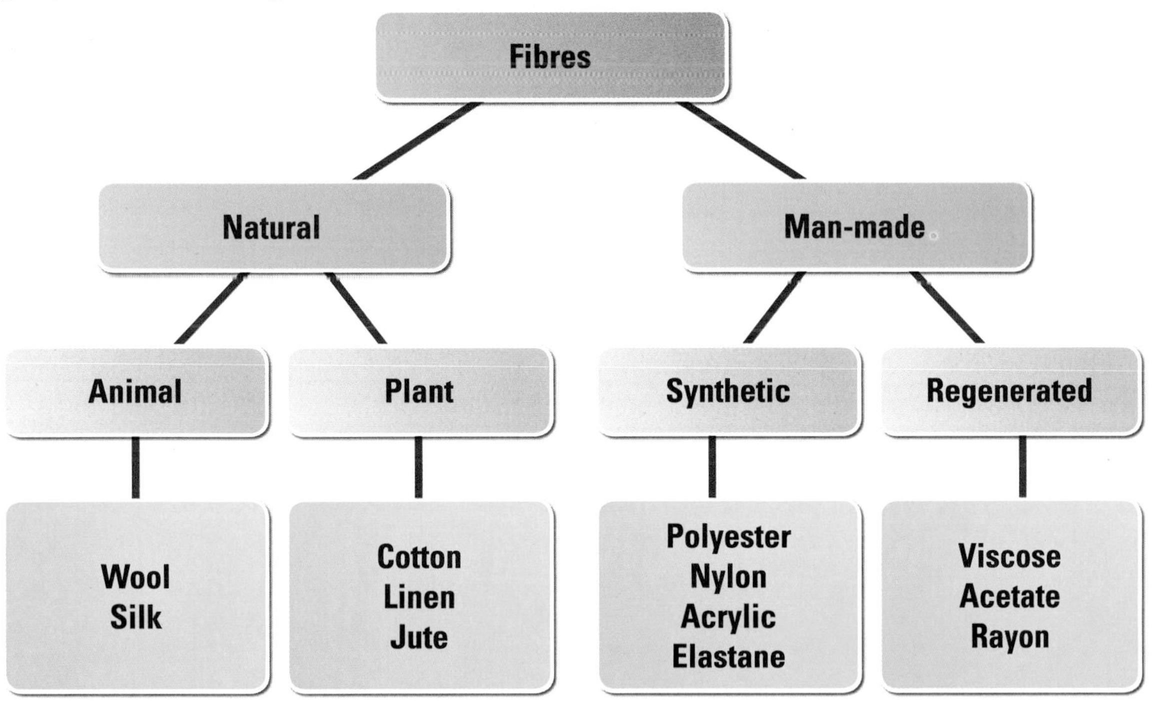

Regenerated fabrics are made from natural fibres to which chemicals are added.

The care of a textile will depend on the fibre used, how it is constructed and any finishes that are applied. The care label of each textile item describes accurately how the textile should be cared for.

Natural fibres

Animal sources

Wool

Wool is a natural animal fibre. Most wool comes from sheep, but other varieties can also come from goats, alpacas, rabbits and camels.

Cashmere goat

Angora rabbit

Mohair goat

Alpaca

Merino sheep

Camel

Wool fibres are covered in scales, which interlink and trap air, making wool a good insulator.

Examples: Tweed, gabardine, jersey, velour, flannel

Production: The animal is sheared annually. The fleece is graded, washed and dried, then the fibres are teased apart with wire covered brushes (**carding**). Finally, the fibres are spun into a yarn, which is used to make fabric.

Uses in clothing: coats, shawls and scarves, trousers, skirts, dresses, jumpers and hats.

Uses in household items: carpets, rugs, upholstry, cushions, blankets and throws.

Properties of wool	
Desirable:	**Undesirable:**
Warm	Irritates sensitive skin
Insulating	Scorches easily
Absorbent	Can be damaged by moths
Soft	Weak when wet
Comfortable	Can shrink and felt if washed carelessly
Durable	Pills easily
Elastic	
Resilient	
Does not burn easily	

Did You Know?

Pilling occurs when groups of fibres break, tangle, and mat together, making the texture of the garment rough and really unattractive.

Can you find out how to prevent pilling and how to remove it after it occurs?

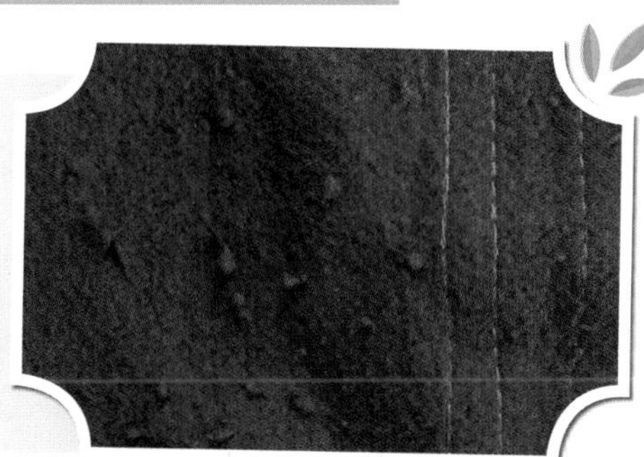

The Woolmark is the internationally-recognised symbol for 100% wool items.

The Woolmark Blend symbol is for any fabric that contains 50% to 99% wool.

The Wool Blend symbol is for any fabric that contains 30% to 49% wool.

Caring for wool:

- Remove any pilling.
- Turn garment inside out to prevent pilling during washing.
- Handwash in tepid water or use a machine setting for wool.
- Never wring or stretch when wet.
- Use a towel to absorb the water and dry flat.
- Do not tumble dry (**why?**).
- Press with a cool iron.

Further Investigation

To learn more about where our wool comes from, watch 'How It's Made: Wool' (5:34) on YouTube. For tips on how to take care of your woolly jumpers, go to **www.marthastewart.com**, search for 'How to care for your sweaters' and watch the video.

Silk

Silk is a natural animal fibre that comes from the **silkworm**.

Silk fibres are smooth, lightweight and are a **continuous filament**.

Examples: raw silk, Charmeuse, chiffon, satin, crêpe de chine, taffeta

Did You Know?
The production of silk is called **sericulture**.

Production: A silk moth lays eggs onto mulberry leaves. These eggs hatch into silkworm larvae, which feed on the mulberry leaves. The larva – or worm – then spins a cocoon of silk around itself. If left alone, it will transform into a moth and lay more eggs. However, if the cocoon is immersed in hot water, the silk softens and the filament is drawn off (raw silk). This is then twisted and spun into thicker yarn, which is used to make fabric.

Uses in clothing: evening and bridal wear, shawls and scarves, shirts, ties and dresses.

Uses in household items: lampshades, curtains, bedlinen and cushions.

Properties of silk	
Desirable:	**Undesirable:**
Lightweight but warm Crease resistant Usually smooth to the touch Absorbent Soft Comfortable Drapes well Dyes well	Expensive Can be damaged by chemicals, sunlight and moths Flammable Weak when wet

Discovery Learning

For a long time, making silk meant killing the silkworms. But Kusuma Rajaiah, an Indian man, has developed a new technique for producing silk that does not kill the silkworms. Find out the advantages and disadvantages of producing so-called 'Ahimsa' silk.

Did You Know?

Leather is a durable and flexible material created by tanning animal rawhide (skin). Leather can be made from cows, pigs, goats, and sheep and exotic animals such as alligators, ostriches, and kangaroos and even dogs and cats, who are slaughtered for their meat and skin in China.

Caring for silk:

- Never spray silk with perfume or deodorant
- Never bleach silk or expose it to direct sunlight for long periods of time
- Don't spray silk with water while ironing or treat individual stains with water
- Never wring or stretch when wet
- Hand wash silk clothes in cold water
- Rinse well
- Use a towel to absorb the water and dry flat
- Do not tumble dry
- Press with a cool iron

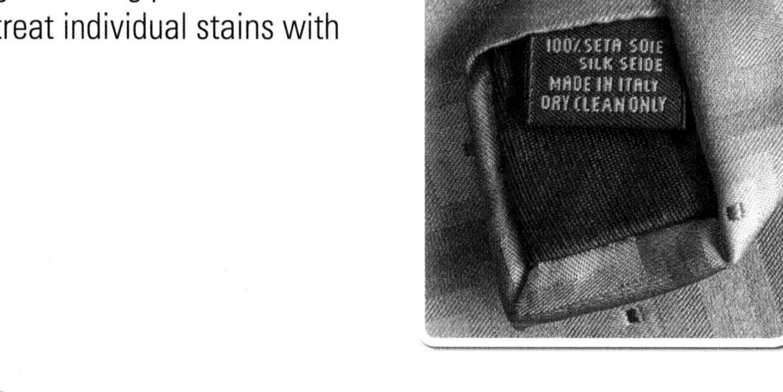

Further Investigation

To learn more about where our silk comes from, watch 'How It Is Made: Silk' (5:06) on YouTube.

Some fabrics are made from **continuous filaments** which are long smooth thin, unbroken threads which are twisted to make a very smooth yarn and very smooth silky fabrics, e.g. silk and viscose. The filament can be chopped to make short **staple fibres**, which are fluffier, thicker and softer, e.g. wool, cotton, linen and some man-made fibres.

Plant sources

Cotton

Cotton is a natural fibre that comes from the cotton plant. Cotton is a soft, fluffy, staple fibre that grows in a 'boll', or protective case, around the seeds of the cotton plant. It grows in hot climates, in countries like the USA, India and Egypt.

Examples: Muslin, flannelette, denim, towelling, corduroy, canvas, velvet, lawn, poplin.

Production: When the flowers fall from the cotton plant, pods called 'bolls' develop. When the seeds inside them ripen, the bolls burst open, releasing fluffy white fibres. The bolls are picked, cleaned and graded. The seeds are removed, then the fibres are combed into strands and spun into yarn, which is used to make cotton fabric.

Uses in clothing: shirts, blouses, t-shirts, sweatshirts, joggers, jeans, skirts and dresses.

Uses in household items: towels, kitchen cloths, curtains, cushions, bedlinen and duvet covers, upholstry.

Properties of cotton	
Desirable:	**Undesirable:**
Strong wet or dry	Creases easily
Absorbs moisture	Little elasticity
Cool, good for summer	Can be damaged by mildew
Easy to wash and dry	Shrinks unless pre-shrunk
Can be bleached and dyed	Burns easily
Easy to dry clean	
Does not pill easily	
Comfortable	

Did You Know?

Producing a single pair of jeans requires around 11,000 litres of water! All this water goes into growing cotton (production process) and then wet processing, i.e. dyeing, treating and washing the fabric.

Discovery Learning

Find out what denim companies are doing to make their products more sustainable. Feed back to the class.

Did You Know?

While cotton is planted in only 2.4% of agricultural land, it accounts for nearly 11% of pesticide sales in the world.

Caring for cotton:
- Machine wash in cold water
- Do not soak
- Do not bleach
- Only tumble dry on low heat
- Press with a warm iron

Further Investigation

To learn more about where cotton comes from, watch 'How It's Made: Cotton Yarn' (4:49) on YouTube.

Linen

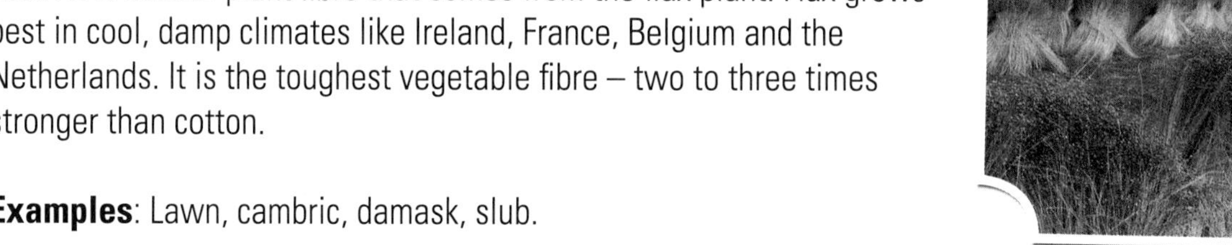

Linen is a natural plant fibre that comes from the flax plant. Flax grows best in cool, damp climates like Ireland, France, Belgium and the Netherlands. It is the toughest vegetable fibre – two to three times stronger than cotton.

Examples: Lawn, cambric, damask, slub.

Production: The stem is pulled and left to soak until the tough, outer part rots away, exposing the inner fibres (retting). These fibres are dried and combed, and are then spun into yarn, which is bleached and dyed.

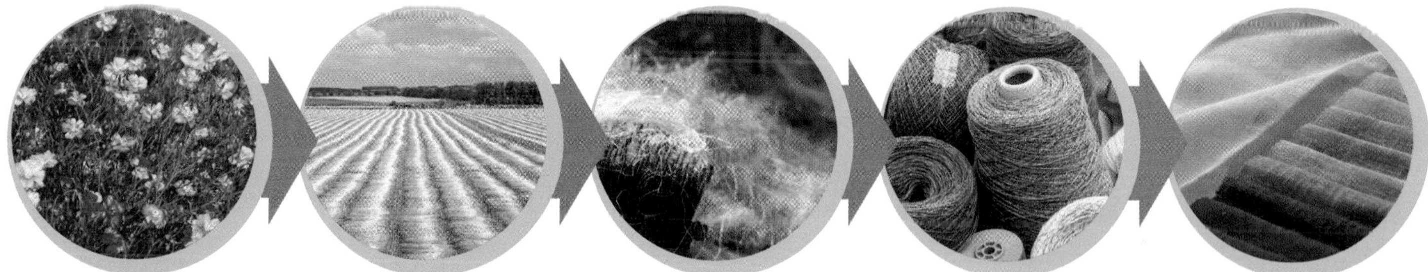

Uses in clothing: shirts, jackets, trousers, suits, dresses, coats.

Uses in household items: curtains, cushions, tablecloths, tea towels.

Properties of linen	
Desirable:	**Undesirable:**
Strong wet or dry	Creases very easily
Absorbs moisture	Shrinks easily
Cool	Can be damaged by mildew
Easy to wash and dry	Difficult to dye
Dirt resistant	Burns easily
Can be bleached and dyed	
Easy to dry clean	
Smooth and lint-free	
Comfortable to wear	

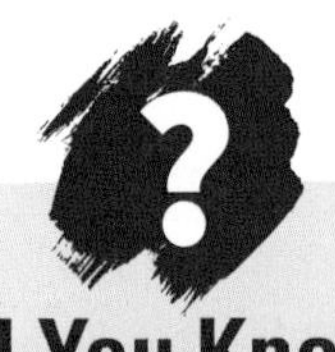

Did You Know?

The word 'linen' is derived from the Latin for the flax plant, which is '*linum*', and the earlier Greek '*linon*'. Linen is one of the world's oldest fabrics – mummies have been found wrapped in linen shrouds dating as far back as 4500 BC.

Discovery Learning

Find out about the Irish linen industry, which was established in the 17th century. Present your findings to your classmates in a creative way.

Caring for linen:

- Machine wash in cold water
- Do not bleach or tumble dry
- Line dry, out of direct sunlight
- Press with a warm iron
- Do not dry clean

CARE INSTRUCTIONS

Cold Machine Wash
Mild Detergent
Do not Bleach
Do not Tumble Dry
Line Dry in Shade
Warm Iron
Do Not Dry Clean

100% Linen

Further Investigation

To learn more about where linen comes from, watch 'How Linen is Made' (4:22) on YouTube.

Did You Know?

Jute is known as the 'Golden Fibre' due to its golden brown colour and its importance in terms of usage, production and global consumption. It is the fibre used to make hessian sacks, twine and sandals, and by designers in their clothes collections. Jute is environmentally friendly as well as being one of the most affordable fibres, it is easy to grow and has a high yield per acre.

Further Investigation

To find out more about jute, watch 'Jute production' (6:30) on YouTube.

Man-made fabrics

Man-made fabrics are also known as 'artificial' fabrics. They were invented at the end of the 19th century, when scientists looked at how the silkworm produced cellulose fibres and created an artificial silk, known as rayon. Later, synthetic fibres were invented that were made entirely from chemicals such as petroleum. The first called nylon was made in the late 1930s and it was used to replace silk for stockings and in parachutes.

Synthetic fibres

What are they? These fibres were developed in a laboratory using coal, oil and chemicals.

Examples and uses

Fabric	Clothes	Household items
Nylon	• Tights • Waterproof jackets • Linings • Underwear	• Carpets • Shopping bags • Tents • Sleeping bags
Polyester	• Suits • Trousers • Shirts and blouses • Dresses	• Duvets • Sheets • Pillowcases • Cushions • Wadding
Acrylic (including Dralon®)	• Jumpers • Jacket linings	• Upholstery • Blankets • Cushions
Elastane (including Lycra®)	• Sportswear • Leggings	• Upholstery

Properties

- Elastic
- Strong
- Warm
- Crease resistant

Regenerated fibres

What are they? These fibres come from plant materials (wood, seaweed, cotton or cellulose waste) with chemicals added to them.

Examples and uses

Fabric	Clothes	Household items
Viscose (Tencel) Rayon	• Scarves • Shawls • Formal dresses • Shirts	• Netted cloths • Mop heads • Napkins • Tablecloths • Curtains
Acetate	• Coats • Jackets • Shirts • Cheap lace	• Kitchen cloths • Mop heads

Properties

- Smooth
- Cool
- Easily dyed
- Drapes well

Man-made fibre production

- The raw materials (wood, seaweed, cotton, cellulose waste, petroleum, etc.) are mixed with chemicals.
- The resulting liquid is heated, then forced through a spinneret (nozzle).
- This cools and dries to form the fibres in a continuous filament, which is drawn and twisted to make yarn, or chopped to make staple fibres.

Did You Know?

All man-made fibres are flammable, and some (like nylon) cling, cause static and are uncomfortable to wear in hot weather. Regenerated fabrics are not very strong.

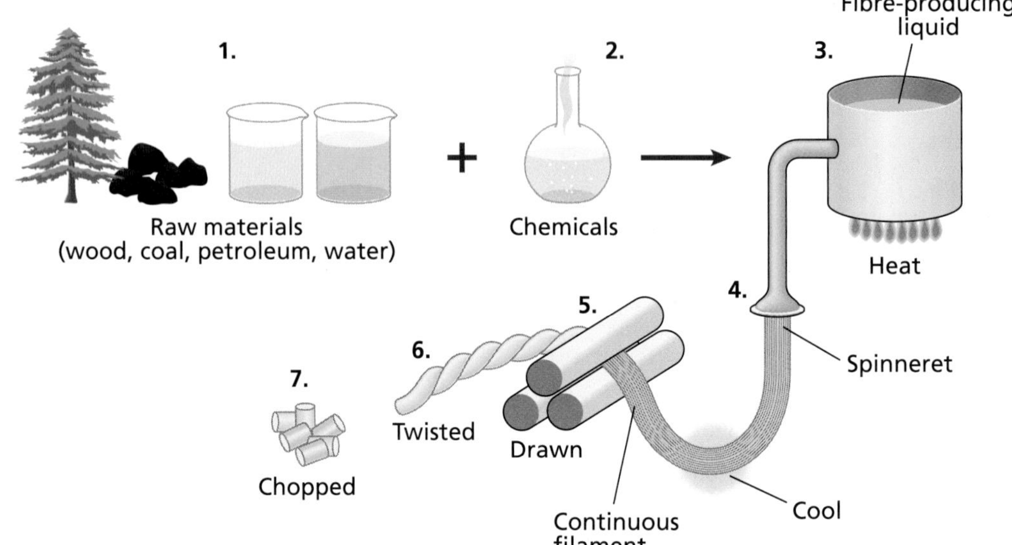

Did You Know?

'Denier' refers to the thickness of man-made fibres. The lower the number, the finer the yarn. Tights have a denier rating on the packet, so the higher it is, the thicker (and warmer) the tights are.

Further Investigation

To find out how fibre is turned into fabric, watch 'Fibre to Fabrics' (3:18) on YouTube.

Changing fibres into fabric

Spinning is the process of twisting fibres into yarn. It gives strength to the fibres; a loose twist produces soft, bulky yarn while a tight twist produces a finer, stronger yarn.

Spinning produces a single yarn (or 'thread'). These can then be twisted together to produce plied yarns, e.g. 'two ply' is two threads twisted together, 'three ply' is three threads twisted together, and so on.

Blended fabrics are created when two or more different kinds of fibres are mixed together (natural and man-made) to create a new fabric with unique properties. For example, a polyester/cotton blend combines the coolness of cotton with the crease resistance and easy-care qualities of polyester. An 80% wool/20% nylon blend often used in carpets combines the strength of nylon with the resilience of wool.

Yarn is changed into fabric by weaving, knitting or bonding.

Weaving

Weaving is the most common method of producing fabric. Woven fabric is made using a large tool called a loom.

Lines of strong yarn are stretched lengthwise on the loom: these are called warp threads. Then another set of weaker threads are passed over and under the warp threads from one side to the other: these are the weft threads. The selvage is the finished edge of the fabric, which does not fray. The **straight grain** means the direction in which the warp threads run in a fabric. **Bias** is the diagonal line of a fabric; the fabric stretches a little bit when it is pulled along this line. Examples of woven fabrics include tweed, denim, gabardine and towelling.

Further Investigation

If you would like to find out how to weave fabric, watch 'How To Weave On A Traditional Loom' (3:01) on YouTube.

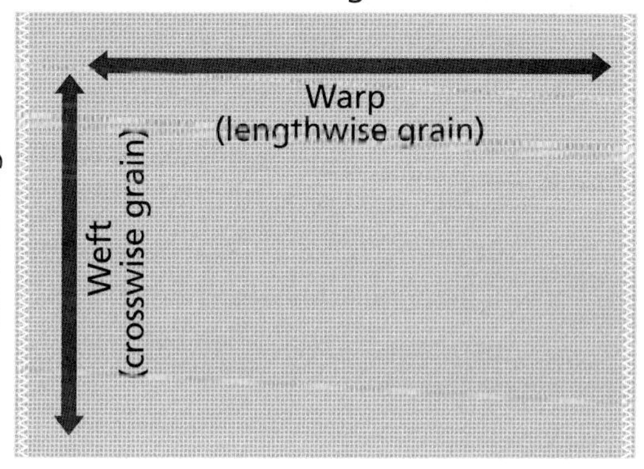

Knitting

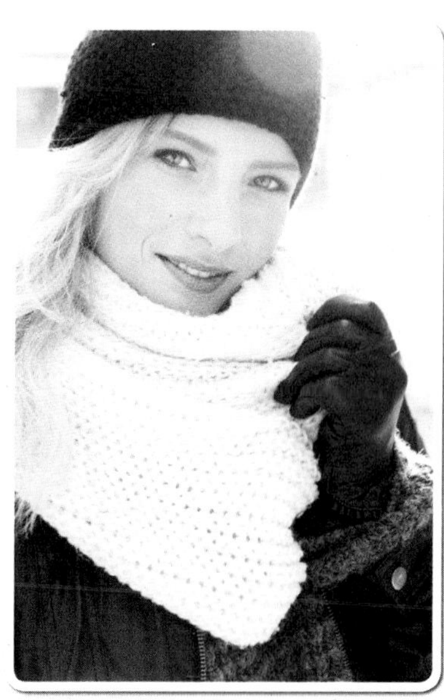

Knitting links or interlocks loops of yarn together. This can be done either by hand or by machine. All knitted fabrics are stretchy, the amount of stretch depends on the fibre and the stitch used. There is a huge variety of knitting stitches, all of which give different effects, like chunky (e.g. Aran) or decorative (e.g. lacy), but most are based on the two basic stitches: plain and purl. Knitting results in stretchy, comfortable, warm and crease-resistant fabrics. It is used in jumpers, hats, scarves socks and sportswear.

Bonding

Bonded or non-woven fabrics are made by bonding short staple fibres together using heat, moisture, pressure and adhesive. Examples of bonded fabrics include felt and interfacings. Bonded fabrics are used for hats, blankets, carpet underlays, and disposable cloths and

clothes, such as hospital gowns. They are cheap to produce, do not fray and hold their shape, but do not wear well. Felt can be damaged by water and bonded fabrics do not trap air, so are not as warm.

Finishes

Finishes are applied to fabrics to make caring for them easier, and to improve their appearance and performance. Some finishes need special treatment during cleaning, so be sure to read the care labels.

Finishes that improve the appearance of fabrics

Colour and pattern can be applied to fabric in a variety of ways.

> **Classroom-Based Assessment**
> This section can be linked to CBA1: Creative Textiles.

1. Dyeing

- Textiles can be dyed as fibres, yarn, fabric, or as finished garments or household items.
- First, the textiles are washed and bleached, so that the colour of the dye can be absorbed easily. This is assisted by a substance called a **mordant**, which enables the textiles to take up the dye.
- Before commercial dyes were available, people used natural dyes made from fruit and vegetables. Commercial dyes, however, are more permanent and are colourfast, which means they don't wash out.
- Tie-dyeing and batik are techniques that allow patterns to be created.

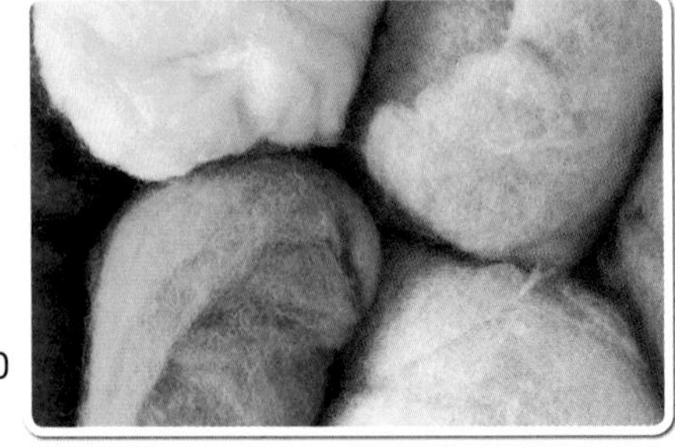

2. Printing

- Printing involves applying dyes to the surface of fabric in a pattern or a design on one side of the fabric only.
- It can be applied using a block, screen or roller. You can paint free-hand onto the surface too.

Don't Forget!
Pattern and texture can also be introduced by the arrangement of yarn in woven and knitted fabrics and with fibres in non-woven fabrics.

Fabric finishes that enhance the properties of a fabric

Finish	Purpose	Uses
Anti-static	Prevents the build-up of static which causes clinging and slight shocks	Underwear, clothes and curtains, also in fabric conditioners and tumble dryer sheets
Brushing	Makes fabrics warmer by giving them a fluffy texture, trapping air thereby acting as an insulator	Wool blankets, brushed nylon and brushed cotton, e.g. flannelette
Crease resistance ('easy care')	Reduces creasing, making it easier to iron	Cotton and rayon clothing and furnishing fabrics
Flame-resistant (e.g. PROBAN®)	Makes fabric more resistant to fire	Children's nightwear and furnishing fabrics
Mothproof	Protects fabrics from moths	Clothes, furniture and carpets
Polishing ('mercerising')	Makes fabric smoother and gives it a sheen	Cotton clothing and furnishing fabrics, embroidery and sewing threads
Permanent pleating	Saves ironing as pleats do not fall out	Clothes, e.g. shirts, skirts and trousers, soft furnishings, e.g. curtains and cushions
Shrink resistance	Prevents shrinkage	Natural and synthetic clothing and furnishing fabrics
Stretch finish	Makes fabrics more stretchy, flexible and comfortable	Swimwear, tights and trousers
Stiffening	Gives a crisp finish	Shirt collars and cuffs
Stain repellent (e.g. Scotchgard™)	Makes fabric more resistant to stains	Household textiles, such as upholstery and carpets, and clothing fabrics
Waterproofing (e.g. Scotchgard™)	Prevents water soaking through the fabric	Rainwear

Revision Questions

1. Classify fabrics into natural and man-made, and suggest a use for each.
2. Explain what a blended fabric is and the advantages of using blended fabrics.
3. Explain how to convert fibres into fabrics.
4. Investigate finishes that are applied to fabrics and discuss why they are used.

Caring for clothes

Clothes that are well looked after last longer and look better.

- Wash soiled or stained clothing as soon as you can. The longer they are left the harder it will be to remove the stains and dirt.
- Hang clothes straight after use on shaped or padded hangers; close any zips and buttons.
- Fold knitwear and store it flat.
- Mend clothes before storing, e.g. fix hems, sew on buttons.
- Polish shoes and leather accessories to preserve them and keep them looking smart.
- Store clothes in a wardrobe or in drawers.

Further Investigation

Why do we hang some clothes and fold others? Can you come up with a set of guidelines for the best way to arrange a wardrobe?

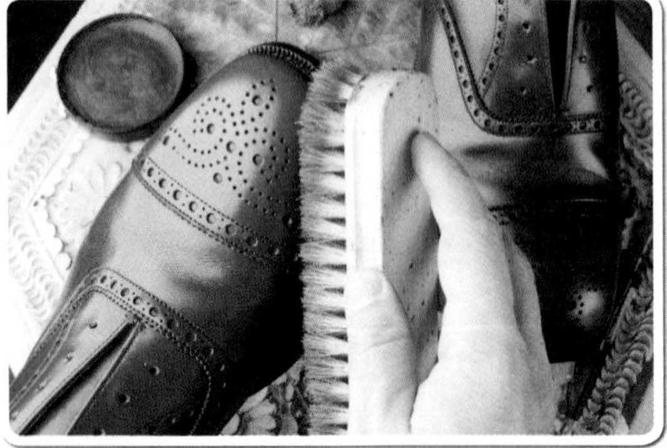

Care labelling

Care labels are found on most clothes and household items. Care labels may contain written instructions or symbols devised by the International Care Labelling System. They can be on a woven or printed label that is sewn into a garment which shows the manufacturer's name, the size, fibre content and care information.

Why care labels are important:

- To help you make an **informed decision** when buying clothing.
- They provide **useful information** that can save you time and money.
- Your clothes **last longer** if you know how to care for them properly.
- A garment that can only be **dry cleaned** could end up being very **costly**.
- If you have an **allergic reaction** to certain fibres (e.g. wool) you can avoid these.

Care label law:

- Clothing and other textile products for sale in the EU must be labelled with the fibre content, e.g. '100% cotton' or '50% wool, 50% acrylic'.
- Manufacturers do not have to put the country of origin or any wash symbols on the care label, but most do anyway.

Further Investigation

To find out more about the standards of product labelling of clothes and household products, go to **www.citizensinformation.ie**, scroll down the home page and click on 'Consumer Affairs'.

Care labelling instructions

Many of the care label instructions are in symbols. The International Care Labelling System has five basic symbols:

- A **washtub** showing the washing temperature to be used

- An **iron** with dots to indicate the temperature to be used

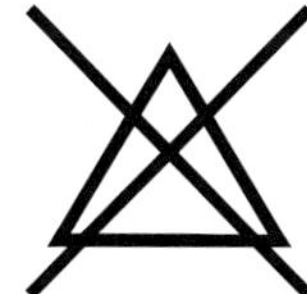

- A **triangle** which indicates if chlorine bleach can be used

- A **circle** for dry cleaning instructions for the dry cleaner

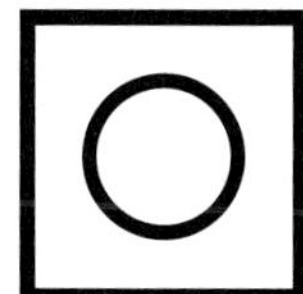

- A **square** containing drying instructions

Drying	Ironing	Bleach	Dry cleaning
Dry flat	Hot iron	Bleach may be used	A
Line dry	Warm iron	Do not bleach	P
Drip dry	Cool iron		F
Tumble dry	Do not iron		Do not dry clean
Do not tumble dry			

Washing instructions

There are three basic factors to consider when machine washing textiles:

- **Water temperature**, which is written inside the washtub symbol.
- **Wash action**: How fast the machine moves the clothes around during the cycle.
- The bar symbol under the washtub tells you the correct wash action and spin length for the item you are washing.
  - No bar indicates maximum washing action and spin.
  - One bar indicates medium washing action and a short spin.
  - A broken bar indicates minimum washing action or a wool cycle spin.
- **Spin length**: Spin (full) or short spin.

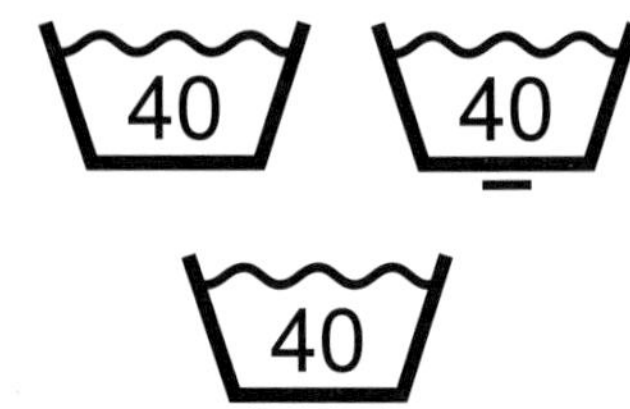

Symbol	Machine wash	Hand wash	Fabric
95	Maximum wash in 'cotton' cycle	Hand hot (50°C) or boil. Spin or wring	White cotton and linen items without special finishes
60	Maximum wash in 'cotton' cycle	Hand hot (50°C). Spin or wring	Cotton, linen or viscose items without special finishes where colours are fast at 60°C
50	Medium wash in 'synthetic' cycle	Hand hot. Cold rinse. Short spin or damp dry	Polyester/cotton mixtures, nylon polyester, cotton and viscose items with special finishes, cotton/acrylic mixtures
40	Maximum wash in 'cotton' cycle	Warm. Spin or wring	Cotton, linen or viscose where colours are fast at 40°C but not at 60°C
40	Medium wash in 'synthetic' cycle	Warm. Cold rinse. Short spin. Do not hand wring	Acrylics, acetate and triacetate, including mixtures with wool; polyester/wool blends
40	Minimum wash in 'wool' cycle	Warm. Do not rub. Spin. Do not hand wring	Wool, wool blends, silk
	Hand wash only	See item care label for washing instructions	Items that must not be machine washed; glass fibre fabrics and some pleated fabrics
	Do not wash	Do not wash	Items that cannot be washed: see item care label for cleaning instructions

Stain removal

Most stains can be removed from fabrics by washing. However, some stains can be difficult to remove so another method of stain removal treatment will depend on:

- The type of stain
- The type of fibre
- If the fabric is washable or not

Don't Forget!
Keep detergents, liquid-filled tablets, fabric conditioners and stain removers well away from small children.

Guide to stain removal

Did you know that many household stains can be removed with other household items?

Guidelines for removing stains

- ✓ Act quickly or the stain will set.
- ✓ Remove excess by blotting gently, but do not rub.
- ✓ Check the care label to see if item is washable.
- ✓ Remove stains **before** washing.
- ✓ Always start with mild treatments, like soaking in cold water.
- ✓ Always test commercial stain removers on a part of garment that will not be seen, e.g. inside seam or hem, in case it damages the fabric.
- ✓ Try 'green' stain removers first.

Get rid of this stain ...	Using this ...	Get rid of this stain ...	Using this ...
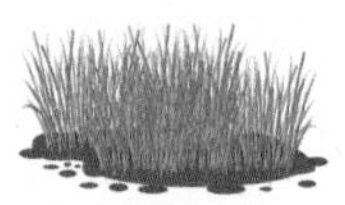 Grass	 Vinegar	 Ink	 Milk or toothpaste
 Red wine	 White wine or salt	 Lipstick	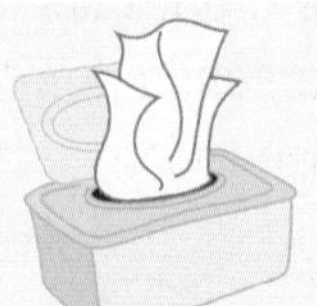 Baby wipes
 Deodorant	 Denim	 Coffee	 Baking soda
 Blood	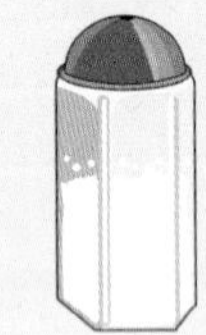 Salt and cold water	 Make-up	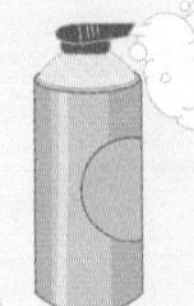 Shaving cream
 Sweat	 Lemon juice	 Oils	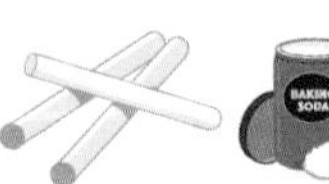 Chalk or baking soda

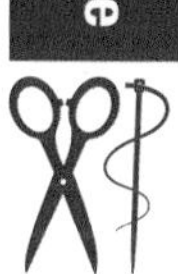

After treatment, wash according to the instructions on the care label.

If you need to use a commercial stain remover, it is important to:

- Follow the instructions on the product.
- Use in a well-ventilated room, as many are dangerous to inhale.
- Use gloves and wash your hands.
- Not use it near flames.
- Store it upright, in a cool, dry place, away from children (**why?**).

Preparing a wash

1 Repair any clothes that need mending.
2 Remove stubborn stains.
3 Close up zips.
4 Empty pockets.
5 Turn t-shirts and sweatshirts with ironed-on logos inside out (**why?**).
6 Sort clothes according to their colour and their care labels – the colour in some clothes is **colourfast**, meaning it will not run. Others clothing has colours that are **non-colourfast**. These clothes need to be washed separately, as their colour will run into other clothing in the wash.

Don't Forget!
A cross through the care symbol means the treatment should not be attempted.

Delicate fabrics should be washed by hand:

1 Use a mild detergent.
2 Rinse twice.
3 Squeeze to remove excess water.
4 Roll in a towel to remove water.
5 Drip dry or dry flat.

Detergents

Detergents are available in powder, liquid, 'liquitab' or tablet form. They are made from a mixture of chemicals including enzymes, bleaching agents, optical brighteners and perfumes. Some have added conditioners.

Types	Functions
• Biological detergents that contain enzymes that break down protein stains at low temperatures • Detergents for delicate fibres • Eco-friendly detergents	• Helps remove dirt and grease • Softens the water • Reduces the surface tension so the fabric can get wet through

Discovery Learning

Many washing machine manufacturers offer eco-friendly features on their machines. Can you find out what these features are and what brands are most environmentally friendly?

Discovery Learning

Investigate eco-friendly detergents and compare them to another detergent on the market in terms of ingredients, cost and information on the packaging. Share this information with someone else in your class.

Fabric conditioners

Fabric conditioners are added to the final rinse to:

- Reduce static electricity
- Soften clothes
- Give fabrics a pleasant smell
- Make ironing easier

Did You Know?

Liquitabs are very dangerous for children, so many manufacturers put child safety warnings on their products and even have advertisements to alert parents to the dangers.

Discovery Learning

There are things we can do to make our laundry routines more eco-friendly. Do some research to find out how to do laundry in an environmentally-friendly manner. Present your findings to your classmates in a creative way.

Drying clothes

Clothes can be dried on a clothes line outside or on a clothes horse inside or by using a tumble dryer.

Line drying costs nothing and clothes remain soft and smell fresh. It is the most eco-friendly method of drying, but Irish weather is not always suitable for drying outside.

Clothes horses are used when the weather is bad, but it causes condensation so the room must be well ventilated.

A tumble dryer contains an element that heats the air coming into the machine. The clothes are rotated gently in the warm air and the moisture is removed through a vent in the wall, or is condensed from steam back into a water tank, which can be emptied. Tumble dryers are costly to run, but they remove wrinkles and reduce ironing.

Ironing

An iron contains a heating element that heats the shiny base plate. A thermostat controls the temperature and a light turns off when the correct temperature is reached (see p. 112). Irons contain a small water tank that creates steam which is released through the base making it easier to remove creases.

- Check the care label and select the correct heat setting.
- Iron clothes while they are still slightly damp or use a steam iron for a smoother finish.
- Iron some items inside out (**why?**).
- Iron carefully to avoid creasing.

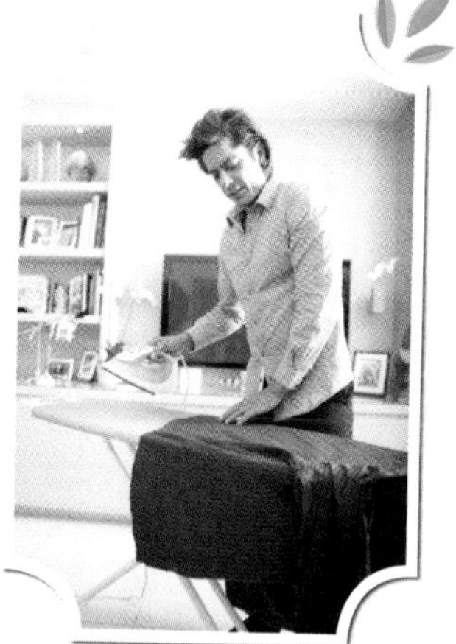

Classroom-Based Assessment

This section can be linked to CBA1: Creative Textiles.

Revision Questions

Use your workbook to revise this chapter

1. Give three reasons why care labels are attached to textiles.
2. Sketch and describe a care label for (a) a wool jumper and (b) a pair of denim jeans.
3. Suggest a stain remover for each of these stains (a) blood, (b) oil and (c) ink.
4. What guidelines should be followed when washing and drying a linen dress?
5. List four guidelines to follow when ironing clothes.

Summary

- Textiles get dirty and stained easily, so it is important to clean them before the dirt and stains become ingrained into the fabric. Clean clothes that are well cared for look better and last longer.
- **Fibres** are tiny hair-like threads. They are twisted together into **yarn** and the yarn is then made into **fabric**.
- Fibres are classified into **natural** fibres (plant and animal) and **man-made** fibres (synthetic and regenerated).
- Blended fabrics are a mix of two or more fibres. **Denier** is the thickness of the fibre. Fibres are **woven**, **knitted** or **bonded** into fabric.
- **Finishes** are applied to fabrics to make caring for them easier, and improve appearance and performance. Fabric finishes include brushing, anti-static, flame resistance, and waterproofing, dyeing and printing.

- **Care labels** are found on most clothes and household items. Care labels may contain written instructions or symbols devised by the International Care Labelling System. They help you make an **informed decision** when buying clothing, provide **useful information** that can save you time and money, help clothes **last longer**. A **dry-clean only** garment will be very **costly**. Certain fibres can cause an **allergic reaction**.
- Most **stains** can be removed from fabrics by washing. Some can be difficult to remove so treatment will depend on the type of stain and fibre and if the fabric is washable or not. Remove stains before washing.
- **Preparing a wash**: repair any clothes that need mending, remove stubborn stains before washing. Empty pockets, turn inside out and close zips. Sort clothes according to their colour and their care label. Delicate fabrics should be washed by hand, with a mild detergent, and drip- or flat-dried.
- **Detergents** are available in powder, liquid, liquitab or tablet form. They are made from a mixture of chemicals including enzymes, bleaching agents, optical brighteners and perfumes.
- **Fabric conditioners** are added to the final rinse to reduce static electricity, soften clothes, give fabrics a pleasant smell and make ironing easier.
- Clothes can be **dried** on a clothes line outside, on a clothes horse inside or by using a tumble dryer.
- When **ironing** check the care labels and select the correct heat setting, while the clothes are still slightly damp or use a steam iron for a smoother finish. Iron carefully to avoid creasing.

Section 2: Sew Successfully

29 LEARN TO SEW

Learning Outcomes 1.8, 2.4, 2.5, 2.6, 2.7, 2.8, 2.9, 2.10, 3.1, 3.2, 3.3, 3.4, 3.5, 3.6, 3.7, 3.8, 3.9

What I Will Learn

- to appreciate the importance of being able to sew
- to identify and use basic sewing equipment
- to compile a set of guidelines for hand stitching
- to work a variety of hand stitches
- to create a textile item using a variety of hand stitches
- to state the points to consider when choosing sewing equipment
- to identify the parts of a sewing machine
- to thread and use the sewing machine correctly
- to repair and mend items
- to select appropriate fabrics for sewing
- to use stitches to make and/or embellish a textile item

Key Words

- ✓ Sewing
- ✓ Crafts
- ✓ Stitches
- ✓ Equipment
- ✓ Tacking
- ✓ Running
- ✓ Gathering
- ✓ Backstitch
- ✓ Hemming
- ✓ Slip hemming
- ✓ Embroidery
- ✓ Embellish
- ✓ Stem stitch
- ✓ Satin stitch
- ✓ Long and short stitch
- ✓ Chain stitch
- ✓ Notions
- ✓ Nap
- ✓ One-way design
- ✓ Straight grain
- ✓ Bias
- ✓ Patch
- ✓ Darn
- ✓ Seam
- ✓ Hem

Learn to sew

The term '**textile item**' includes all textile-based crafts for an individual and the home. **Sewing** includes stitching by hand and using a sewing machine. Stitches can be both functional and decorative.

29.2 Knowing how to sew is a useful and creative skill in modern society. It is used to make clothes and soft furnishings, in many crafts, and to repair and alter textile items. Creative sewing, e.g. embroidery, quilting or knitting, can become a rewarding hobby. Recycling and upcycling textile items enables us to make sustainable decisions as consumers; we can be creative while saving money.

29.3 Although a lot of sewing is done by machine, the first step is to learn to sew by hand.

Don't Forget!
Use the 'Safety' mnemonic to help you remember the sewing room safety rules:

Switch off machine when not in use
Always walk, not run
Flexes are to be placed safely away
Ensure that hair is tied up
Turn on bright light to ensure clear vision
Your safety comes first

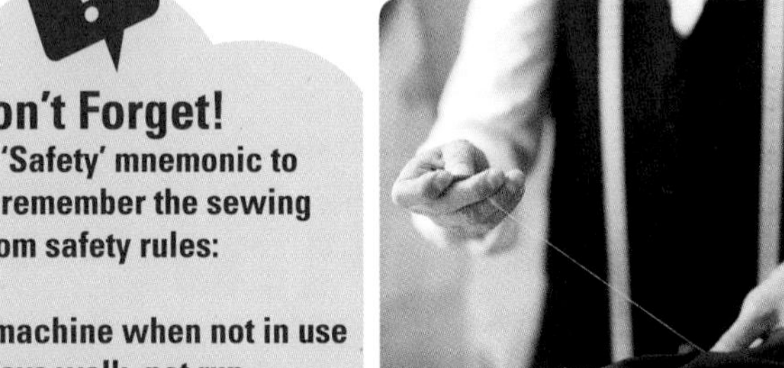

Hand stitching

Hand stitching can be functional or decorative, temporary or permanent. It is used for temporary stitching, e.g. tacking, for awkward areas, e.g. backstitch, hemming and slip hemming, and for decorative work.

Sewing equipment

It is important to be organised, so gather your sewing equipment and keep it together safely and out of reach of young children. The basic equipment you need includes pins, needles, thread, stitch ripper, measuring tape, tailor's chalk, thimble, scissors, pinking shears, tracing wheel and carbon paper, iron and ironing board.

Discovery Learning

Using a recycled item from your home, make a storage box or bag to store your sewing equipment safely. At least one element must be textile-based. Follow the Design Brief Process and be creative (**see p. 437**).

Classroom-Based Assessment

This section can be linked to CBA1: Creative Textiles.

Hand sewing guidelines

- Use a single thread and avoid having thread too long, as this leads to knots.
- Pin and tack seams and hems before stitching.
- Begin and finish stitches securely to prevent your sewing from coming undone.
- Usually stitches are worked from left to right – unless you are left-handed. If you are left-handed and finding it hard to learn how to stitch watch another left-handed person sewing or the mirror reflection of a right-handed person sewing. You will find it much easier to see what is happening.
- Stitches should be even, and not too long.
- Use a thimble to protect your finger when working with tough materials like denim.

Tacking

Tacking is also known as 'basting', and is a temporary stitch used to hold two or more pieces of fabric together until they get sewn properly. It acts as a guide for the permanent stitches and holds a garment together for fitting.

Did You Know?

Tacking should be done in a contrasting colour of thread so it is easier to remove once the permanent stitching is in place.

Method:

1. First, pin the fabric in place.
2. Use a single contrasting colour of thread with a knot at one end.
3. Begin with one backstitch to secure the stitching.
4. Make your stitches around 1 cm long, with 1 cm spaces between them.
5. Do not pull the thread too tightly or the fabric will gather up.
6. Finish with at least two backstitches to secure.

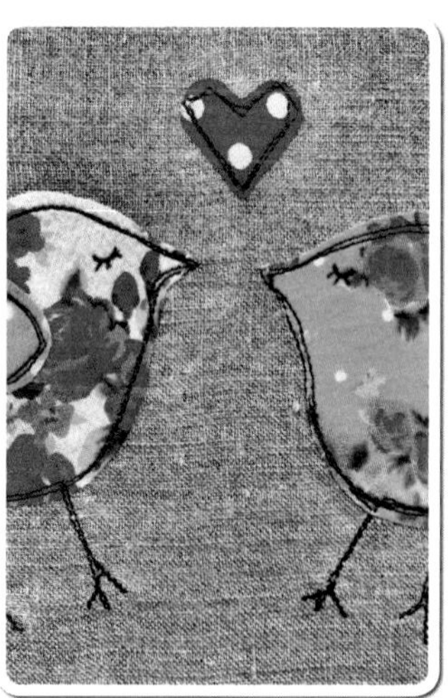

Running stitch

Running stitch is worked like tacking, except that is much smaller (1–2 mm instead of 1 cm) and is used as a functional stitch for sewing seams. It can be larger when used as a decorative stitch in appliqué or embroidery.

Gathering stitch

Gathering stitch is used to make a wide piece of fabric fit into a narrower piece, e.g. gathered skirt into a waistband. It can be done by hand or on a sewing machine.

Method:

1. Using the largest stitch width and loosest tension, sew two parallel lines along the area to be gathered. Alternatively, use two lines of running stitch.
2. The threads are then carefully pulled gathering the fabric until it fits into the required size.
3. The gathering stitches are then removed to give a neater finish.

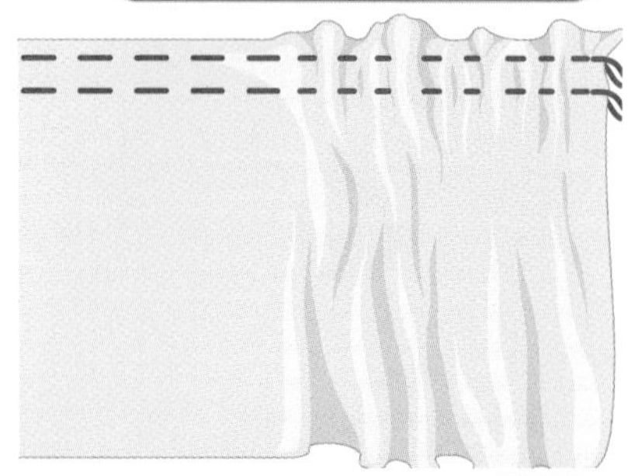

Backstitch

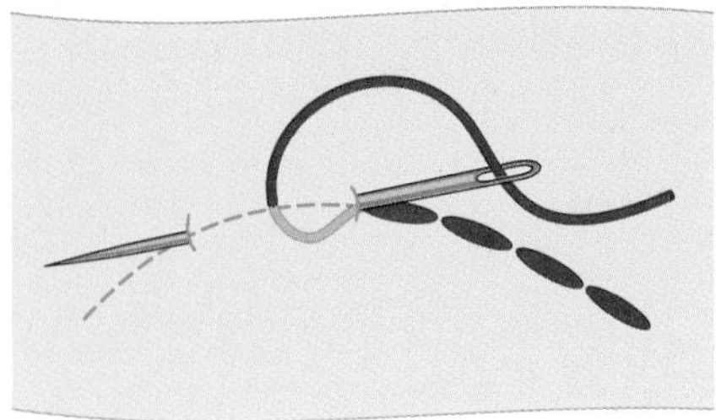

Backstitching is used instead of machine stitching when a sewing machine is not available. It can also be used to repair garments in awkward places, or as a decorative stitch.

Method:

1. Pin and tack fabric in place; remove pins.
2. Start with a couple of single backstitches to secure the thread.
3. Bring needle up 3 mm past end of last stitch.
4. Put needle into cloth at end of last stitch.
5. Bring needle out 3 mm beyond end of new stitch.
6. End with two single backstitches, bring the needle out between the two layers of fabric and cut the thread.
7. Remove tacking and press.

Hemming

Hemming is a small slanted stitch used to sew hems on garments or household textile items. Care must be taken to make stitches as small as possible, so they are almost invisible.

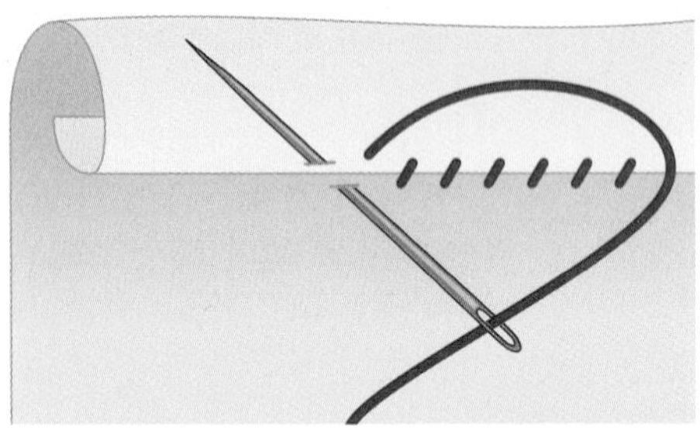

Method:

1. Pass needle through fold of the hem and make a small backstitch.
2. Make a small slanted stitch picking up two threads of the single fabric.
3. Pass the needle through the fold for 5 to 10 mm depending on thickness of fabric.
4. Continue sewing quite loosely.
5. Finish with backstitch through the fold of the hem.

Slip hemming

This is used to sew the hems of skirts, dresses and trousers because it is almost invisible on the right side. It is not as secure as hemming, but it can be secured by sewing a backstitch from time to time into the fold along the hem.

Method:

1. Pass needle through fold of the hem (left to right) and make a small backstitch.
2. Pick up only one or two threads from the single fabric.
3. Slip the needle through the fold for 5 to 10 mm depending on thickness of fabric and depth of hem.
4. Continue sewing quite loosely.
5. Finish off securely with a double backstitch through fold of hem.

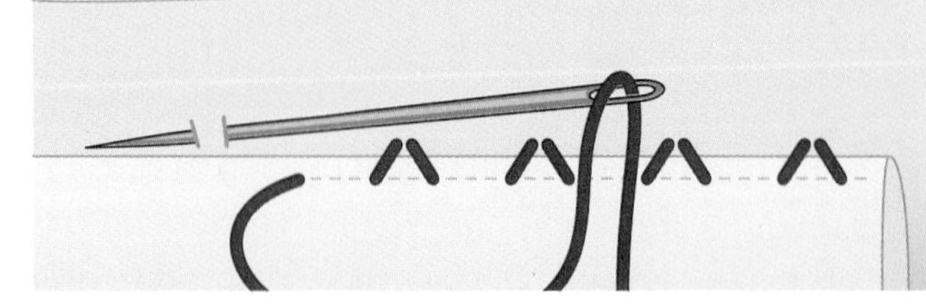

Embroidery stitches

Embroidery is used to decorate or embellish fabrics. It can be done by hand or machine. For hand embroidery we use skeins of thread. There are a wide variety of stitches and effects that can be worked in.

- Embroidery thread is made up of six strands; use two to three strands at a time.
- Use **crewel** needles (large eye) for embroidery.
- Start with a few running stitches along the line to be embroidered. These secure the stitching and are covered as you work embroidery stitches over them.
- Finish by weaving thread through stitches at the back.

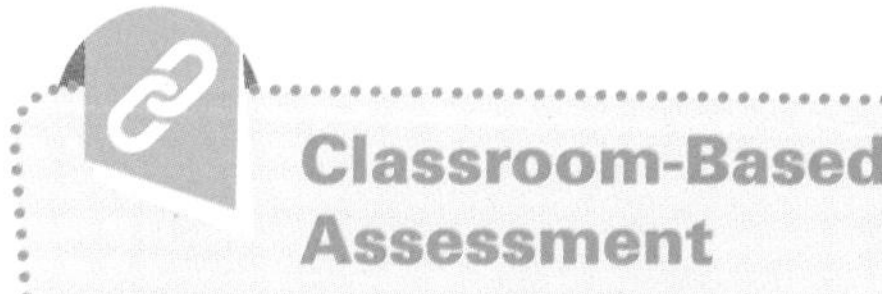

Classroom-Based Assessment

This section can be linked to CBA1: Creative Textiles.

To **embellish** means to make an item more attractive by the addition of decorative details or features. In textile items this can be done during the manufacture by dyes, patterns and weaves. Stitching, appliqué, beading, lace, ribbons and jewels can also be used.

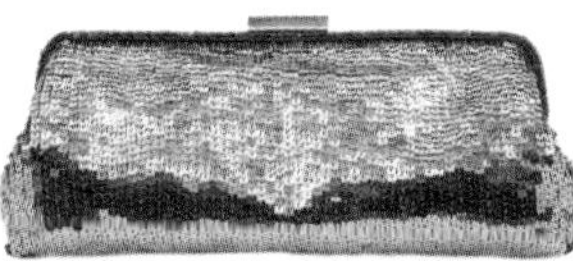

Stem stitch

Stem stitch is used to outline shapes or initials in crafts like embroidery, appliqué or tapestry. It forms a rope-like effect and can be worked on straight and curved lines.

Method:

1. Begin with a backstitch to secure the thread.
2. Work from left to right along the design, taking even-sized, slightly slanted stitches.
3. The thread should always come out above the previous stitch, about half-way along that stitch.

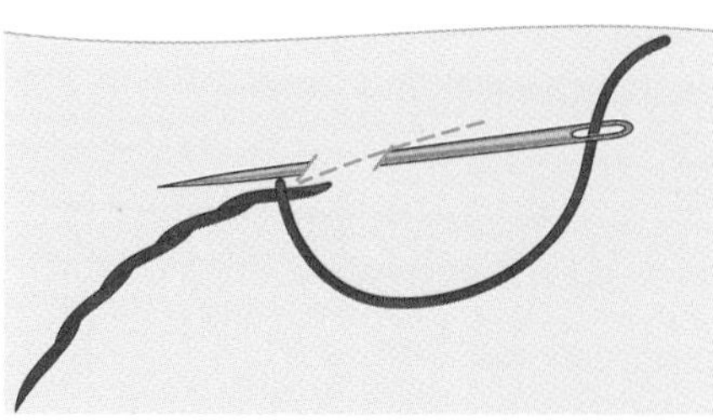

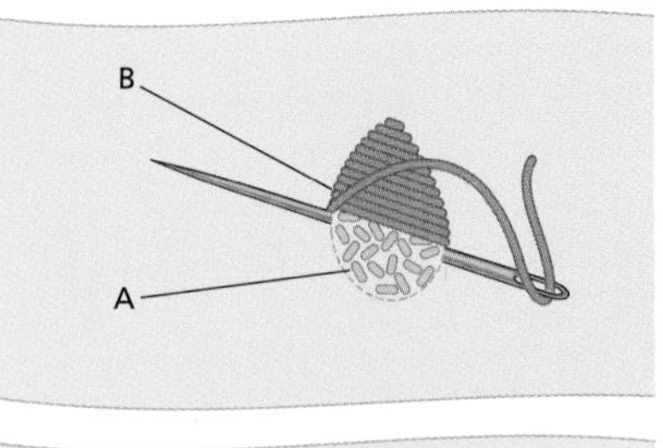

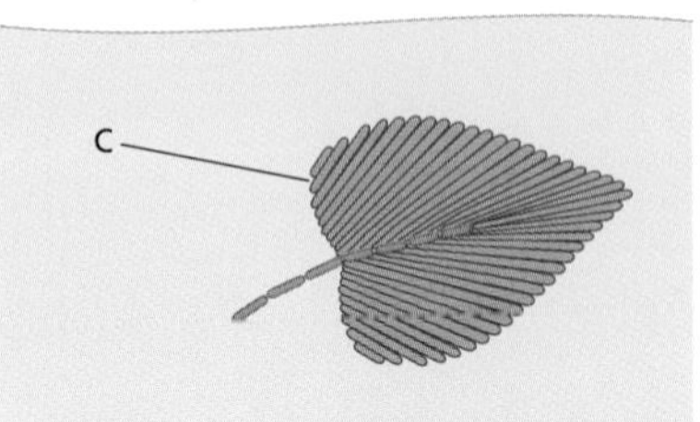

Satin stitch

Satin stitch is used to fill in small shapes, e.g. petals, animal eyes or noses, while decorating or embellishing textile items.

Method:

1. Start by doing some running stitches up and down through the design for extra thickness (A).
2. The threaded needle goes in one side of the design and out the other; the stitches can be straight or slanted but they must bc close together (B).
3. Use short stitches as longer stitches pull the fabric; for wider designs, use two short stitches (C), or use the long and short stitch below.

Long and short stitch

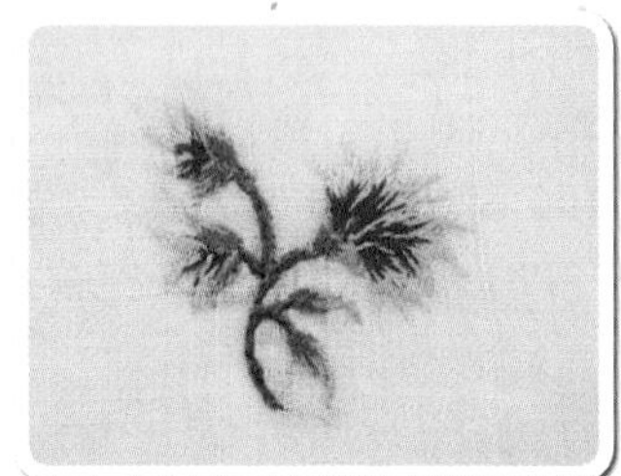

Long and short stitch is used to fill in larger designs or to give texture and shade to shapes, giving a more natural appearance, while decorating or embellishing textile items. Different shades of thread can be used to create a nice effect.

Method:

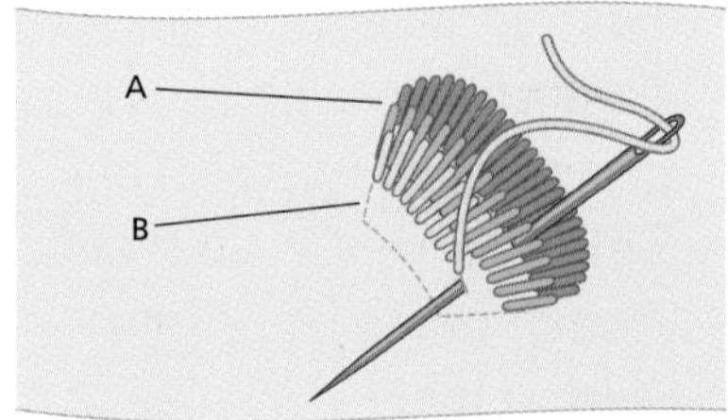

1. Begin with a backstitch to secure the thread.
2. Row one: first do a long stitch then a short stitch (A).
3. Row two: first a short stitch, then a long stitch so that the rows fit neatly into each other (B).

Chain stitch

The chain stitch is used as an outline stitch or to fill up a design.

Method:

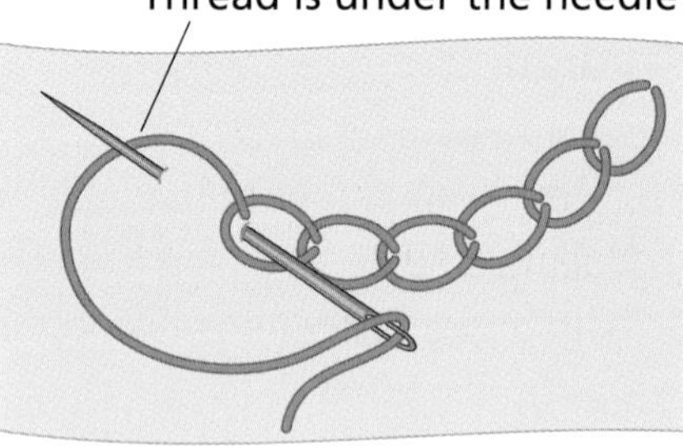

1. Begin with a backstitch to secure the thread.
2. Work down the design, holding the thread with your thumb to form a loop.
3. Insert the needle inside the loop beside where it came out last.
4. Finish with a secure stitch, bring the thread to the back and weave through a few stitches, then cut the thread.

Discovery Learning

There are a wide variety of embroidery stitches that can be used. Investigate one stitch, explain its uses, and how to work it. Find a tutorial on YouTube and work a small sample. Present all your findings and sample in a creative manner to your classmates or display it on the textiles wall.

The sewing machine

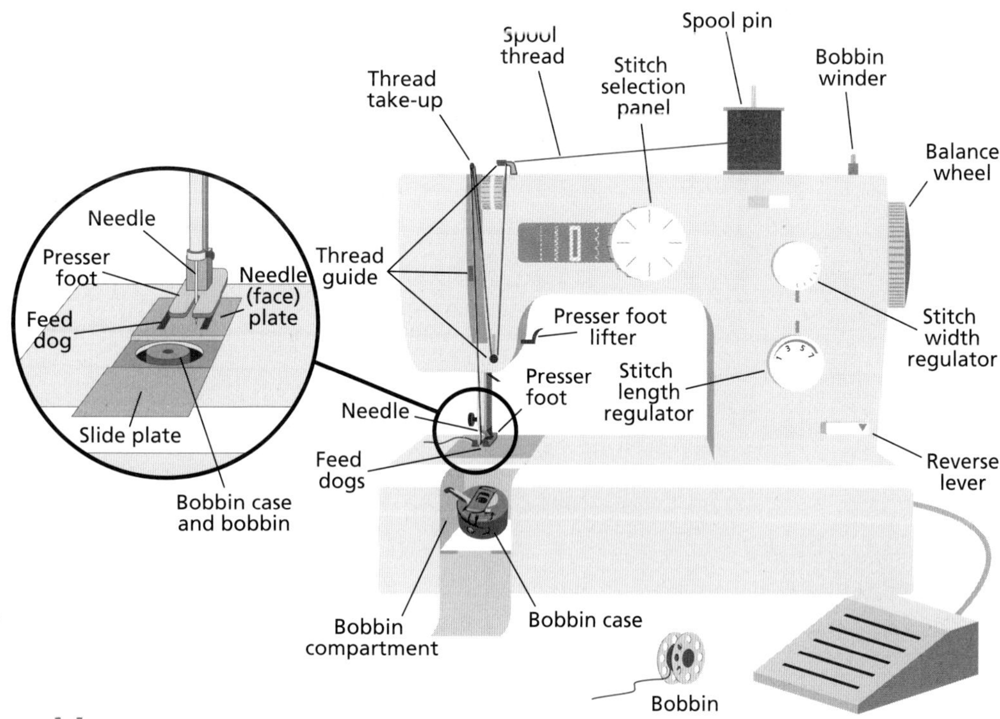

The sewing machine is a very important sewing resource when creating textile items, upcycling items, mending or repairing clothes.

Choosing a sewing machine

When choosing a sewing machine consider:

- **Cost**: consider what you can afford to pay.
- **Features**: consider what you might need, e.g. one-step button hole, adjustable presser foot, etc.
- **Reliable** brands and seek an informed and knowledgeable retailer.
- **Attachments** and **extras** that are included, e.g. embroidery functions.
- **Guarantee** and after-sales service.
- **Ease of use**: is there a demonstration available and can you test it out in the shop before you buy (**consumer awareness, see p. 345**)?

Revision Toolkit

Can you come up with a mnemonic to help you remember what to consider when choosing a sewing machine? When you do, share it with your class.

Modern features of the sewing machine

Sewing machines used to offer only very basic stitches, but nowadays they have become more advanced and can have a lot of useful 'added' features, such as:

- Needle down
- Automatic needle threader
- One-step button hole
- Lightweight
- Adjustable presser foot
- Free arm
- Top loading bobbin
- Electronic controls
- Embroidery stitches

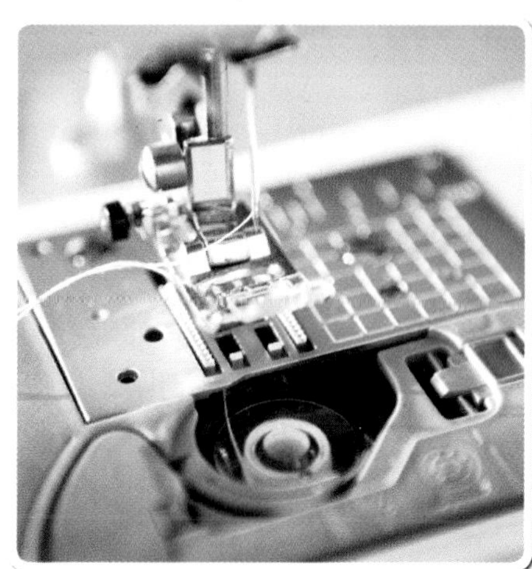

Machine stitches

Type	Description	Diagram
Straight stitch	All machines sew straight stitch, both forwards and in reverse. It is used for seams and hems on all types of non-stretch fabrics. Length can be adjusted to suit the thickness of the fabric. It is used in many crafts like quilting and patchwork.	
Zig-zag stitch	A zig-zag stitch can be used on most types of fabric, and is especially useful for fine and stretchy materials, e.g. lace and for sewing on elastic. It is used for finishing seams and for appliqué.	
Buttonhole stitch	Most modern machines have a buttonhole function; it can be done in four stages or automatically. It is useful for making garments and upcycling items.	
Blind stitch	The blind stitch can be used on most types of fabric, for blind hemming, shell edging or decoration.	
Embroidery stitches	Embroidery stitches are available on most modern machines, and are used for decorating and embellishing textile items.	

How a sewing machine stitches

- There are two threads involved – the thread from the spool and the thread from the bobbin.
- The stitch is made when these two threads twist around each other.
- The interlocking takes place between the two layers of fabric.
- If the tension on the thread is too loose or too tight the stitches won't form properly.

Further Investigation

Sewing machines use clever twisting to secure threads and create stitches. To find out how sewing machines work, watch 'Sewing Machine Anatomy; How a Stitch is Made' (1:24) on YouTube.

Threading a sewing machine

1. Put spool on spool pin and bring the spool thread …
   - i through the first thread guide,
   - ii around the tension spring,
   - iii through the take-up lever,
   - iv through the thread guide at the top of the needle, and
   - v through the needle, from front to back.
2. Put the filled bobbin into the bobbin case and pull the thread through the bobbin tension.
3. Put the case into the machine.
4. Turn the hand wheel until the needle thread catches the bobbin thread.
5. Pull both threads to the back of the machine.

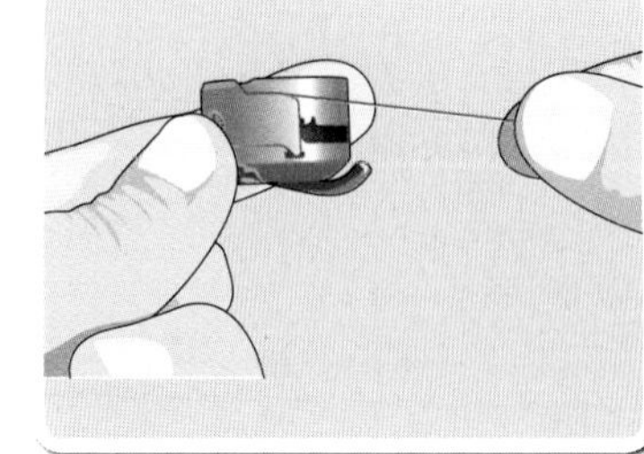

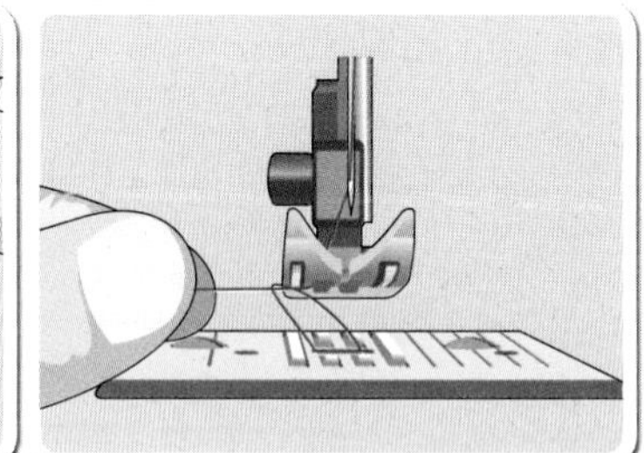

Using the sewing machine

1. Thread the machine properly.
2. Raise the needle to highest point.
3. Adjust stitch and test stitch on spare fabric.
4. Put the part of fabric to be sewn under the presser foot, with the bulk of the cloth to the left of the needle.
5. Lower the presser foot to hold the fabric in place.
6. Lower needle into the fabric by turning wheel towards you.
7. Begin machining by pressing the foot pedal gently.
8. Guide the fabric – do not push or pull it!
9. Leave needle in fabric when turning a corner (pivot).
10. When finished, lift the presser foot, raise the needle and pull fabric gently out the back of the machine.
11. Cut the thread.

Care of sewing machine

- Follow the manufacturer's instructions.
- Cover when not in use to keep out dust.
- Oil moving parts.
- Have repaired by qualified person.
- Do not run a threaded machine without material.

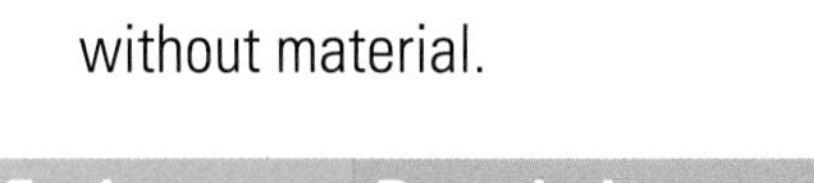

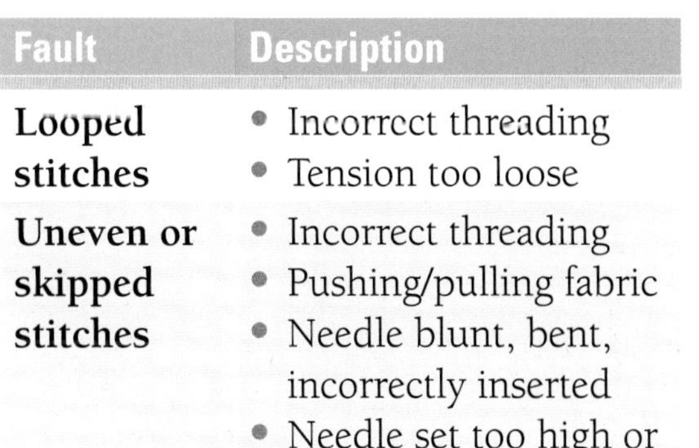

Fault	Description
Looped stitches	• Incorrect threading • Tension too loose
Uneven or skipped stitches	• Incorrect threading • Pushing/pulling fabric • Needle blunt, bent, incorrectly inserted • Needle set too high or too low

Fault	Description
Needle breaking	• Incorrectly inserted, bent or too fine for fabric • Pulling fabric out before needle is raised • Top tension too tight • Loose presser foot
Needle thread breaking	• Needle wrongly inserted • Top tension too tight • Incorrect threading • Bad quality thread

29.6

Mending and repairing clothes

Sometimes, with wear and tear, clothes may need to be repaired.

- Match the thread or wool as closely in terms of colour, thickness and fibre as possible if you want the repair to blend in. Or choose contrasting threads to add a decorative feature to the textile item.
- A patch or darn should extend beyond the hole on all sides to strengthen the area around the patch or darn.
- Iron-on patches can be bought for quick repairs.
- Hems and seams may need to be repaired either by hand, e.g. backstitch or by machine.

Darning

This is weaving over the hole and surrounding area.

By hand: Use matching wool/thread; do not pull tightly. Work very long stitches over the hole in one direction first and then weave in and out through these in the other direction, keeping the threads close together to fill in the hole.

By machine: Tack a finer piece of fabric over the section to be repaired. This is then machined up and down and over and back. Then the fabric is trimmed.

Patching

This can be done by hand, machine or is ironed in place.

Cut a shape larger than the area to be repaired, turn a hem on the wrong side all around, tack in position and follow the grain of the fabric. Machine stitch or hem in place, remove the tacking and trim and neaten the back of the patch.

Alternatively, use an 'iron-on patch' to cover the tear or hole.

By being creative, fashionable items can be created with clever repairs, e.g. using a crochet patch or patterned fabric.

Hem

A hem is the finished edge of a garment, such as the lower edge of a trouser leg, a dress, around the top of a bag or laundry bag. There are a number of ways to make a hem, depending on the fabric you are using and the finish you want:

Type	Description	Diagram
Turned and stitched hem	Cut edge is turned over and pressed. The hem is then slip-hemmed by hand.	
Machine stitched hem	Cut edge is turned over and pressed. It is then stitched using the machine to hold the hem in place.	
Zig-zag hem	A zig-zag is stitched close to the cut edge, and excess fabric trimmed off. This is a fast and easy way to finish fabric.	

Seams

Seams are used to join pieces of fabric together to make clothing and other textile items. The flat seam is the most common type and needs to be finished off to prevent fraying.

Type	Description	Diagram
Flat seam	Basic seam used for most types of seams, but raw edge needs to be finished off.	
Flat zigzagged seam	Quick method of finishing a raw edge. Not very neat only used when the seam will not be seen.	
Flat pinked seam	Made using the pinking shears. Quick method of finishing a seam but not very secure.	

Type	Description	Diagram
Turned and stitched seam	Raw edge of material is turned over and machine stitched close to the folded edge, giving a secure and neat finish to the fabric.	
Overlocked seam	Seams are stitched and neatened to give a secure and neat finish.	

Choosing a fabric for project work

Successful sewing depends largely on the right choice of fabrics and accessories.

- Choose a fabric that is easy to work with. Stretchy or slippery fabrics are more difficult to work with and to sew. Polyester-cotton or cotton is good for beginners.
- Fabrics are sold in different widths. The wider the fabric you buy, the less of it you will need. If recycling fabrics, ensure you have enough to complete your project.
- If you are making a garment or a household item from a commercial pattern, calculate the amount of fabric you will need using the grid on the back of your pattern envelope.
- Check washing and care instructions on the fabric roll or label before you buy it in case it is unsuitable.
- Buy or recycle anything else you need to complete your project.

A list of requirements or '**notions**', e.g. matching thread, zip, buttons, hooks and eyes will be given on your pattern envelope. If designing your own textile item, gather everything you need before you start and keep all together in a bag or box for the duration of the project.

- Fabrics that have a nap, e.g. velvet, or a one-way design are more difficult to cut out properly and need more fabric.

Nap is a pile on the fabric that can be brushed one way to be rough and another way to be smooth, creating a different shading, e.g. velvet. When fabric has a **one-way design**, e.g. an animal pattern, pattern pieces must be laid in the same direction to make sure everything is the right way up.

A one-way pattern

Velvet, a fabric with nap

Further Investigation

If you want to use a commercial pattern when making a textile item, watch these informative videos on YouTube to find out everything you need to know:

- 'How to Cut Out Sewing Pattern Pieces' (8:33)
- 'How to Arrange Sewing Pattern Pieces' (12:10)

Tips for cutting out a pattern

- Arrange the pattern pieces on the fabric. Straight-of-grain arrows should run parallel with selvage edges. Place fold arrows on fold or follow bias arrow if required. Pattern instructions will suggest a layout.
- Pin in position.
- Using a sharp scissors, cut around each pattern piece. Leave a 1.5 cm seam allowance if not already allowed. Most patterns include this allowance, in which case cut fabric to exact size of pattern pieces.
- Keep fabric flat on the table with one hand. Do not lift the fabric up to cut it. Cut notches outwards.

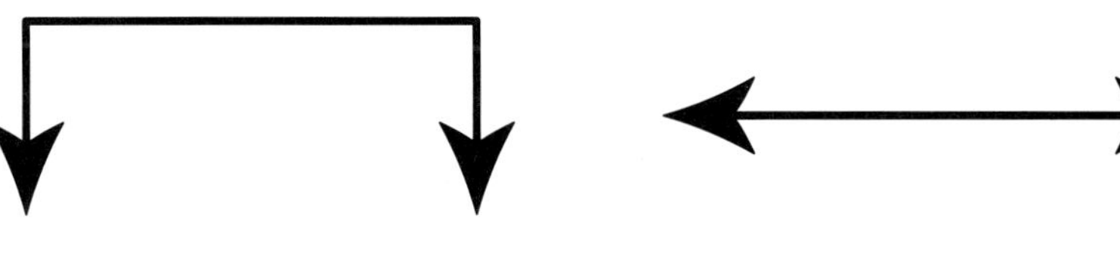

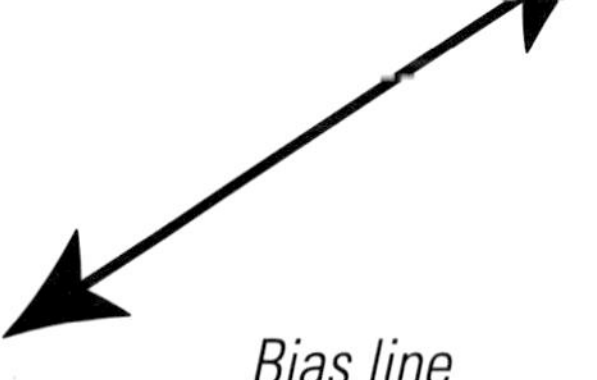

Fold arrows *Straight grain* *Bias line*

Transferring pattern markings

Transfer important pattern markings from a pattern to the fabric using any of the following methods:

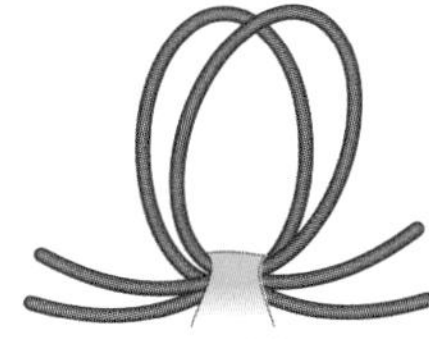

- Tailor tacking

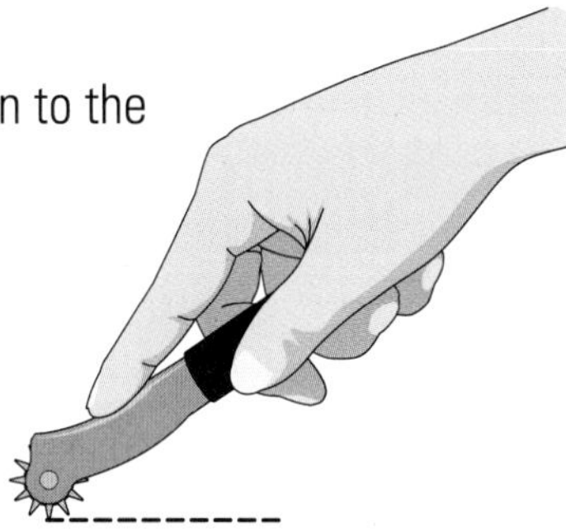

- Tracing wheel and carbon paper

- Thread marking

- Tailor's chalk

Revision Questions

1. Compile a set of guidelines for hand stitching.
2. Give two uses for (a) tacking, (b) backstitching and (c) hemming.
3. Draw and label a diagram of a sewing machine.
4. What should be considered when choosing a sewing machine?
5. Why is it important to repair and mend clothes and household items?
6. You are making a bag to store your creative textile project in. Can you suggest (a) three suitable fabrics, (b) three fabric embellishments you could use, and (c) what stitches and techniques you could use to assemble your bag?

Summary

- Sewing is a **useful** and **creative** skill. It is used to make clothes and soft furnishings, in many crafts, and to repair and alter textile items. Recycling and upcycling textile items enables us to make sustainable decisions as consumers and is a therapeutic and rewarding experience.
- '**Textile item**' includes all textile-based crafts for an individual and the home. **Sewing** includes stitching by hand and using a sewing machine.
- **Sewing equipment** includes pins, needles, thread, stitch ripper, measuring tape, tailor's chalk, thimble, scissors, pinking shears, tracing wheel and carbon paper, iron and ironing board.
- **Hand stitches** include tacking, backstitching, hemming, slip-hemming and gathering.
- **Embroidery stitches** include stem, satin, long and short stitch and chain stitch.
- The **sewing machine** is a very important sewing resource. When choosing a sewing machine consider cost, features, reliability of brand, attachments and extras, guarantee and after-sales service as well as ease of use.
- To **care** for your machine always follow the manufacturer's instructions, cover when not in use to keep out dust, oil moving parts and have it repaired by a qualified person. Do not run a threaded machine without material.
- When **using a sewing machine**, thread it correctly, insert fabric carefully, lower the presser foot and needle, press the foot pedal gently and guide the fabric through.
- **Mending and repairing** clothes is important, and can be done by replacing buttons, repairing seams and hems, darning and patching.
- A **seam** joins two pieces of fabric together: a flat seam is used most and the seams are finished by pinking, stitching and zig-zag stitching on a machine.
- When **choosing fabrics** for a textile project choose the correct amount and type of fabric for the purpose of the item.
- When **cutting out fabric**, pin the pattern pieces into position, use sharp scissors to cut out the fabric and transfer fabric markings carefully.

30 CREATIVE TEXTILES PROJECT

Learning Outcomes 1.8, 2.4, 2.5, 2.6, 2.7, 2.8, 2.9, 2.10, 3.1, 3.2, 3.3, 3.4, 3.5, 3.6, 3.7, 3.8, 3.9

What I Will Learn

- to discuss the importance of craftwork in a modern society
- to demonstrate basic hand sewing techniques
- to demonstrate basic machine sewing techniques
- to apply the design brief process and principles to the making of a creative textile item for an individual or the home
- to design and create a textile item using a variety of hand sewing and/or machine sewing techniques
- to demonstrate fabric embellishment techniques
- to demonstrate ways in which clothing and/or textile household items can be repaired
- to examine how textile items can be re-used, re-purposed, recycled and upcycled

Key Words

✓ Craft
✓ Craftwork
✓ Appliqué
✓ Batik
✓ Crochet
✓ Cross stitch
✓ Embroidery
✓ Fabric painting
✓ Knitting
✓ Lacemaking
✓ Patchwork
✓ Printing
✓ Quilting
✓ Rug making
✓ Soft toy making
✓ Tapestry
✓ Weaving

Craft in Ireland

Ireland has a long tradition of producing high-quality crafts that are exported all over the world. We have a history of craftwork that may go back 3,000 years into Ireland's past. The art of craftworkers can be seen in our museums, e.g. Bronze Age ornaments, religious objects like chalices, pewter vessels, jewellery, illustrated manuscripts (like the Book of Kells), woven textiles (lace, crios), Aran knitting and Irish crochet.

Irish Felt Fairy

Traditional crafts began to die out when the industrial revolution made it possible to mass-produce goods by machine, much more quickly and cheaply. Today, there is a renewed interest in handcrafted items, as many tourists want to buy high-quality indigenous crafts to bring home with them. The term craft is now associated with items that are beautiful and useful, but are high-end unique items.

Ana Fay Bags

Many craftworkers have set up small enterprises around Ireland to create high-quality Irish craft products, e.g. Irish Felt Fairy and Ana Faye Bags. Taken nationally, the craft industry is a significant employer and is important in providing viable, sustainable enterprises in local communities – especially in rural areas – and keep crafting skills vibrant and relevant in modern society.

Craftwork and sewing have recently seen a surge in popularity in people of all ages, as they offer an opportunity for self-expression and being creative, develop fine motor skills, relax people and reduce stress. People can get great personal satisfaction from making new products from old through upcycling and recycling clothes and household items; this also saves money.

Discovery Learning

There are lots of creative textile craftworkers in Ireland. Research one textile enterprise and present your findings to your classmates in a creative manner.

Further Investigation

Visit the DCCoI website at **www.dccoi.ie**. Visit their learner section to find lots of interesting information on the Irish craft industry, particularly the Craft Career Sheets and Second Level Craft Resources.

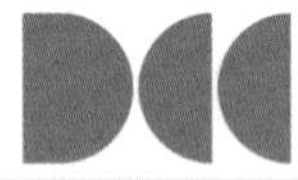

Design & Crafts Council of Ireland

Design & Crafts Council of Ireland (DCCoI) is the national agency for the commercial development of Irish designers and craftworkers. It encourages and stimulates innovation, educates, and helps inform government policy. DCCoI is funded by the Department of Business, Enterprise and Innovation via Enterprise Ireland.

Textile crafts

Textile crafts encompass all craft using threads and/or fabrics. Textile crafts have evolved over time from traditional crafts like patchwork, tapestry and quilting to modern creative embroidery and knitting.

Textile crafts include:

Tapestry Appliqué Crochet Batik Embroidery Weaving Cross stitch Fabric painting Knitting Rug making Patchwork Felting Soft toy making Lacemaking Quilting

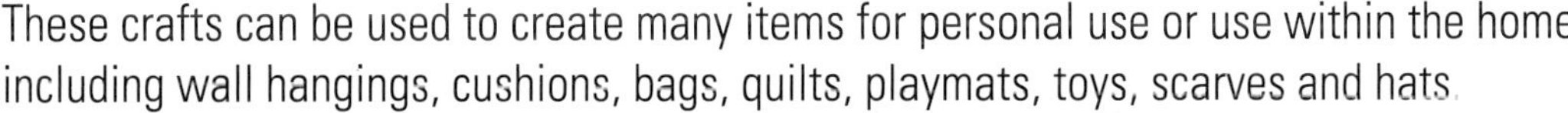

These crafts can be used to create many items for personal use or use within the home, including wall hangings, cushions, bags, quilts, playmats, toys, scarves and hats.

Craft skills

Craftwork is the use of personal skills to design and create objects that are both beautiful and useful. A well-designed craft item will look attractive, be fit for purpose and have a high standard of workmanship. Craftworkers need the following:

- The ability to design
- Skill with their hands (good 'manual dexterity')
- An artistic eye
- A good imagination
- The ability to explore different options, implement ideas and take actions

New from old

We all have stuff that no longer serves any purpose around the house, but we still have trouble getting rid of it because it is still in good form, or might come in handy in the future, or just has sentimental value. However, if you are creative enough, you can solve the problem by re-purposing, upcycling and reusing your old things. As well as serving a purpose again, repurposed items add a touch of creativity and uniqueness to the home and avoid waste.

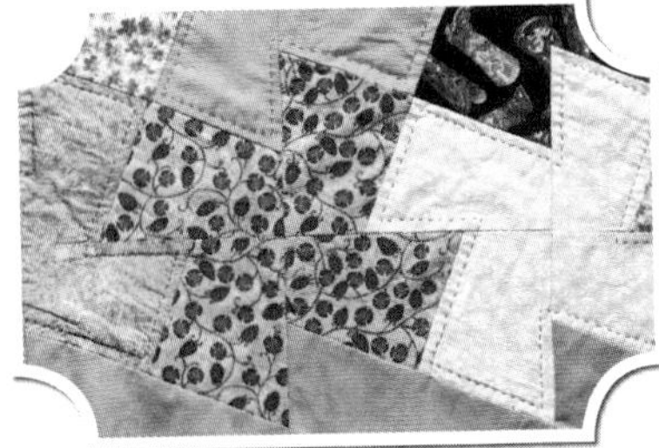

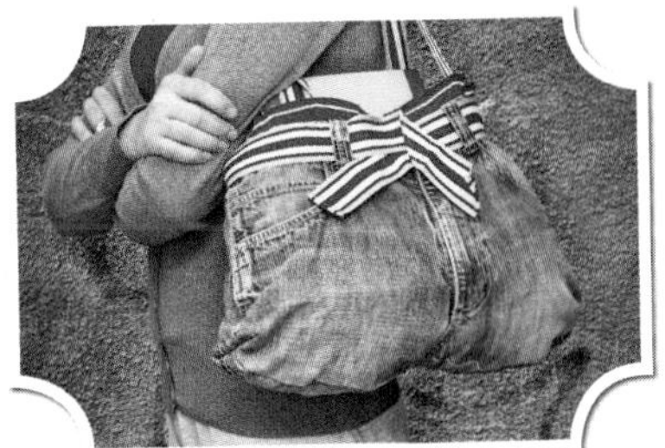

Classroom-Based Assessment 1: Creative Textiles

The Classroom-Based Assessments will provide an opportunity for you to:

- **research** information using a variety of methods
- **analyse** data and evidence to make informed value judgements and decisions
- **organise** information and plan logically
- **communicate** clearly and effectively
- **collaborate** with others on tasks
- **reflect** on your own learning

There are **two** options, from which you can choose **one** Creative Textiles project:

1. Make a textile item for an individual or the home; or
2. Recycle or upcycle a textile item for an individual or the home

Option 1

Make a textile item for an individual or the home.

Applying the design brief process and the principles of design and sustainability, students make a textile item for an individual or the home.

As part of the project, students will show evidence of:

- applying the design brief process
- applying the principles of design and sustainability
- using basic hand sewing and/or machine sewing techniques in the making of the product
- fabric embellishment techniques (where applicable)
- appropriate textile care and maintenance

Option 2

Recycle or upcycle a textile item for an individual or the home.

Applying the design brief process and the principles of design and sustainability, students recycle or upcycle a textile item for an individual or the home.

As part of the project, students will show evidence of:

- applying the design brief process
- applying the principles of design and sustainability
- using basic hand sewing and/or machine sewing techniques in the making of the product
- fabric embellishment techniques (where applicable)
- appropriate textile care and maintenance

For successful completion of the Classroom-Based Assessment, students will submit a textile item and evidence of the application of the Design Brief Process (a portfolio).

This Classroom-Based Assessment is an individual project and will be completed by **the end of year two**. It will be assessed by the teacher.

The Design Brief Process is ideally cyclical and reflective, and may involve the following stages:

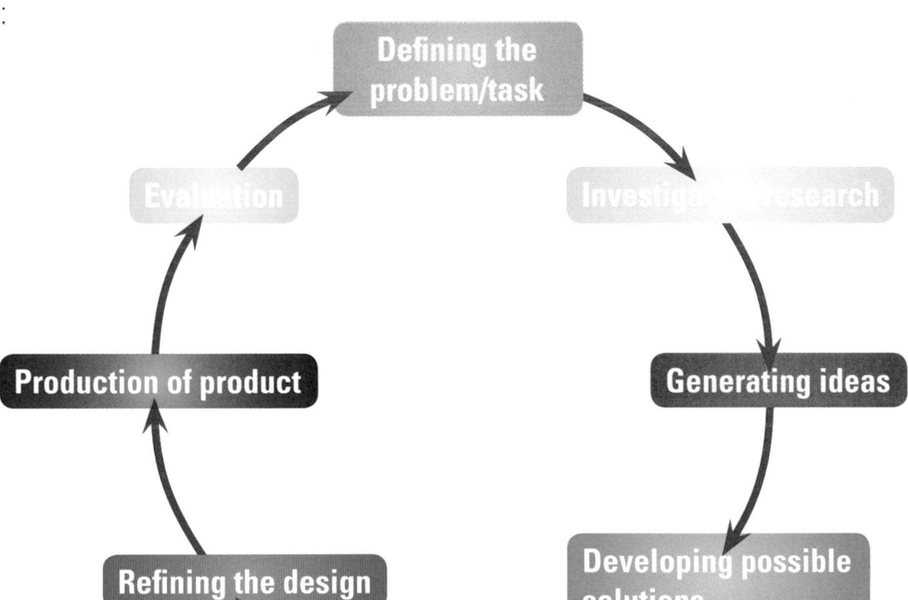

Let the information below guide you to complete your CBA1:

Design Brief Process	How to do this
Defining the problem/task	• You need to examine what the brief is really asking you to do. You must **identify the problem** to be solved. • The best way is to write out the brief on a page, then using a highlighter or coloured pen **underline all of the key words**. These describe what needs to be done. Look up the definitions for these words, particularly the ones you do not understand. • **Now re-write this brief** in your own words. • List the **requirements** of the design; ask yourself what must be done to satisfy the brief.

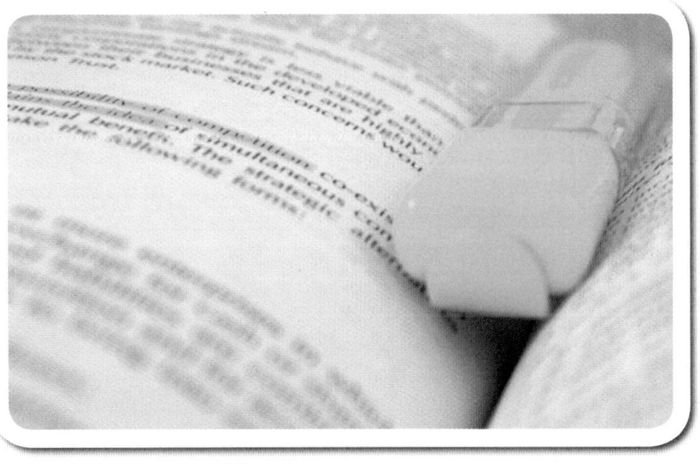

Design Brief Process	How to do this
Investigation/ research	Now that you have a good understanding of the problem, it's time to start looking for the answers. **Show evidence at all stages of this work** (sketches, mood board, photos and written notes from people from whom you received advice), and look for inspiration in books, magazines, interviews, etc. Produce a bibliography. • Try to find other designs of this item in catalogues, in shops, online, at home, etc., and make notes and sketches of their **key design points**. • Use your textbook and other sources to **research stitches, construction methods and embellishments** you could use to suit your design. Remember to include **safety considerations** when designing, especially for children. • If using the internet, do not copy material straight from the computer to your report. Cut and paste text and drawings/pictures, stick onto page and **write your own notes** on these. • **Take measurements** of items which are to be stored or accommodated in or on your creation. These will assist you in the design (e.g. pocket for a mobile phone – you need to measure a range of different models to ensure your design will work). • **Ask your teacher** what they think of your findings and if you are stuck, they will help you get back on track.
Generating ideas	• Draw out **at least three different designs** using sketches on blank or square grid paper. • They must show a **link with your analysis and research**. You must show by notes and sketching how the project will be stitched together. • **Discuss your designs**, i.e. include written notes around sketches to help explain your choices. Use colours in your sketches where appropriate. Label your ideas 'Design Idea 1', '2' and '3', etc.
Developing possible solutions	• **Evaluate** each design idea: write out why they are or are not fully meeting the brief, and whether or not you like your design.

A **bibliography** is a list of books, magazines or websites you used during your research.

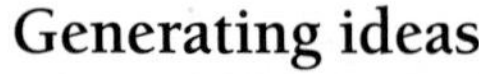

Design Brief Process	How to do this
Presenting ideas to others for feedback	• At the end of this section, you must ensure that your project design is **different** from other students', so look at other students' designs and discuss your idea with them. • Your teacher will be the person to assess this.
Refining the design	• Take on board the feedback of your classmates and teacher and refine your design. • Show on a separate **sheet a sketch** of your **final chosen design**. This will be inspired closely by your three or more design ideas. Name the **materials** you hope to use and show that you have examined the final design with **user safety** in mind (e.g. considerations for a child's toy, bag, wall hanging, etc.).
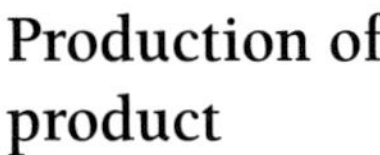 Production of product	**Complete the product and portfolio**, which should include: • Templates or patterns used • Order of work or time plan • List of materials used • Stitches used • Costs involved • How to care for your textile item
 Evaluation	**Evaluate** the project by asking: • Does the design meet the **purpose** it was made for? • Is the **appearance** pleasant or otherwise? Were **materials** used effectively? • Is the final product **safe and fit for its intended use**? If not, list the things that require improvement. • Should there be **modifications** or alterations made to the final presented work? • How effectively was the project **executed**? • Are you happy with the **overall** result? • If you were to start again **would you do anything differently**?

Don't Forget!
When doing your CBA1, it is important to apply the Design Brief Process, keeping in mind the principles of design and sustainability, and to annotate your sketches clearly and detail any craft, embellishment and sewing techniques used. Explain how to care for your finished item.

See Zest for Life Skills Book pp. 275–280 for a sample CBA1 project. This sample will help when following the Design Brief Process.

Summary

- Ireland has a long **tradition** of producing high-quality crafts that are exported all over the world. Traditional crafts began to die out when the industrial revolution made it possible to mass-produce goods by machine, much more quickly and cheaply. Today, there is a renewed interest in crafts, as many tourists want to buy high-quality indigenous items to bring home with them.
- The term **craft** is now associated with items that are beautiful and useful, but are high-end individual items.
- The **Design and Crafts Council of Ireland** is the national agency for the commercial development of Irish designers and craftworkers. They encourage and stimulate innovation, and educate with their teaching resources. They help inform government policy and they are funded by the Department of Business, Enterprise and Innovation via Enterprise Ireland.
- We all have stuff that no longer serves any purpose around the house. If you are creative enough, you can solve the problem by **re-purposing, upcycling and reusing** your old things.
- This **Classroom-Based Assessment** is an individual project and will be completed by the end of year two. It will be assessed by the teacher.
- The **Design Brief Process** is ideally cyclical and reflective and may involve the following stages: defining the problem/task; investigation/research; generating ideas; developing possible solutions; presenting ideas to others for feedback; refining the design; production; and evaluation.

Index

Q

R

S

T

U

V

W

Y

Photo Acknowledgements

For permission to reproduce photographs, the author and publisher gratefully acknowledge the following:

Advertising Standards Authority of Ireland: 366C; © Alamy: 17T, 23C, 34B, 38T, 38B, 40, 43, 55, 62B, 69B, 71BCR, 71BL, 81, 87BC, 91C, 102C, 108B, 110B, 114TC, 114B, 121, 139CB, 142B, 143C, 148B, 150T, 152, 154, 160CL, 163C, 165BL, 165BR, 167C, 168C, 174C, 177B, 195B, 196L, 196C, 202CR, 203C, 204, 207, 208, 209BL, 210TL, 210TR, 210B, 211, 216, 223B, 227T, 227B, 229, 241C, 243CL, 245T, 246, 254, 258T, 267T, 276C, 292CT, 292C, 292CB, 292B, 300TL, 305L, 317C, 326, 328B, 333, 338T, 340BC, 342CR, 349B, 351C, 353T, 353B, 355CL, 363T, 369B, 370, 371L, 372, 373TR, 374B, 375, 376, 378TC, 378TR, 378CR, 385BL, 385BR, 386, 387B, 389BR, 391T, 391CT, 392TR, 392CL; 399T, 399B, 401T, 402B, 403T, 403BCL, 404C, 405B, 406, 408BL, 408BR, 409, 415B, 416C, 420, 421B, 424, 428C, 435TC, 435TR, 435BL, 435BC, 438T; Courtesy of Ana Faye: 434T; An Post: 299L; An Taisce: 342CL; Aurivo: 210CB; Avonmore: 173C, 176B, 225T; Ballymaloe: 140B, 224; © BananaStock: 17CL; Bord Bia: 188, 200B; British Standards Institution (BSI Group): 356CB; Citizens Information Board: 297, 365C; Competition and Consumer Protection Commission: 351B, 364C; Connacht Gold: 175T; © Cultura: 46B, 284, 389C; Design and Crafts Council Ireland: 434C; © DigitalVision: 15L, 17L, 58, 84, 107, 138T, 281CR, 286L, 305R, 373B, 374T, 387T, 388T, 407B; © E+: 14B, 53B, 54CL, 54C, 57T, 60, 61, 86TR, 92B, 93, 110CL, 122B, 125, 135CT, 136R, 140C, 143B, 145B, 146CR, 146CL, 156, 187TC, 189B, 191, 192T, 192B, 193L, 195C, 199C, 222, 232T, 233, 235, 236R, 238, 242T, 244T, 249C, 251, 252T, 257C, 265C, 274, 283, 291C, 293T, 299R, 300C, 303L, 310R, 321CR, 321C, 323, 327B, 335, 345, 351T, 355TL, 355BL, 371R, 377, 383BL, 398CL, 398BL, 400R, 402TCL, 408CL, 410C; Eco Egg: 416T; Environmental Protection Agency: 342TL; EU Ecolabel: 338BR; European Commission: 356B; European Consumer Centre: 365B; Excellence Ireland Quality Association: 356CT; Fairtrade: 102B; Food Safety Authority of Ireland: 88; Gas Networks Ireland: 315C; © Getty Images: 33, 54BC, 157, 168CB, 168B, 385C; Courtesy of goingfreelance.com: 362C; Green-Schools Ireland: 343; Guaranteed Irish: 356T; © Hemera: 167B, 340BR; © Image Source: 187TL; Courtesy of Irish Felt Fairies: 433B, © iStock: iv, 1, 3, 4, 5, 7, 8, 9, 10, 11, 12, 14T, 15R, 16T, 16B, 17L, 17CR, 17R, 18, 20, 23BL, 23BR, 25, 26, 27, 28, 29, 34C, 35, 36, 38C, 39, 46T, 53T, 54CR, 54BL, 54BR, 57B, 59, 62T, 63, 65, 66, 67, 69T, 71T, 71CL, 71CR, 71BR, 71BCL, 75, 76, 77, 85, 86TL, 86TC, 86C, 87CL, 87TR, 87BL, 87CR, 87BR, 92T, 92TC, 92BC, 95, 97, 104, 108T, 109, 110C, 110CR, 112, 113, 114TL, 114TR, 114CL, 114C, 115, 117, 118, 120, 122T, 124, 126, 127, 128, 130, 131, 132, 133, 135T, 135CB, 135B, 136L, 136C, 138B, 139T, 139BL, 139BR, 141T, 141CL, 141C, 141CR, 141R, 142C, 144, 145T, 145CT, 145CB, 146T, 146B, 148C, 149, 150C, 153, 158, 160B, 161, 162, 163T, 164, 165C, 166, 167T, 168T, 169, 170, 172, 173B, 174T, 175B, 176T, 177T, 179, 181C, 184, 187TR, 187CL, 187C, 187CR, 189T, 190, 192C, 193R, 194, 195T, 196R, 197, 199T, 199B, 200T, 201, 202T, 202CL, 202B, 203T, 203B, 206T, 206 , 212, 214, 215, 217, 218, 219, 218T, 220, 223T, 223C, 226, 231, 232C, 234, 236L, 239, 240, 241T, 242C, 243T, 243CR, 244C, 245C, 247, 248, 249T, 250, 252C, 253, 255, 256, 257T, 258C, 259, 260, 261, 262, 263, 264, 265T, 266, 267C, 268, 269, 270, 271, 272, 273, 275, 276T, 277, 278, 280, 281TL, 281CL, 285, 286, 289, 290, 291T, 291CL, 291CR, 291BL, 291BC, 291BR, 292T, 292C, 293C, 293B, 295T, 298, 300TR, 302, 303R, 304, 306, 307, 308, 309, 310L, 312CL, 312C, 312CR, 312BL, 312BR, 313T, 314, 315T, 315B, 316T, 317T, 318, 319, 321TL, 321TC, 321TR, 321BR, 322, 327C, 328T, 329, 330, 331, 332, 334, 338BL, 339, 340TL, 340TC, 340TR, 340BL, 346, 347, 349C, 353C, 355TC, 355TR, 355CR, 359, 360, 361, 362B, 366B, 367, 369T, 373C, 378TL, 378CL, 378BR, 381, 382, 383CL, 383CR, 384, 387C, 388B, 389BL, 391B, 392TL, 392CR, 393, 396, 397, 398TL, 398TC, 398TR, 398C, 398CR, 398BCL, 398BC, 398BCR, 398BR, 400T, 400L, 400CL, 400C, 400CR, 401B, 402TL, 402TCR, 402TR, 402C, 403C, 403BL, 403BC, 403BCR, 403BR, 405T, 407T, 408T, 408CR, 410BL, 410BR, 412, 415C, 416B, 419, 421T, 423, 425, 426, 428B, 430, 433T, 435TL, 435CL, 435CL, 435CR, 435BR, 437, 438B, 439; Kerry Group: 210CT; National Dairy Council: 181B; National Standards Authority of Ireland: 356C, 365T; Nest Box Egg Company: 200C; Northern Ireland Fire Service: 333C; Odlums: 160CR; Office of the Ombudsman: 364B; © OJO Images: 2, 139CT, 141L, 279, 281TR, 311, 312BC, 313C, 363C, 383BR, 391CB, 417; Organic Trust: 143TR; Origin Green: 143TL; Courtesy of payback.ie: 295B; © PhotoObjects: 225B; Repak: 338BC; © RooM: 373TL; Second Nature Oils: 209BR, © Shutterstock: 427, Sustainable Energy Authority of Ireland: 342TR, The Consumers' Association of Ireland: 355BR, 366T; WEEE Ireland: 338C; The Woolmark Company: 399CL, 399C, 399CR; XV Kings: 385BC.

The author and publisher have made every effort to trace all copyright holders, but if any have been inadvertently overlooked we would be pleased to make the necessary arrangement at the first opportunity.